Hiedra, el hada verde

A las hadas que habitan en lo
más profundo de mi jardín

Un agradecimiento especial
a Narinder Dhami

Originally published in English as
Rainbow Magic: Fern the Green Fairy

Translated by María Cristina Chang

ISBN 978-0-545-23988-2

12 11 10 9 8 7 6 5 4 3   11 12 13 14 15/0

Printed in the U.S.A.   40
First Spanish printing, September 2010

Hiedra,
el hada
verde

por Daisy Meadows
ilustrado por Georgie Ripper

SCHOLASTIC INC.
New York Toronto London Auckland
Sydney Mexico City New Delhi Hong Hong

Que sople el viento, que haya hielo.
Creo una tormenta y no tengo miedo.
A las hadas del arco iris las he mandado
a las siete esquinas del mundo humano.

Miro el reino y yo solo me río.
porque está gris y siempre habrá frío.
En todas sus esquinas y rincones,
el hielo quemará los corazones.

Rubí, Ámbar y Azafrán están
fuera de peligro. ¿Podrán Raquel y
Cristina rescatar a
Hiedra, el hada verde?

Contenido

El jardín secreto

—¡Qué maravilla! —dijo encantada Raquel Walker al mirar a su alrededor—. Es el lugar perfecto para hacer un picnic.

—Es un jardín secreto —dijo Cristina Tate. Le brillaron los ojos al decirlo.

Las chicas se habían detenido en un jardín muy grande. Parecía abandonado desde hacía mucho tiempo.

Rosas blancas y rosadas crecían
alrededor de los troncos de los árboles y
llenaban el aire con su dulce aroma. El
jardín estaba lleno de estatuas de
mármol, la mitad de ellas cubiertas por

una hiedra verde. Y, justo en el medio,
estaban las ruinas de una torre de piedra.

—Aquí hubo una vez un castillo
llamado el Castillo Moonspinner —dijo
el Sr. Walker mientras caminaba por

detrás de la torre y revisaba su guía turística—. Pero lo único que queda ahora es la torre.

Raquel y Cristina observaron la torre. Sus piedras amarillas brillaban bajo la luz del sol, aunque también tenía partes cubiertas de musgo verde. Cerca de la parte superior de la torre había una ventanita cuadrada.

—Se parece a la torre de Rapunzel —dijo Cristina—. Me pregunto si podremos llegar allá arriba.

—Vamos a averiguarlo —dijo Raquel entusiasmada—. Quisiera explorar todo el jardín, ¿nos das permiso, mamá?

—Vayan. Tu papá y yo vamos a preparar la comida —dijo sonriente la Sra. Walker mientras abría la canasta—. Pero no se tarden mucho, chicas.

Raquel y Cristina corrieron apresuradas hacia la puerta que estaba a un lado de la torre. Cristina tiró de la manilla de hierro, pero la puerta estaba cerrada.

—¡Qué lástima! —dijo Raquel.

—Sí, tenía la esperanza de que Hiedra, el hada verde, estuviera aquí —dijo Cristina, y dejó escapar un suspiro.

Raquel y Cristina guardaban un secreto. Estaban ayudando a encontrar a las hadas del arco iris durante sus vacaciones en la isla Lluvia Mágica. El malvado Jack Escarcha las había hechizado y expulsado del Reino de las Hadas y, sin ellas, el Reino se había quedado sin color. El Reino de las Hadas no volvería a ser un lugar bello y resplandeciente hasta que las siete hadas regresaran a su hogar.

—Hiedra —susurró Raquel—. ¿Estás aquí?

—Aquí… aquí… aquí…

Sus palabras resonaron contra las piedras. Raquel y Cristina esperaron ansiosas una respuesta, pero sólo escucharon el crujir de las hojas.

—Este es un lugar muy especial. Se siente como si la magia estuviera cerca —dijo Cristina. De pronto, añadió sorprendida—: ¡Mira la hiedra, Raquel!

Raquel miró. En el muro, que estaba cubierto por la espesa enredadera, se veía un círculo en el que no había hojas.

A Raquel el corazón le dio un salto en el pecho.

—Parece un anillo de hada —dijo.

Raquel había escuchado que si las plantas crecían en un círculo se debía a la magia de las hadas. La chica corrió alrededor de la torre para mirar de cerca y casi se cae al pisar uno de los cordones del zapato.

—¡Ten cuidado! —dijo Cristina agarrándola por un brazo.

Raquel se sentó en una piedra llena de musgo para amarrarse los cordones del zapato.

—Hay plantas por todas partes —dijo mirando la tupida grama y los frondosos árboles—. Hiedra debe de estar por aquí cerca.

—Entonces tenemos que encontrarla rápido —dijo Cristina con un escalofrío—. O si no, los duendes de Jack Escarcha la encontrarán primero.

Jack Escarcha había enviado a sus duendes a la isla Lluvia Mágica para que impidieran el regreso de las hadas al Reino de las Hadas. Los duendes eran tan malvados que todo a su alrededor se tornaba frío y helado.

—¿Por dónde comenzamos a buscar? —dijo Raquel al levantarse de la piedra.

Cristina miró a su amiga y se echó a reír.

—Tienes la falda sucia —dijo.

Raquel miró. La parte de atrás de su falda estaba verde y llena de polvo.

—Debe ser el musgo —dijo molesta mientras se sacudía la falda.

El viento levantó una nube de polvo. El sol de la mañana lo hacía brillar en el aire. Al caer en el suelo, brotaron unas pequeñas hojas verdes que llenaron el aire de un fresco aroma a grama recién cortada.

Raquel y Cristina se miraron emocionadas.

—¡Es polvo de hada! —gritaron.

¿Dónde está Hiedra?

—¡Está aquí! —dijo Cristina.

—¡Menos mal que me senté sobre ese polvo de hada! —dijo Raquel.

Las chicas empezaron a buscar alrededor de la torre, bajo los arbustos y dentro de las flores aromáticas. Mientras caminaban, llamaban a Hiedra en voz baja, pero el hada verde no aparecía por ningún lado.

—¿Crees que los duendes ya la atraparon? —preguntó Raquel preocupada.

—Espero que no —respondió Cristina—. Estoy segura de que Hiedra estuvo aquí, pero parece que ya se fue.

—Sí, ¿pero adónde? —preguntó Raquel mirando en vano alrededor del jardín.

—Quizás la magia que dejó nos pueda ayudar a encontrarla —dijo

Cristina y bajó la mirada para observar las pequeñas hojas que revoloteaban por todo el jardín—. ¡Ya sé, sigamos su rastro!

Las hojas verdes y el polvillo de hada fueron flotando hacia un sendero estrecho. El camino las llevó hacia un hermoso huerto. Raquel vio manzanas, peras y ciruelas que colgaban de los árboles.

—¡Es un sendero mágico! —dijo Cristina emocionada.

—¡Rápido! No perdamos de vista el polvo de hada —dijo Raquel.

Raquel y Cristina emprendieron su camino por el sendero, el cual atravezaba la arboleda.

De repente, el sendero las condujo a un gran claro. Cristina se quedó boquiabierta.

—¡Es un laberinto! —gritó.

Un seto tupido surgía imponente frente a ellas. Sus hojas no paraban de crujir con el viento.

—¡Mira! —le dijo Raquel a Cristina—. ¡El polvillo de hada se dirige al laberinto!

—Tendremos que tomar ese camino
—dijo Cristina valientemente.

Las chicas siguieron las hojas mágicas
que volaban hacia la estrecha entrada del
laberinto. Cristina sintió miedo cuando
vio que el polvo de hada iba de un
lado a otro. ¿Qué
pasaría si el polvillo se
acababa? ¿Cómo
saldrían ellas del
laberinto?

—Quizás
encontremos otra
pista más adelante
—dijo Cristina
esperanzada.

—O a lo mejor encontremos a Hiedra
—agregó Cristina.

Las chicas doblaron una esquina y llegaron al centro del laberinto. Un roble enorme se alzaba justo en medio.

El polvo de hada se acercó al árbol y ahí se detuvo.

—¡Hiedra debe de estar aquí! —dijo Raquel emocionada.

Cristina frunció el ceño.

—Sí, pero ¿en dónde? —dijo mientras miraba a su alrededor.

Toc, toc, toc.

Las chicas brincaron del susto.

—¿Qué fue eso? —dijo Raquel asustada.

Toc, toc, toc.

Cristina abrió los ojos asombrada.

—El ruido viene de allí —dijo señalando el roble.

—Espero que no sea una trampa de los
duendes —susurró Raquel.

Toc, toc, toc.

El ruido se escuchaba cada vez más alto.
Lentamente, Raquel y Cristina caminaron
alrededor del árbol. Al principio, no encon-

traron nada que les llamara la atención, pero un momento después, Raquel señaló el tronco del árbol.

—¿Qué hace una ventana en un árbol? —preguntó.

En la mitad del tronco había un pequeño orificio, ¡cubierto con una ventana de vidrio!

Cristina tocó la ventana. Estaba helada.

—No es de vidrio —susurró—. ¡Es de hielo!

Las chicas se acercaron para ver mejor. De repente, algo se movió detrás de la ventana de hielo. Cristina apenas pudo ver a una niña pequeñita vestida de verde brillante.

—¡Raquel, la encontramos! —dijo Cristina feliz—. ¡Es Hiedra, el hada verde!

Perdidas en el laberinto

Hiedra saludó a las chicas a través de la lámina de hielo. Su boca se abrió para decir algo que Raquel y Cristina no entendieron. El hielo era demasiado grueso.

—Hiedra debe estar congelándose —dijo Raquel preocupada—. Tenemos que sacarla de ahí.

—Podríamos romper el hielo con una rama —dijo Cristina entusiasmada, pero inmediatamente se desanimó—. Pero podríamos herir a Hiedra.

Raquel intentó buscar otra solución.

—Podemos derretir el hielo —dijo.

—Pero ¿cómo? —preguntó Cristina.

—Así —respondió Raquel.

La chica levantó la mano y la colocó firmemente contra la ventanita de hielo. Cristina

hizo lo mismo. El hielo estaba muy frío,
pero ellas siguieron presionándolo con sus
manos calentitas.

Después de un rato, algunas gotas de
agua comenzaron a deslizarse por la
ventana.

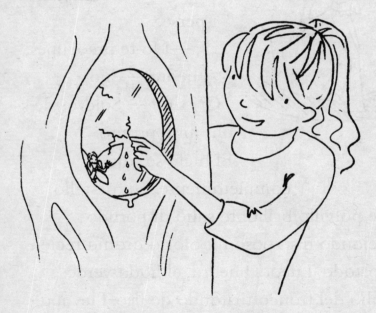

—¡Se está derritiendo! —dijo
Raquel—. Creo que ahora podemos

abrir un huequito en el hielo. Con la punta del dedo, golpeó en el medio de la ventanita y el hielo comenzó a romperse.

—No te preocupes, Hiedra —dijo Cristina—. Saldrás de ahí muy pronto.

El hielo se rajó completamente. Un destello de polvillo brillante salió disparado, dejando a su paso un olor a grama recién cortada. Luego, Hiedra, el hada verde, salió del tronco tiritando de frío. Llevaba puesto una blusa y unos pantalones verde brillante y bellos adornos en forma de hojas en la cintura y el cuello. En sus diminutos pies llevaba unas botitas color bellota. Su largo cabello castaño estaba atado en dos colitas, una a cada lado. Su fina varita color esmeralda tenía la punta cubierta de oro.

—T-tengo tan-to frí-í-í-frío —dijo el hada temblando.

Luego, voló hasta el hombro de Cristina.

—Déjame calentarte un poquito —dijo Raquel. Tomó al hada, la colocó entre sus manos y empezó a soplar suavemente.

El aliento cálido de Raquel calentó a
Hiedra, que dejó de temblar y estiró sus
alas.

—¡Gracias!
—dijo—. Ahora
me siento
mejor.

—Yo soy
Raquel y ella
es Cristina
—explicó
Raquel—.
Estamos aquí para
llevarte a la olla que
está al final del arco
iris.

—Rubí, Ámbar y
Azafrán te están esperando allí
—agregó Cristina.

Los ojos verdes de Hiedra se iluminaron.

—¡Están a salvo! —dijo Hiedra—. ¡Qué alegría!

Salió volando de la mano de Raquel dejando a su paso una ráfaga de polvillo verde y dando piruetas de felicidad en el aire.

—Pero, ¿qué pasará con mis otras hermanas?

—No te preocupes, nosotras las encontraremos —dijo Cristina—. Pero ¿cómo te quedaste atrapada detrás de esa ventana de hielo?

—Cuando llegué a la isla Lluvia Mágica, me enredé en la hiedra de la torre —explicó el hada—. Logré desenredarme, pero los duendes de Jack Escarcha empezaron a perseguirme.

Así que volé hacia el laberinto y me escondí en el roble. Estaba lloviendo y cuando los duendes pasaron por aquí, su malvada magia convirtió el agua de lluvia en hielo, así fue como quedé atrapada.

De repente, Raquel sintió un escalofrío.

—Está haciendo frío —dijo.

Miró hacia el cielo. El sol había desaparecido detrás de una nube.

—Los duendes deben estar cerca —susurró Cristina asustada.

Hiedra asintió.

—Sí, debemos salir de este jardín de inmediato —dijo calmadamente—. Ustedes saben el camino de regreso, ¿verdad?

Raquel y Cristina se miraron.

—No estoy segura —dijo Cristina un poco asustada—. ¿Raquel, conoces el camino?

—No —respondió Raquel—. Pero podemos seguir el rastro del polvillo para regresar a la entrada del laberinto.

Cristina miró alrededor.

—¿Y dónde está el polvillo? —preguntó.

En ese momento comenzó a soplar un airecillo frío. Las hojas verdes mágicas empezaron a dispersarse y a desaparecer.

—¡Ay, no! —gritó Cristina—. Y ahora, ¿qué vamos a hacer?

De pronto, escucharon unas pisadas que se acercaban a ellas.

—Sé que esa hada está por aquí cerca —refunfuñó una voz áspera.

Hiedra, Raquel y Cristina se miraron preocupadas.

—¡Los duendes! —susurró Raquel.

Fuegos artificiales de hada

Hiedra, Cristina y Raquel escucharon aterrorizadas a los duendes que se acercaban. Como de costumbre, peleaban entre ellos.

—¡Apúrate! —dijo uno de los duendes—. No podemos dejar que se escape esta vez.

—Deja de dar órdenes —dijo el otro duende—. Voy tan rápido como puedo. ¡AUCH!

En ese instante se escuchó un ruido, como si alguien se hubiera caído.

—Si tus pies no fueran tan grandes, no tropezarías con ellos —dijo un duende burlándose.

—Son lo suficientemente grandes para darte una buena patada —contestó el otro.

—Vamos a escondernos en el árbol —Hiedra les sugirió a Raquel y a Cristina—. Las transformaré en hadas para que así podamos meternos debajo de una hoja.

Hiedra se alzó en el aire y esparció
polvillo de hada sobre las chicas.

Raquel y Cristina miraban admiradas
cómo se volvían cada vez más pequeñitas.
¡Era increíble!

Cuando las chicas fueron lo
suficientemente pequeñas, Hiedra las
tomó de las manos.

—Vamos —dijo.

Las tres agitaron sus alitas y volaron
hasta aterrizar en una rama. Grandes
bellotas marrones crecían en el árbol, eran
tan grandes como pelotas de playa. Incluso
las ramas más pequeñas parecían troncos
de árboles para las diminutas chicas.

Hiedra levantó el borde de una hoja,
que parecía un mantel gigante, y las tres
se escondieron debajo de ella.

Un momento después, los duendes se
acercaron al árbol.

—¿Dónde podrá estar esa hada? —refunfuñó uno de los duendes—. Sé que estuvo por aquí.

Comenzaron a buscar alrededor del árbol.

—¿Cómo vamos a regresar a la olla? —le preguntó Raquel a Hiedra—. Cristina y yo no somos muy buenas volando. Los duendes nos atraparían si lo intentamos.

Hiedra empezó a reír.

—No se preocupen, conozco a alguien que nos puede ayudar —dijo mientras señalaba detrás de ellas.

Raquel y Cristina se voltearon.

Una cara gris peluda se asomó
tímidamente. Era una ardilla.

—Hola —dijo Hiedra suavemente.

La ardilla saltó y se escondió detrás de
una rama. Luego, asomó sus curiosos
ojitos negros.

—A lo mejor quiere una bellota
—sugirió Cristina.

Había una bellota grande y reluciente
justo al lado de ella. La envolvió entre sus

brazos, pero no pudo arrancarla... ¡era muy grande! Raquel y Hiedra trataron de ayudarla. Las tres tiraron muy fuerte hasta que la bellota se desprendió de la rama con un chasquido.

Hiedra le acercó la bellota a la ardilla.

—Ummm... ¡Qué rica! —dijo para animar a la ardilla.

La ardilla corrió por la rama moviendo su cola larga y peluda. Tomó la bellota entre sus patas delanteras.

—¿Cómo te llamas? —preguntó Hiedra amigablemente.

—Soy Peludín —dijo la ardilla sin dejar de mordisquear la bellota.

—Yo soy Hiedra —dijo el hada—. Y
ellas son mis amigas, Raquel y Cristina.
Necesitamos alejarnos de los duendes.
¿Nos puedes ayudar?

Peludín empezó a temblar.

—No me gustan los duendes —dijo.

—No vamos a dejar que te hagan
daño —dijo Hiedra mientras le

acariciaba la cabeza—. ¿Podemos viajar
encima de tu lomo? Tenemos que salir de
este laberinto y tú puedes saltar de seto
en seto mucho mejor que nosotras.

—¡Sí, yo las ayudaré! —dijo Peludín
mientras se comía el último pedazo de
bellota.

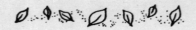

Hiedra, Cristina y Raquel saltaron al lomo de la ardilla. Cristina se sentía como sumergida en una manta grande y suave.

—¡Esto es fantástico! —dijo Hiedra abrazando a la ardilla—. ¡Vamos, Peludín!

La ardilla giró y empezó a correr a lo largo de la rama. Hiedra, Cristina y Raquel se aferraron con todas sus fuerzas a Peludín cuando éste saltó del árbol, justo por encima de los duendes, y aterrizó en el seto más cercano. Los duendes estaban tan ocupados peleando que ni cuenta se dieron.

—¡Bien hecho, Peludín, ahora al siguiente! —le susurró Hiedra al oído.

Raquel tragó en seco al ver lo lejos que estaba el siguiente seto.

—Quizás Peludín necesite un poco de magia de hada —dijo ella.

—No, no la necesita —respondió Hiedra entusiasmada—. Él puede hacerlo.

Peludín saltó, flotó en el aire y aterrizó en el siguiente seto. Raquel y Cristina se miraron sonrientes. ¡Qué emocionante! El

aterrizaje había sido un poco brusco, pero el pelaje de Peludín sirvió de amortiguador. La ardilla se movía tan rápido que en un abrir y cerrar de ojos se alejaron de los duendes.

—¡Lo logramos! —dijo Hiedra mientras Peludín alcanzaba el borde del laberinto.

—¿Y ahora hacia dónde vamos, chicas?

Raquel y Cristina se miraron preocupadas.

—Nosotras no entramos por este lado
—dijo Raquel—. No sé cuál es el camino
hacia la olla desde aquí. ¿Y tú, Cristina?

Cristina negó con la cabeza.

Hiedra parecía preocupada.

—Pero tengo que llegar a la olla
—dijo—. Mis hermanas me esperan ahí.

—¡Ya! —dijo Cristina, a quien se le
acababa de ocurrir una idea—. Raquel,
¿qué te parece si buscamos ayuda en la
bolsa mágica?

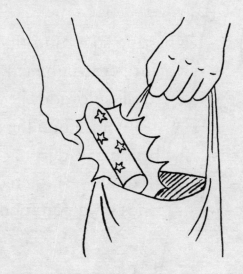

—¡Qué buena idea! —dijo Raquel.

Titania, la Reina de las Hadas, les había dado a Raquel y a Cristina dos bolsas mágicas para que las usaran si necesitaban ayuda durante el rescate de las hadas. Las chicas siempre las tenían a mano.

Cristina abrió su bolsa y echó un vistazo. Algo dentro de ella brillaba con una luz plateada.

—Me pregunto qué habrá adentro —dijo metiendo la mano en la bolsa.

Cristina sacó una fina varita verde cubierta de estrellas doradas.

—Parece una luz de bengala —dijo Raquel—. No creo que nos sirva para nada.

—¡Es una bengala de hadas! —dijo
Hiedra emocionada—. Puedo usarla para
escribir un mensaje en el cielo. Mis
hermanas podrán verlo desde la olla y
sabrán que necesitamos ayuda.

—¿Y que pasará con los duendes?
—preguntó Raquel—. Ellos también
podrán verlo y sabrán dónde estamos.

Hiedra se puso seria.

—Tendremos que correr ese riesgo
—dijo.

Hiedra tomó la bengala en una mano
y prendió la punta con su varita mágica.
Después, salió volando hacia el cielo.

Raquel y Cristina esperaron ansiosas.
El hada verde no paraba de ascender en
el cielo, dejando a su paso una estela de
brillantes chispitas verdes.

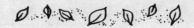

Cuando Hiedra estuvo muy alto en el firmamento, escribió con la bengala un mensaje de estrellas color esmeralda que decía:

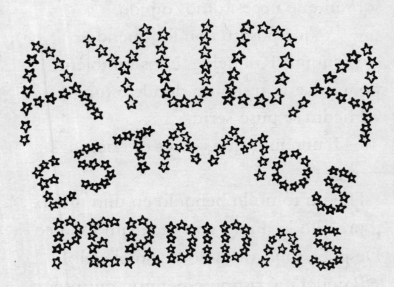

Las estrellas titilaron fuertemente en el cielo y luego desaparecieron.

—No tendremos que esperar mucho tiempo —dijo Hiedra mientras aterrizaba en el suelo, en medio de Raquel y Cristina—. Pronto vendrán a ayudarnos.

Raquel y Cristina estaban preocupadas. ¿Cómo vendrían las hadas a rescartarlas? ¿Qué pasaría si los duendes las encontraban?

En ese momento, Hiedra, Cristina y Raquel escucharon unas hojas crujir.

—¿Viste la bengala de hadas? —gritó uno de los duendes—. Vino de aquel lado. Apúrate antes de que el hada escape otra vez.

Puercoespín al rescate

Raquel y Cristina se miraron alarmadas. Peludín también parecía preocupado. Los duendes estaban siguiéndoles los pasos, ¡otra vez!

—Vienen hacia nosotros —susurró Raquel al oír que las voces de los duendes sonaban cada vez más fuertes.

—No se preocupen —dijo Hiedra sonriendo tranquilamente—. Mis hermanas pronto enviarán ayuda.

En ese momento, Raquel vió una línea de chispitas doradas que brillaban a lo lejos, entre los árboles frutales.

—¿Qué es eso? —susurró Raquel.

—¿Será la magia de los duendes? —preguntó Cristina.

Hiedra negó con la cabeza.

—Son luciérnagas. Seguro que mis hermanas las enviaron para que nos indiquen el camino hacia la olla.

De repente, se escuchó un grito proveniente del laberinto.

—Mira, ¿qué son esas lucecitas de allá arriba?

—Los duendes han visto a las luciérnagas —dijo Raquel asustada.

—¡Rápido, Peludín! —dijo Hiedra mientras se subía al lomo de la ardilla—. ¡Sigue a las luciérnagas!

Las chispitas doradas bailaban entre los árboles. Peludín empezó a corretear

detrás de las luciérnagas
justo cuando los
duendes salieron del
laberinto.

—¡Ahí está el
hada! —gritó uno
de los duendes
apuntando a
Hiedra—. ¡Detengan
a esa ardilla!

—¡Regresen aquí!
—refunfuñó el otro mientras
Peludín seguía corriendo.

Hiedra, Cristina y Raquel se
agarraron fuertemente
a Peludín mientras éste
iba de un lado a otro
intentando alejarse de
los duendes.

La ardilla trepó el tronco del árbol más cercano. Estaba a punto de saltar hacia el siguiente árbol cuando escucharon una voz que los llamaba desde abajo.

—¡Hola!

—¿Quién es? —preguntó Raquel.

Hiedra, Cristina y Raquel miraron al suelo. Un puercoespín estaba parado al pie de un manzano.

—¡Hola! —gritó nuevamente—. Los animales del bosque escucharon que estaban en problemas y queremos ayudarlas.

—¡Gracias! —respondió Hiedra un poco nerviosa al ver a los duendes entre los árboles.

—¿Adónde se habrá ido esa ardilla?
—gritó uno de ellos.

Sin perder ni un segundo, Peludín saltó
hacia el siguiente manzano. Los duendes
chillaron rabiosamente y se echaron a

correr tras ellos. En ese momento, el
puercoespín se enrolló en una pelota y
rodó hacia los duendes. Raquel pensó que
parecía una gran pelota de fútbol con
púas.

—¡Auch! —gritaron los duendes—. ¡Mi
pie!

Raquel y Cristina no paraban de reír
al ver a los duendes saltando de dolor.

—¡Viva el puercoespín!
—gritaron las chicas.

A medida que
Peludín saltaba de
un árbol a otro,
las luces de las
luciérnagas iban
desapareciendo.

—¿Quién
apagó las luces?

—dijo uno de los duendes mientras seguía sobándose el pie—. ¿En qué dirección debemos ir?

—¿Qué voy a saber yo? —contestó el otro duende.

Sus voces se escuchaban cada vez más lejanas.

—¡Gracias, luciérnagas! —gritó Hiedra, despidiéndose de las últimas chispitas de luz que quedaban—. Necesitamos encontrar el camino hacia el huerto. Seguro que no estamos muy lejos de la olla.

—Si tuviera el tamaño de un ser humano, sabría qué dirección tomar —dijo Cristina—. ¡Pero todo se ve tan grande!

—Pero si volvemos a nuestro tamaño normal, los duendes podrían descubrirnos —dijo Raquel.

—Yo los puedo ayudar —susurró una vocecita.

Una venadita estaba parada al pie de un árbol y los miraba fijamente con sus grandes ojos marrones.

—¿Nos puedes mostrar el camino? —dijo Cristina.

—Sí, les puedo mostrar un atajo —dijo la venadita moviendo su colita y echándose a correr entre los árboles.

Peludín la seguía saltando de rama en rama.

Raquel estaba muy emocionada. Se encontraba encima del lomo de una ardilla y una venadita les mostraba el camino hacia la olla al final del arco iris.

Un rato después, llegaron al muro de ladrillo que rodeaba el huerto. Peludín saltó sin pensarlo dos veces. Raquel y Cristina miraron felices: del otro lado del muro había una pradera y más allá un terreno lleno de árboles.

—¡Mira! —gritó Raquel—. ¡Ahí está la olla!

Volando muy alto

—¡Gracias! —gritaron las chicas a la venadita.

La venadita respondió con un guiño y se fue trotando.

Un mirlo de plumas oscuras y brillantes que estaba posado en el muro muy cerca de ellos, se les acercó.

—Estoy aquí para llevarlos a la olla que está al final del arco iris —dijo—. ¡Todas a bordo!

Peludín se puso triste al ver que Hiedra, Raquel y Cristina se bajaban de su lomo y se montaban encima del pájaro, cuyas plumas eran tan suaves y sedosas que no se podían comparar con el grueso pelaje de Peludín.

—¡Adiós, Peludín! —gritó Raquel tristemente y le lanzó un beso—. ¡Gracias!

Mientras se despedían, el pájaro alzó el vuelo.

—Llévanos al gran sauce llorón —dijo Raquel.

—¡Tengo muchas ganas de ver a mis hermanas otra vez! —dijo Hiedra emocionada.

El pájaro voló sobre el bosque y aterrizó en el claro, cerca del sauce llorón. Hiedra, Cristina y Raquel saltaron al suelo y se despidieron de él.

—¿Quién está ahí? —dijo una voz muy grave.

Un ranita verde saltó entre las ramas de un árbol.

—¡Beltrán, soy yo! —gritó Hiedra.

Sin perder ni un segundo, el hada sacudió su varita y Raquel y Cristina volvieron a su tamaño normal.

—¡Srta. Hiedra! —dijo Beltrán muy feliz—. ¡Está a salvo!

—Seguimos a las luciérnagas —dijo Hiedra mientras abrazaba a la rana—. ¡Gracias por enviarlas!

—Vimos la luz de bengala en el cielo —explicó Beltrán—, así supimos que estaban en problemas. Pero no se preocupe, aquí estará bien. La olla está escondida debajo del árbol y los duendes no tienen ni idea de que está aquí.

Raquel y Cristina corrieron hacia el árbol y empezaron a abrirse paso entre las frondosas ramas. La olla al final del arco iris estaba donde la habían dejado. De repente, un chorro de polvillo rojo, anaranjado y amarillo brotó de la olla. Rubí, Ámbar y Azafrán salieron volando muy contentas. Una enorme abeja reina zumbaba detrás de ellas.

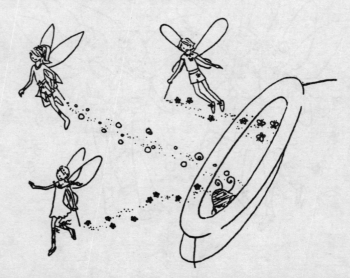

—¡Hiedra! —gritó Rubí—. ¡Estoy tan feliz de verte!

Raquel y Cristina sonreían al ver que las hadas se abrazaban. El aire se llenó de flores rojas, burbujas anaranjadas, mariposas amarillas y hojas verdes.

—¡Te extrañamos muchísimo! —dijo Azafrán.

La abeja se acercó a Azafrán y la rozó con su pequeña antena.

—¡Ay, disculpa, Reinita! —dijo
Azafrán—. Ésta es mi hermana, Hiedra.

Reinita zumbó de alegría.

—¿Cómo llegaron tan rápido?
—preguntó Azafrán—. ¡Si apenas
acabamos de enviar a las luciérnagas!

—Nuestros amigos del bosque
nos ayudaron —dijo Hiedra
despidiéndose del pájaro,
que ya se iba volando—. En
especial Peludín, la ardilla.
Fue muy triste decirle adiós.

Rubí empezó a reír.

—Y entonces, ¿quién es ese?
—dijo señalando un árbol que se
encontraba al otro lado del claro.

Raquel y Cristina miraron hacia el lugar.
Peludín las miraba tímidamente medio
escondido detrás del tronco de un árbol.

—¡Peludín! —Hiedra voló hacia él y le dio un abrazo—. ¿Qué haces aquí?

—Estaba preocupado por ustedes —explicó Peludín—. Quería asegurarme de que llegarían a la olla sanas y salvas.

—¿Te gustaría quedarte con nosotras? —preguntó Ámbar—. Podrías vivir en el sauce, ¿no crees?

—¡Sí, me encantaría! —dijo Peludín—. Estoy muy solo. Vivo en el roble del laberinto yo solito.

Rubí se dirigió a Raquel y a Cristina:

—¡Muchas gracias otra vez! —dijo—.
No sé qué haríamos sin ustedes.

Hiedra voló hacia el hombro de
Raquel. Una de sus alas rozó suavemente
la mejilla de la chica.

—Las veremos pronto, ¿verdad?

—Claro que sí —prometió Raquel.

—¡Sólo nos falta encontrar a tres
hadas! —dijo Cristina.

Raquel y Cristina se tomaron de la
mano, se despidieron de las hadas y se
marcharon corriendo.

—Debemos regresar con tu padres,
Raquel —dijo Cristina—. Deben estar
muy preocupados.

—Buena idea —dijo Raquel con una
sonrisa—. Si no regresamos pronto mi
papá se va a comer toda la comida.

Rubí, Ámbar, Azafrán y Hiedra
están a salvo.
Ahora Raquel y Cristina
tienen que encontrar a
¡Celeste, el hada azul!

Pero, ¿dónde podrá estar?
Únete a las aventuras de
Raquel y Cristina
en este adelanto del próximo libro…

Un mensajero mágico

—¡El agua está tibia! —dijo Raquel Walker sonriendo.

Estaba sentada en una piedra, agitando con los dedos del pie el agua cristalina de una de las marismas de la isla Lluvia Mágica. Su amiga Cristina Tate buscaba caracolas muy cerca de ella.

—Ten cuidado de no resbalarte, Cristina —gritó la Sra. Tate, que estaba un poco más lejos en la playa, sentada junto al Sr. Tate.

—¡Está bien, mamá! —respondió Cristina.

La chica bajó la vista para mirar sus pies descalzos y descubrió algo azul brillante debajo de un manojo de algas marinas.

—¡Raquel, ven acá! —gritó.

Raquel se acercó a Cristina.

—¿Qué pasa? —preguntó.

Cristina apuntó hacia las algas.

—Hay algo azul debajo de esas algas —dijo—. Me pregunto si es…

—¿Celeste, el hada azul? —dijo Raquel emocionada.

Jack Escarcha había hechizado y expulsado a las siete hadas del arco iris del Reino de las Hadas. Ahora, estas se encontraban escondidas en la isla Lluvia

Mágica. El Reino de las Hadas no recuperaría su color hasta que todas las hadas estuvieran reunidas. Raquel y Cristina les habían prometido al Rey y a la Reina del Reino de las Hadas que ellas las encontrarían.

Las algas se movieron nuevamente.

Raquel sintió que el corazón le dio un vuelco.

No te pierdas el próximo libro de la serie

RAINBOW magic™

Celeste, el hada azul

y entérate de la magia que se esconde entre las algas brillantes.

Talk Your Way Out of Credit Card Debt by Scott Bilker

"I had to write and thank you so much for the book. I just got it yesterday afternoon and started reading it. This morning I decided to try it out on one of my cards that has a very high interest rate. This card had been only about 9.99%, but the interest rate skyrocketed last May and I didn't know why and I really didn't know what to do about it. I called the company this morning and in less then 5 minutes I found out why (I'd had trouble with another card issued by the same company) and got the interest rate lowered from 23.99% to 8.99%. One point lower than it had been before! This one call paid for the book and way more. I figured out how much I saved. It's a good thing I was sitting, because I'm sure I would have fallen on the floor when I realized I saved $10,706.50."—Jill King, Philadelphia, PA

"Scott, I wanted to thank you. I ordered your books a few weeks ago and read them right away. I had an incredible amount of confidence when I called to get my credit card rate lowered. It was so easy! They lowered my rate from 10.45% to 3.9% (for a large balance too) for the life of the balance, with no fees. I calculated my savings at $3,968. WOW! Thanks again for your terrific advice!"
—Lisa Harris, DE

"A valuable book from day one! It contains a large amount of information your banks don't want you to know. My first night of reading the book, I got up to about page 70 and made my first phone call, with the intent of gaining information about the account and possibly getting a fee reversed. I ended up getting a $50 credit to the account, relatively easily. I cannot praise this book enough! If you need to reduce your credit card debt, this book may very well be your solution."—Monica Rice, PA

"I tried calling my credit card bank and using one of the things you said on Friday's TV show. Well, I called and they raised my limit to $1,000 from $300 and dropped my rate from 17.9% to 15.3%. Thank you!"—Mark Crilley

"5 stars! Easy to understand, anyone can use it, very informative. I used Scott's advice in the book about calling the credit card companies and having the interest rate lowered on my credit card. I have learned what I need to say and how to negotiate. Whatever you need to know it's in the book. Before I called I had a 14.99% for purchases and 19.99% for cash advances. After speaking to the representative for 7 minutes I had my rate drop to 12.99% for purchases and 14.99% for cash. Not only that but I have another card with them and the rate went from 19.99% for both to 15.99% for both. Not bad for 7 minutes. I wish everything was this easy. Total Saved $1,000.00!"—Scott Morey, NJ

"I ordered your books and studied them and I have read your newsletter for quite some time. I had close to $55,000 in credit card debt with high interest rates. Following your advice I did balance transfers until I was able to get the interest rate to 3.9 percent, and I have paid off four cards and cancelled them. In two years the total has dropped to about $25,000 and is dropping fast with the low interest rate. My son lost his job 7 months ago and your advice saved their home. Keep up the good work and especially keep telling everyone not to trust the banks who issue the credit cards."—Jimmy Thomas, Texas

"I just got your books and was inspired to call my major credit card to ask for a reduction in APR. The current rate is variable 12.74%; with a $10,000 balance that's costing more than $100 per month in interest. They reduced that rate to 9.9% with no discussion. But here's where I really benefited from having read your book: In talking about that rate, the account supervisor told me they will wire cash advances to my bank account for only 2.99% APR. They will provide as much as $10K per month. So, I could reduce the 19.74% rate to 2.99% rate by having the money wired to my bank and then writing a check to pay off the entire balance! Amazing—they told me how to save money. So, I just wanted to say that I feel I've already gotten my $19.95 worth from your books. Thanks!"—Kathy

"I have recently found your book *Talk Your Way Our of Credit Card Debt* and it has really helped me. I have had excellent credit until very recently. I had an automatic payment through the credit card. A few months ago, the minimum payment was $3 over what I had set as the auto pay. I had not noticed that there was a difference until too late. This one time problem cause my interest rates to go up from 3.9% fixed balance transfer rate and a 13% purchase rate to 24.9% and 5.9% fixed balance transfer rate and a 10.9% purchase rate to 27.9%! It affected more than just the one card. I read your book and called customer service on all of my credit card today. I had amazing success. Most of my interest rates went back to their original rates and a few I was able to get lower! One account would not budge, so I transferred to a lower rate. Thank you!!!! You have saved me a bundle of money!"—R.J.

"I give this book my full recommendation! I've never seen a more detailed how-to book. If you have a credit card, you need this book! I think Scott outdid himself on this one. Almost everyone I know, and myself included, has been intimidated by credit card banks. To have an actual script to follow for all situations will be a godsend to a lot of people. *Talk Your Way Out of Credit Card Debt* is the one book that every credit card holder should have."—Terry Rigg, *The Budget Stretcher*

"Scott Bilker is one of the most effective negotiators that I know. If you're going to be talking to credit card companies it's well worth getting his book *Talk Your Way Out of Credit Card Debt*."—Tom Allan, host of the *I Hate Debt* radio show in San Diego, CA

Please submit your review at: http://www.debtsmart.com/reviews

TALK YOUR WAY OUT OF CREDIT CARD DEBT!

PHONE CALLS TO BANKS THAT SAVED MORE THAN $43,000 IN INTEREST CHARGES AND FEES!

Scott Bilker

Press One Publishing, Barnegat, NJ

TALK YOUR WAY OUT OF CREDIT CARD DEBT!

PHONE CALLS TO BANKS THAT SAVED MORE THAN $43,000 IN INTEREST CHARGES AND FEES!

by Scott Bilker

Published by:
Press One Publishing, PO Box 563, Barnegat, NJ 08005-0563
Tel: (609) 660-0682, Fax: (609) 660-1412, Email: scott@debtsmart.com

Visit DebtSmart® Online at http://www.debtsmart.com

Copyright © 2003 by Scott Bilker
First Printing 2003
10 9 8 7 6 5 4 3 2
Printed in the United States of America

Publisher's Cataloging-in-Publication
(Provided by Quality Books, Inc.)

Bilker, Scott.
    Talk your way out of credit card debt! : phone calls to banks that saved more than $43,000 in interest charges and fees! / by Scott Bilker.
    p. cm.
    Includes index.
    LCCN 2002095765
    ISBN 0-9648401-5-4

    1. Credit cards--United States. 2. Consumer credit-- United States. 3. Finance, Personal--United States. I. Title.

HG3756.U54B547 2003   332.024'02
                    QBI02-200863

For my mother, Audrey L. Bilker, who was always so proud of her only son—I miss you.

TABLE OF CONTENTS

ACKNOWLEDGEMENTS

Writing a book is a long and difficult process. I could not have completed this new title without the help of many people. Most notably all my friends that trusted me to help them save money.

Thanks to Jen and Joe Macedo, Matt Macedo, Greg Hussey, Deborah Cohen, Barbara and Richard Crammer, Richard K. Crammer, Harvey L. Bilker, Greg Mador, Paul S. Bilker and everyone that let me call and save them money. I enjoyed every minute of it. Thanks again for allowing me to share your experience with others.

Special thanks to editors Larissa S. Bilker and Richard K. Crammer! Also, extra thanks to Rick for transcribing 80% of those tapes! It took Rick weeks to listen, and type, every word spoken—over 10 hours of recordings!

Additional thanks to my cousin Paul S. Bilker, Esq. for all his legal advice with copyrights and trademarks (and editing)! His expertise has been crucial for all my projects in print and online!

Thank you Christopher Norris Crammer for the great job you've done with all the cartoon illustrations! Your drawings truly complement the message of this book.

Thanks to Robert Gamble, Claude Tygier, and my father Harvey L. Bilker for your help with my first book *Credit Card and Debt Management*! Without its success I would not have been able to create DebtSmart.com or write this book.

Thanks to Master Art Beins, my karate instructor, mentor, and friend. Karate has taught me much over the years. I'm always referring back to my philosophical training for guidance. My hope is that this book becomes the consumer-credit self-defense, training manual!

Thanks to all my DebtSmart® Online and Email Newsletter readers! I've learned much from your survey responses and truly enjoy delivering to you what I consider to be the best money-saving information available.

Thanks to all radio and TV hosts and producers that have had me on their shows over the years. I appreciate your trusting me to inform your audience about credit cards, debt, and money.

I'd like to thank all the bank representatives for helping train us all as consumers to fight back! Not only did they help train me, they also provided much "financial entertainment," if there is such a thing. ☺

WARNING—DISCLAIMER

Everyone's financial situation is different. This book is designed to provide information in regard to the subject matter covered. It is sold with the understanding that the publisher and author are not engaged in rendering legal, accounting, financial planning, or other professional services. If legal or other expert assistance is required, the services of a competent professional should be sought. Your call results may vary compared to those discussed herein.

It is not the purpose of this manual to reprint all the information that is otherwise available to the author and/or publisher, but to complement, amplify and supplement other texts. You are urged to read all the available material, learn as much as possible about credit cards/debt management, and to tailor the information to your individual needs. For more information on this subject visit your library or ask a trusted financial professional where you can locate more details pertaining to your personal finances.

Negotiating with your bank alone will not entirely solve all your credit problems. Your results may be different than those in this book.

The author and publisher are not suggesting that you misrepresent yourself to your bank. You can have a friend or relative help you as long as the bank knows whom they're dealing with.

Every effort has been made to ensure this book is as complete and as accurate as possible. However, there may be mistakes: typographical, mathematical or in content. Therefore, this text should be used only as a general guide and not as the ultimate source of credit card and debt management information.

The purpose of this book is to educate and entertain. The author and Press One Publishing shall have neither liability nor responsibility to any person or entity with respect to any loss or damage caused, or alleged to be caused, directly or indirectly by the information contained in this book.

The information, methods and techniques described by the author are based on his own experience. They may not work for you and no recommendation is made to follow the same course of action. No representation is made that following the advice in this book will work in your case. The author and publisher expressly disclaim any and all warranties, including but not limited to warranty of fitness for particular use.

INTRODUCTION

WE'VE ALL BEEN THERE

When I was younger and naïve many businesses easily took advantage of me. Like with the purchase of my first car. Hey, even my second car! Apparently I didn't learn my lesson the first time. This is what happened...

I paid $1,000 for a car that had no floor. And I mean no floor—just a rug! I discovered that it had no floor when I was driving to get that heap a front-end alignment.

It was raining that day and I hit a large puddle in the road. Suddenly a tsunami comes from beneath my feet and gushes over my head, while I was driving.

I pulled over, removed the rug from the driver's side floor, and found that the rug had been merely resting on a few strands of rust. It was like something out of the Flintstones. I could just put my feet on the road and start running!

Within a few years I became a vigilante during car purchases! I learned everything I could about negotiating for a fair price. It wasn't long before my friends started asking me to accompany them on their car shopping journeys.

I quickly discovered that overpriced rip-offs didn't stop at the price of the car. The gouging continued in the bowels of the financing room as the dealers increased the interest rate of the loans, added in more fees, and attempted to sell unwanted warranties and under coatings.

I eventually lost all my fears about speaking up and negotiating, and now I refuse to let anyone, or any business, take advantage of me!

I've reached the point in my life where I simply cannot accept being ripped-off anymore without putting up a major fight! I refuse to pay any fees that are not necessary or have anything extra charged to my accounts simply "because they can."

BACKGROUND

I wrote my first book, *Credit Card and Debt Management* to help people start saving money on their debts by learning how to determine which credit deals are best and devising a payment strategy that is financially efficient. Later, I created DebtSmart.com as an ongoing effort to help inform the readers of my web site, and email newsletter of the new, money-saving techniques I'm always learning. The most popular articles were then released in my second book, *How to be more Credit Card and Debt Smart*.

I've put this book together for the sole purpose of empowering you to take action and stop banks from taking too much of your money! To stop them from charging you late fees, annual fees, astronomically high interest rates, and more. The book contains details of what to say to get banks to give you the credit deals you deserve!

I've been making these calls for years, and now I want to show you the power that we have as consumers. The power to make the credit card banks beg for our business! And they should! It's very difficult for them to get their paws on profitable consumers and we should not allow them to continue charging us high rates and fees!

I promise that you'll learn something by reading my phone transcripts; at least one thing that will work to save you more money. You'll also see some of the mistakes I've made and how to avoid them. But the bottom line is that you'll read how to save a bundle of cash!

YOU HAVE THE POWER

Between my wife and I we have over 80 credit cards! Yeah, I know what you must be thinking, "Scott, you're insane! Why should I listen to you? You obviously have a credit problem."

Actually, it's just the opposite. First of all, most of those cards carry a zero balance. If I were to actually charge them all to the max, this book would be about bankruptcy recovery. ☺

Secondly, who would you want advice on negotiating with your banks from? Some "expert" that hasn't had a credit card in the last 10 years, buys everything with cash, and thinks you've got problems because you can't stick to using cash? Or me, the guy that talks to the credit card banks all the time because I've got 80 cards? Someone who preaches it or someone who lives it?

I'm not suggesting that you go out and get 80 credit cards. I just like to have credit options. By having many accounts I have control over the banks. They must fight for my business. If they don't, I can take my business, and their profits, elsewhere in a heartbeat!

Over the years I have made hundreds of calls to credit card banks for others and myself. In this book I'm going to share many of my personal phone calls with banks. Also included are numerous calls I've made to help my friends and family save money.

All of these phone conversations are recorded. I started recording the conversations to keep a record of what was promised to me by the banks. There were many times I called the bank and they told me one thing, like they'd waive a fee, but the fee was never waived. I called them back and told them "I spoke to Mr. X on blah-blah-date who said they'd waive the fee," but they just didn't remember and had no record of that promise.

What you're going to read are the exact transcripts of these phone conversations, plus my comments throughout each call. I hope you'll find them to be entertaining and informative. You'll see exactly what I said and the results those words produced.

I always kept good notes, but the recordings are absolute proof. Plus, when I call the banks they always say they're "recording this conversation for training purposes." You know that those training purposes are to teach the bank representatives how to deter you from pursuing the deals you deserve. But it seems the opposite has occurred. Because as it turns out, they have also been recorded for training purposes—by me! I am going to use these recorded calls to train people on how to get better deals from their banks.

Please keep in mind that there is a difference between knowing what to do and being trained to do it. I know this from karate. You can tell someone how to throw a kick, but actually showing that person how to do the kick properly, then practicing, is the key to truly learning with the confidence that the kick will actually work when needed. The same is true for learning how to negotiate with banks.

Knowing what to say may come naturally for some people but it may not be so natural for others and must be learned. Or, like in my case, you get so mad that it just starts to become natural.

It's easy for someone to say, "just call the banks and get the fees waived," but actually calling is a different story. Without training you risk not knowing exactly what to say in a highly pressured moment. And not having that sound of confidence in your voice that makes the difference between success and continued gouging. How do you know when they're giving you the best deal? What option do you have if they don't give you their best deal? And what should be your next move?

There are many details to consider when you're going to start dealing with your banks to shop for money. Knowing exactly what to say and how to "manipulate the system" to your advantage is very, very important.

Having debt isn't something to be ashamed of. Not doing something about it, when you can, is. This book is meant to inspire and motivate you to take action! To help you build your self-confidence. To show you that you can do it! You can control your financial destiny. You can **talk your way out of credit card debt** and have a fun time doing it!

By reading the transcripts from each call in this book, you're going to gain the confidence and knowledge you need to start calling your banks today! You're going to feel involved with these real demonstrations of how to deal with banks and their reps. Get mad, get smart, DebtSmart®, and pick up that phone!

As Benjamin Franklin wisely stated, **"Tell me and I forget; Teach me and I remember; Involve me and I learn."**

CHAPTER 1

THE BANKS ARE AT OUR MERCY

A GREAT PAYING JOB

Everyone wants to get out of debt, but few are willing to do the work it takes to make this goal a reality. As it turns out, looking into all your credit options is going to be one of the best paying jobs you'll ever have. That's because the money you save more than compensates you for your time.

If you have high-rate debt and spent just 10 hours per year working on getting better deals, you might easily save $1,000 or more. That's $100 per hour!

In this book I make 52 phone calls that take 403 minutes (6 hours, 43 minutes) and save $43,147.68. Let's do the math on that. What a fast way to make/save $6,423.97 per hour, which works out to be $107.07 per minute! Not bad, huh? And the great news is that you may be able to achieve the same results!

All the real names of banks have been changed to avoid providing free advertising. The names of the bank representatives have also been changed as well to protect the innocent.☺ If I happen to accidentally select a real bank or person's name, it is merely coincidental. Bank names have been renamed to dog breeds and bank representatives to bug names.

YOU'RE IN CONTROL

You read that right. You are in control! The banks are at our mercy!

I know you're thinking, "Yeah right, easy for you to say, you've got great credit. These things only work for people with great credit." That may be true to some extent. However, you can also have great credit by continuously working on your credit card and debt management. You may not be able to reduce your rates from 26% to 3% in a day but perhaps to 18%; maybe a month later to 9% then in a year all the way down to 0%.

In today's economy, nearly all of the buying-public, we, the consumers, have credit cards. Credit card banks start marketing to us as early as possible, because the younger you are when you start to use credit, the more likely you are to remain loyal to that original bank throughout your life.

At this point in time, the market for new credit-card customers is nearly saturated. Banks are propositioning college students since banks know, and it's true, that they are more likely to have higher-paying jobs in the future. But aside from this "new blood," where are the banks going to get more customers? They have to steal profitable customers from their competitors!

The only way to get you as a customer is to take you away from your current credit card bank. Because of this fact, there are many banks from which you can choose to do business with. I know it may not feel like that right now, especially if you have had credit problems in the past, but no matter your credit situation, you still have the power to decide whom you wish to give your money.

There are just too many banks out there that want your business. You shouldn't accept being treated poorly by any bank. I don't accept it and neither should you! I let them know that they will give me that low-rate deal, they will treat me right, or I'll just use one of my other 79 credit cards instead.

The bottom line for my banks is this, they have a choice: (1) continue to make some money at a fair rate or (2) I'm going to start using another bank for all my balance transfers and purchases—they won't make another penny from me!

WHY THE BANKS NEED YOU MORE THAN YOU NEED THEM

Think about the great business that credit-card banks have going. Not only do they charge the public an incredible amount for using their money, but they also charge merchants a percentage of each transaction. How would you like to get 1% of all credit-card purchases in the world in one day? I do not have any sympathy for them.

Add that to the late fees, annual fees, overlimit fees, cash advance fees, etc. Some banks make nearly 50% of their profits just from these fees alone! Naturally, banks want to make money. And they should be able to make money, but it must be a fair amount.

As you know, the only way they can make money is to get it from you, the consumer, either through your purchases with merchants or directly through fees. If they believe you're profitable, they are going to do almost anything to keep you as a customer, or to get you to switch to them from your current credit-card bank.

Banks want to give the appearance that they're in control, but it just isn't the case. They have called and begged me to use my lines of credit too many times for me to believe that they don't really need me. You bet they need me! And to keep me, they're going to have to offer a deal that I would be insane to refuse.

WHAT ABOUT CREDIT COUNSELING SERVICES

I'm always asked "What about those non-profit credit counseling agencies?" What are these companies? They say they can lower your rates, set up a budget, and help you pay off your debts. Many claim that only they can negotiate deals with your credit card banks.

Basically, credit counseling companies set up a payment plan with, hopefully, all of your creditors. You then send the credit counseling company a single monthly payment. The counseling agency then redistributes that payment to all your individual creditors.

So how do they make money?

Most charge very low fees, or ask for "contributions." But more notably, the very same banks to which you owe money compensate them. That's right, they get paid a percentage of what they get you to pay! Your creditors pay them a portion, sometimes called "fair share," of the money that you pay. By the way, banks are always looking to reduce this payment to the counseling agencies.

Sounds very similar to a collection agency. Collection agencies get paid by creditors to collect money from a debtor. That's why I sometimes refer to credit counseling agencies as "voluntary collection agencies."

Credit counseling agencies, and debt negotiation companies, don't want you to know that you can negotiate with your creditors directly. In fact, many credit counseling and debt negotiation companies state in their literature, that they can "negotiate deals with your creditors that you can't."

That's an outright lie! You can negotiate for lower rates. You can negotiate for better deals. You can just pick up the phone, call your banks, and start talking your way out of debt in the next ten minutes.

As with all businesses, there are good credit counseling companies with knowledgeable staff and others that are going to get you into more trouble! If you decide to use a credit counseling company, you must be sure to research the background of that company and the counselors that are working on your accounts. By the way, in the majority of cases, the fact that you are working with credit counseling services will be reported to credit reporting agencies.

Many banks consider people who are working with credit counseling services to be "one step from bankruptcy." Because of this you may have difficulty getting new credit or getting approved for a mortgage.

Ironic isn't it? You'd think that banks would consider you to be responsible since you're working to pay off your debts, but that's not the case.

I always recommend that you start trying to fix your credit problems on your own. Doing so will prove invaluable to your financial future because, no matter which route you choose, your financial fate is ultimately in your hands.

One last thing I should mention. As I stated earlier, there are some good credit counseling companies, and if you have tried everything, and have not gotten the results you're looking for, then you may want to consider talking to a reputable credit counseling company. Be sure to research their background to see if any of their customers have had problems with the company. One of the best places to start is online at the Better Business Bureau (http://www.bbb.org).

Credit counseling is a viable option. An option that may, or may not, be better or less expensive than other options. However, it's certainly a smart strategy to seek all the advice you can. Then it's up to you to decide what's best for your situation.

CAN WE NEGOTIATE?

Americans are very accustomed to the perception of rigid pricing. We go into large department stores for sales to get the best price because we believe that there is no flexibility in the pricing policies of these companies—and we're probably right. However, anybody who has ever purchased a car knows that automobile prices are always negotiable. That's also the case for many big-ticket items.

It seems that in our minds, and culture, there are certain items that we can negotiate a better price for and others that are not negotiable. Actually, you would be surprised to find that there are many more instances in which you can negotiate for a better deal. Of course, this is more likely when big money is at stake. For example, if you were going to buy ten refrigerators for ten rental units you would discover that many major department stores are probably quite willing to talk about giving you a special discount for such a large purchase.

That's great but what about smaller items? Well, that's a different story. It's going to be very difficult to ask for a lower price for a can of soda at the local convenience store. In fact, for most small purchases, that may be impossible.

You can always try the flea market or garage sales for better deals on smaller items, but they are usually pre-owned or irregular, which is why the price is flexible. The truth is that almost anything is negotiable—you simply have to ask.

Can you really just pick up the phone, call your bank, and ask for a better rate? Can you just call and ask to have annual fees waived? How about late fees? And overlimit fees?

The simple answer to those questions is "yes." You can negotiate for better deals with your banks. I have proven it time and time again by getting lower interest rates and having their fees waives as well as shopping for new credit or asking for the availability of better credit offers.

However, most of the time it's not an easy thing to do for many reasons. Some people are not confident enough to call, some are not sure what to say, or don't know how to say it. In fact, many people feel intimidated by their credit card banks. There is a stigma about dealing with banks—even when they treat you poorly. Most people would never accept being treated poorly from other businesses.

Imagine having your car repaired at the local garage. You get the car back and it isn't fixed. In fact, it's worse than when you brought it in! I'm sure you would never go there again. But for some reason, it's different when dealing with credit card banks. People simply accept the fact that they're getting charged 18% APR, or more, and never say a word about it! There was a time in the not too distant past where it was true that the banks did have more control, but now the consumer holds all the cards, literally—credit cards. ☺

YOU NEED A "DEAL BREAKER"

The most important factor in negotiating for anything is your deal breaker. That is simply what you are going to do if you cannot get the deal you want after negotiations. If you are going to buy a car and you can't get the price you want, then your deal breaker may be to leave the dealership and go car shopping somewhere else.

When it comes to dealing with banks it's okay if you have to bluff. You can create a fake deal-breaker and go with it. However, you need to keep in mind that if you cannot carry out your threat, you will not be as effective in the long run. If you do not have a real deal breaker, or you are not willing to follow through with that threat, then you are just begging. You don't want to beg! Begging is like going into your boss's office and snapping, "If you don't give me a raise, then I'll quit!" The boss replies with, "No raise!" And like a whipped puppy you respond, "Okay..." and walk back to your desk.

You need to create as many real options as you can before trying to negotiate a better deal. You need a deal breaker. The best place to find those options for credit is right in your own mailbox. Some of those credit-offers can truly save you money. You may not even have to apply for these new lines of credit. Many people throw out these offers without even considering how much money they can save. Remember that if you aren't happy with your bank, you can fire them! But even if you don't, or can't, take advantage of all these offers, you can still use them as bargaining tools, i.e., deal breakers, with your current banks.

So again, it is very important to have credit options. It doesn't really matter if you have high interest credit options, at least you have something. All the time I hear "If you want to get out of debt, then just cut up your credit cards." What a mistake! **When you cut up your credit cards, you cut out your options.**

You need to have a few banks to deal with to get the best credit deals. Plus you can run into trouble if you only deal with one bank. If you're stuck shopping for money in only one store, that store is going to keep its price very high because they know you have nowhere else to shop. You have to start making those banks fight for your money. You have to make them participate in a bidding war for your business. Once you have many places to shop, then you will really have power. Credit options equal negotiation power!

Suggested deal breakers
1) I'll transfer my balance to another bank. Listen to this great deal I just got in the mail from another credit card bank.
2) I'll close my account(s) {and my spouse's account(s)}.
3) I'll claim bankruptcy.
4) I'll simply pay you off.
5) I'll never use your card again.
6) You might as well give me the lower rate now, because when I transfer my balance, you're going to offer me an even more reduced rate to get me to come back.
7) Review your account history and determine how much money you've spent at that bank in charges and payments and interest. Let the bank know that right now they're making something, and that soon they'll be making nothing, when you pay them off or leave them.
8) See more ideas in chapter 9.

THE PERFECT CARDHOLDER

From the bank's perspective, the perfect cardholder is the most profitable cardholder. What makes you look profitable? Good credit card and debt management—translation, no late payments, good income, and healthy spending. Don't worry if you've had problems in the past, they can all be corrected by starting to use good debt management today!

When it comes to looking good to the banks, the amount of money you earn isn't the most important factor. You could make a million dollars a year but if you don't ever make payments on your debts, there won't be any bank looking to lend you money.

When you manage your credit well, you're in a better position to negotiate better rates and terms. That's the subject of my first book, *Credit Card and Debt Management*. That book covers how to get organized, create a debt reduction plan, enact that plan, and keep track of each debt. Most importantly, the book explains in detail how to calculate how much each debt actually costs, which is very important to know when comparing loan options.

If you start managing your debts today, it won't be long before the credit-card bank marketing computers that hunt for profitable customers find you in their databases and send out some great credit offers.

Above all, you must be careful to not commit the greatest sin in the credit card world—paying late! Your most powerful leverage is the fact that you pay on time. If you have been late in the past, you can fix this by getting organized and starting to pay on time from this moment forward.

If you pay late it will come back to haunt you—for sure. In fact, many credit card companies will raise your rates, some to as high as 26% or more, if you're late to other creditors. Even utility companies! How unfair is that! You're late paying your electric bill and your credit card bank raises your rate to 26%. It happens all the time and it has happened to many people I know personally.

Paying late also impacts your credit report, or as I like to call it, your Financial Résumé. That credit report is used to determine the best interest rate you're eligible to receive on your credit cards, mortgages, car loans, even your life insurance rates! Negative information on your credit report is like getting points on your driver's license. You're going to pay a surcharge in the form of greater interest charges and fees plus some information is going to stay on you record for 7 to 10 years! In fact, if you get too many points against you they'll take away your credit license by making it nearly impossible to get a loan!

From lenders to employers to landlords, your payment history affects your entire financial life and regular life. Even if you have to borrow from one credit card in order to pay another on time, it's better and less costly in the long run than being late.

BE PERSISTENT AND PATIENT

Many times, fixing your credit or negotiating rates and terms is not going to be a one-step process. By that I mean you won't be able to fix it all in a single day. However, to make progress you have to start somewhere! You must start by doing something; taking some action. You might be able to get some fees waived, you might be able to negotiate a few rates, but your credit history in general and your payment history with each specific bank, will ultimately determine how far you can go to reduce the cost of your debts through negotiation.

If you have excellent credit and you're being charged a few late fees, or annual fees, then it's going to be relatively easy to get the bank to refund those charges. On the other hand, as you will see, the more late or missed payments, the more mismanaged your credit, the more difficult negotiation becomes. However, as long as you're persistent in calling banks and looking for better deals, you will prevail!

Patience is also another important skill needed to negotiate. I don't necessarily mean being patient while speaking, but being patient waiting to speak as well.

One of the most truly annoying parts of calling your banks is going to be dealing with the automated voice menu systems. When you call, you'll first be asked to enter your 16-digit credit card number, then maybe a zip code or social security number. It gets worse...you have to sit there and listen to the computer read your balance, available credit, etc. Finally, after being tortured for five minutes, you're given an option to talk to a human only to recite your account number once again!

Sometimes you can get around this by not entering any numbers at the start of the call. The voice menu will automatically send you to a human because it thinks you have a rotary phone. However, there are some systems now that let you speak the numbers. So there may be no escape.

You can also try to evade the voice menu by repeatedly pressing the "0" button or keep pressing the pound "#" sign. It used to be that "selecting 0" got you to a human, but maybe a lot of people were doing that so they changed it to "press 3" or "press 4." After all, the automated system probably does answer most people's questions but it sure seems that banks don't want to make it easy to get through. All I can say is good luck getting to speak with a human! Talking to a real breathing earthling is going to take patience but, again, it's well worth the wait.

START TALKING

After reading this book, you will be prepared to deal with the banks. By learning what worked, what didn't, and why, you'll be in a better position to bargain. You also need to get prepared by imagining how the conversation might go when you call your bank.

Think about how you'll respond in advance. Think about how you believe the bank will respond. Be ready to ask for a supervisor. Finally, look over your past credit card statements so you can tell the bank representatives how good of a customer you've been in the past. And that if they don't treat you properly, you'll stop using their credit card! The key to success is knowing who to talk to and exactly what to say.

I started recording these calls to make sure the banks remembered the deals they said I would be getting, since some conveniently forgot. And now this collection of tapes has turned into a library of conversations that get results! I want to share this with you so that you too can save thousands of dollars. The best part about talking your way out of debt is that you will have fun doing it!

CHAPTER 2

GETTING THAT ANNUAL FEE WAIVED

ANNUAL FEES

An annual fee is a fixed charge that banks stick you with for the privilege of making them money by using their card. Today there is so much competition among banks that annual fees are starting to become a charge of the past. There are, however, cards that are worth paying an annual fee to use. For example, a card with a fixed, low rate may be worth the annual fee depending on the credit limit. The greater the limit, the lower the comparable interest charge to use that money.

For example, let's say you have a credit card with a $500 credit limit that has an APR, of 9.99% and an annual fee of $50. If you used the entire credit limit for one year, you'd pay 10% just for the annual fee, since $50 is 10% of $500! Then when you add that to your APR, you'll find the true cost of that $500 is at 19.99%. If that same card had a $20,000 credit limit, and you use the entire limit for one year, the cost of your annual fee is only 0.25%. That makes the total cost for the $20,000 at 10.24% which is still very good!

Some banks offer other rewards programs like free air miles, free video rentals, etc. for using the card. In those cases banks may be able to justify charging an annual fee. Conversely, credit cards that are making you pay a 21% APR have no right, the way I see it, to charge you an annual fee. The only way they could get away with charging those high rates, and an annual fee, is if your credit report is so bad that you are desperate for credit.

When I call to ask for an annual fee to be waived, my experience has been that 95% of the time they do it! There have been a few times when the bank hasn't waived the fee, so I've simply closed the account. I have too many credit card options to pay any annual fees. That's a position you want to be in. You don't want to be at the mercy of one bank. No matter your situation, bad credit, good credit, or other, you should always call to see if you can make the bank waive your annual fees. Be sure to keep an eye on every transaction in each month's credit card billing statement. If you see an annual fee charge, call the bank and get that fee waived!

CALL #2.01: IT CAN BE THIS EASY

Reason For Call:	Annual Fee Waived
Result:	Mission complete
Difficulty Level:	Easy
Call Time:	2 minutes
Total Saved:	$40.00
$/hour to make call:	$1,200.00

Most of the time, calling to have your annual fee waived is going to be the easiest call to make. My experience has been that banks are very willing to waive annual fees to keep your business. It would be nice if all the calls were as easy as this first one.

SUMMARY

I called to get my annual fee waived and they did it without giving me any problems. A very easy call!

TRANSCRIPT

Went through the voice menu.

Voice Menu: "To ensure the quality of the service we provide, your call may be monitored or recorded."

Scott: "Yeah, I bet. Yours too."
Note: That's me talking to the voice menu.

Rep: "Barbet Bank cardmember services this is Mrs. Earwig speaking. Can I have your name please?"

Scott: "Scott Bilker."

Rep: "Thank you. And how can I help you?"

Scott: "Ummm, can you see my last statement by any chance?"

Rep: "I'd be happy to take a look at that for you. To maintain security on your account can you please verify your mother's maiden name?"

Scott: "It's..." (I tell her the name.)

Rep: "Thank you. Um, yes I can, I do have your information in front of me."

Scott: "Great okay. Ummm, that $40 annual fee, I was hoping that could be waived."
Note: Simply asking to have the fee removed. I don't even need to give a reason.

Rep: "Okay, let me just take a look at that for you. Okay, please verify your social security number please."

Scott: "Sure it's..." (I tell her the number.)

Rep: "Okay, thank you, one moment. Okay, umm, yes, I can go ahead and I can waive the umm, $40 and you will see it as a credit on your next statement as a $40 credit."

Scott: "Ah, that's great. Thank you very much Mrs. Earwig."

Rep: "You're welcome. Thank you for calling Barbet Bank."

Scott: "Bye-bye."

CALL #2.02: I LOVE WHEN THEY JUST AGREE

Reason For Call:	Annual Fee Waived
Result:	Mission complete
Difficulty Level:	Easy
Call Time:	2 minutes
Total Saved:	$50.00
$/hour to make call:	$1,500.00

Here's another example of how you want the call to go. You call, you ask for the annual fee to be waived, and they simply go ahead and waive the fee!

SUMMARY

Again, having the annual fee waived is probably going to be the easiest call you make. In this call I asked to have the fee waived and they did it, pronto!

TRANSCRIPT

Voice Menu: "Welcome to Deerhound Bank..."

Rep: "Deerhound Bank cardmember services, this is Ms. Larva. May I have your first and last name please?"

Scott: "Scott Bilker."

Rep: "Hi Mr. Bilker, how may I help you?"

Scott: "Hi, umm, I noticed on my statement this month, do you have a copy of that right there?"

Rep: "Uh, yes I do."

Scott: "Okay, that I got charged an annual fee, and I was wondering if that fee could be waived."

Rep: "Okay I would be glad to check into that for you Mr. Bilker, but first in order to maintain security in this account, verify for me your mother's maiden name."

Scott: (I give her the name.)

Rep: "And your social security number."

Scott: (I give her the number.)

Rep: "Can you hold on for a second."

Scott: "Sure."

Rep: "Thank you."

On hold...

Rep: "I do appreciate your holding Mr. Bilker, I went ahead and removed it for you."

Scott: "Wow, that's great, that's good customer service."

Rep: "Okay, thank you."

Scott: "Thank you very much."

Rep: "You're welcome, thank you for calling."

Scott: "Bye-bye."

CALL #2.03: ASK FOR A SUPERVISOR

Reason For Call:	Annual Fee Waived
Result:	Mission complete
Difficulty Level:	Medium
Call Time:	4 minutes
Total Saved:	$28.00
$/hour to make call:	$420.00

Many times the first bank representative that answers the phone will not be able to grant your request. You should always, let me repeat, ALWAYS, ask to speak to a supervisor if the first person you speak with says they cannot help you. This next call is the proof.

SUMMARY

I first spoke to Mrs. Milkweed who told me that they're not waiving the annual fee. I then asked to speak to a supervisor and Mrs. Milkweed told me that the supervisor is going to tell me the same thing but she'll transfer me anyway. Nice ploy to get me to give up the fight on the spot! I wonder how many people throw in the towel at that point.

Anyway, I got connected with Mrs. Termite, the supervisor. She said that she was advised about the situation by Mrs. Milkweed and then she immediately went into something like, "I've looked at your account and I can waive the annual fee, although it's unusual. We'll waive it because you've paid more in interest over the past year than the $28 annual fee."

TRANSCRIPT

Voice Menu: "Welcome to Giant Schnauzer Bank services. Please select from our expanded menu of services..."

Scott: "Uh huh. Go ahead." (I go through the phone tree to speak to account rep.)

Rep: "Thank you for calling card services. This is Ms. Milkweed. Can I have your account number please?"

Scott: (I give her the number.)

Rep: "And your name please."

Scott: "Scott Bilker."

Rep: "Mr. Bilker, and your mother's maiden name please."

Scott: (I give her the name.)

Rep: "How can I help you today?"

Scott: "Okay I was hoping you could help me today. I'm looking at my statement, I just got it today, and I noticed I have an annual fee of $28 on here, and I was hoping you could waive that for me."

Rep: "Unfortunately at this time we are not waiving any annual fees."

Scott: "Em hmm."

Rep: "So in order to keep the account you would need to pay the annual fee."
Note: Yeah, right! I've heard this one a thousand times.

Scott: "Hmm. Is there anyone there who might be able to change that for me? A manager maybe?"

Rep: "The only way that we could do that is to close the account. But I will gladly transfer you to a supervisor, they will be able to tell you the same exact thing I have."
Note: Nice attempt to scare me, ooooh, they'll close my account. Actually, I wouldn't mind giving my business to another bank that doesn't charge an annual fee.

Scott: "Okay, sure."

Rep: "Please hold."

Scott: "Thank you Ms. Milkweed."

On hold...

Supervisor: "This is Ms. Termite, I'm a supervisor in customer service. How are you today?"

Scott: "Good. I just spoke with, umm, Ms. Milkweed?"

Supervisor: "Thank you, I couldn't think of her name. She advised me that you are requesting an annual fee to be waived off."

Scott: "Yes."

Supervisor: "Okay, let me look at it real quick for you."

Scott: "Okay, and you're Ms. Termite?"

Supervisor: "I am. Normally, we normally don't waive annual fees unless you close the account, and that's normally within the thirty days. What I will do since you've spent, you know, the only thing on there right now is the annual fee, and your finance charges alone have actually covered your annual fee for the year. So what I'm going to do is just go ahead and waive it as a courtesy."

Note: Notice how she's trying to make an excuse to justify waiving the annual fee, "since your finance charges covered the annual fee." I don't believe it for one second! My feeling is that she could waive the fee if she felt the bank would lose a good customer. Let them save face by making the excuse. You may even suggest, "Hey, my interest fees have more than covered that annual fee, how about, as a courtesy, waiving that fee for me this time?"

Scott: "Wow, that's very nice."

Note: I really want to say, "That's better because I was about to leave your useless, insulting bank!" I bit my tongue since they did waive the fee.

Supervisor: "Give me just one second. Were you going to leave your account open?"

Note: Ah, ha! There it is! The real reason she waived the fee. She was worried that I would close the account!

Scott: "Of course I'm going to leave it open. You guys are waiving the annual fee, and I use my account very responsibly, and I've had a good relation with Giant Schnauzer Bank. I thought that, umm, you might do that."

Supervisor: "Exactly, and I explained to her the reasons why I was waiving it, so that way next time she will...Bear with me just one second. Okay, I've taken care of it for you."

Scott: "Thank you very much Ms. Termite."

Supervisor: "Not a problem, is there anything else I can do?"

Scott: "Umm, no that will do for now, but I'm sure I'll be calling back with other things and balance transfers in the future."

Note: Maybe or maybe not. Just trying to make her feel good about waiving the fee.

Supervisor: "Okay."

Scott: "Thank you."

Supervisor: "Thanks for calling Giant Schnauzer Bankcard services."

Scott: "Bye-bye."

CALL #2.04: DON'T GIVE UP

Reason For Call:	Annual Fee Waived
Result:	Mission complete
Difficulty Level:	Medium
Call Time:	4 minutes
Total Saved:	$40.00
$/hour to make call:	$600.00

This call demonstrates how important it is to keep pushing! To not give up when you're being told that the bank's "policy" doesn't allow them to waive the fees. Since you already made the call, already endured the voice menu, you can't stop simply because the bank representative won't do as you ask. Hang in there—you may be surprised when they waive your fee.

SUMMARY

I called to ask to have the $40 annual fee waived. The rep told me that they're not waiving the fees on certain cards and the Pug Gold Card is one of those cards. I asked to speak to someone about this and was told that they would tell me the same thing. After speaking with her supervisor, the rep gets back on the phone with me and apologized, saying that she gave me the wrong information. She then told me that her supervisor has waived the fee and it will show up as a credit on my next billing statement.

TRANSCRIPT

Scott: "I'm calling Pug Bank to have my annual fee waived. It's April 4th."
Note: Just making a note on my tape so I have another way to cross-reference the call against written notes.

Rep: "Pug Bank cardmember services, this is Ms. Drone, may I have your account number please?"

Scott: "Sure my account number is..." (I give her the number.)

Rep: "And can I have your name please?"

Scott: "Scott Bilker."

Rep: "How can I help you Mr. Bilker?"

Scott: "Okay, well, I got my statement this month, are you looking at that?"

Rep: "Um, hmm."

Scott: "Okay, great. I see this annual membership fee, and I was hoping that could be waived."
Note: Simply ask.

Rep: "Okay, can you please verify your mother's maiden name and your date of birth please."

Scott: (I give her the information.)

Rep: "Okay, Mr. Bilker unfortunately due to the new policy we cannot waive the membership fee from this card."

Scott: "Oh, really?"
Note: Yeah, right! That's what they all say!

Rep: "Yes."

Scott: "Hmm, let's see. Just looking back here at my previous statements, I'm looking at say..."

Rep: "Right, they did waive it for you in the past, that's correct, but as of now we cannot waive the fees on a couple of different cards now."

Scott: "Uh huh."

Rep: "Pug Gold was one of these cards that we cannot take the fee off."

Scott: "Really?"
Note: The rep has told me 3 times that they're not waiving the fee. However, I'm not giving up!

Rep: "Yes."

Scott: "Is there someone else I can speak to who might be able to assist me with this."

Rep: "Yes, they are going to tell you the same thing, but yes, one moment."
Note: I've heard this line before. Sure, they're going to tell me the same thing. ☺

On hold...

Rep: "Hello Mr. Bilker."

Scott: "Yes."

Rep: "Thank you for holding. Yes sir, I do apologize for that information, unfortunately that was for our Pug Gold. I do apologize for that, but our supervisor, Ms. Queen Bee, she did waive the fee for you. So you will, there will be a $40 credit on your next billing statement."

Note: That's better. Good thing I kept on pushing!

Scott: "Okay great."

Rep: "Okay."

Scott: "Alright, so that's all taken care of."

Rep: "Yes. Is there anything else I can help you with?"

Scott: "No, that was it. Thank you."

Rep: "Yes, okay."

Scott: "Bye-bye."

Rep: "You're welcome. Bye-bye."

CALL #2.05: THROW THEM A BONE

Reason For Call:	Annual Fee Waived
Result:	Mission complete
Difficulty Level:	Medium
Call Time:	2 minutes
Total Saved:	$20.00
$/hour to make call:	$600.00

What happens if they don't waive the fee? What else can you do? Throw them a bone! Tell the bank that you're about to use the card to transfer a balance or to make a large purchase. Tell them that if they don't waive the fee, then you'll use another card.

Also, if you can, get some statistics about your account history by reviewing old statements. Total how much you've spent and repaid so you can let the bank know that you're a good customer and you're prepared to take your business elsewhere if they don't waive the annual fee.

SUMMARY

I called to have the annual fee waived. I am prepared with the account's historical statistics: On the Bull Terrier Bank account I've charged and repaid $44,912.59 and paid $972.17 in fees and interest.

My wife and I have a total of 4 Bull Terrier Bankcard accounts with total lifetime charges of $106,341.25 and fees of $3,461.12, all repaid. This total includes many transfers to other credit card accounts over the years.

I spoke to Mrs. Butterfly and she said that Bull Terrier Bank has started charging people who don't use the account. I explained that I have 4 other Bull Terrier Bank accounts that I have used currently. She said that they're charging the annual fee. I then said that I am about to use the 9.9% deal they're offering and she said, in that case, as a courtesy she's going to waive the annual fee. By the way, I never did use their balance transfer deal!

TRANSCRIPT

Scott: "Okay this is Bull Terrier Bank getting the annual fee waived."
Note: I'm just making a memo on the tape so I can match it up with my notes later.

Voice Menu: "Welcome to Bull Terrier Bank. We are pleased to have you as a Bull Terrier Bank credit account member. If you are calling from a touch tone phone please press 1 now."

Scott: (I press one.)

Voice Menu: "Please enter your account number which..."

Scott: (I start pressing random numbers.)
Note: I'm trying to press anything to get to a human.

Rep: "Cardmember services this is Mrs. Butterfly, may I have your account number please?"

Scott: (I give her the number.)

Rep: "Thanks. Your first and last name."

Scott: "Scott Bilker."

Rep: "Hello, Mr. Bilker. How can I help you today?"

Scott: "Hi, can you see my last statement by any chance?"

Rep: "Let me see, for security I need your date of birth please."

Scott: "Sure..." (I give her the information.)

Rep: "Yeah. $20 annual fee."

Scott: "Right, now I was hoping that Bull Terrier Bank might be able to waive that annual fee."

Rep: "They've been waiving it for you when you've been using it. Like in January you never saw the fee."

Scott: "Right."

Rep: "You haven't used the account for one year."

Scott: "Right, you know in fact I'm about to use it actually, now with this 9.9% offer. But I also have 4 other Bull Terrier Bank accounts that I have been using."
Note: Quick thinking Scott. ☺ Let's see if she goes for it.

Rep: "Sir I understand, it's just Bull Terrier Bank, they have decided to charge annual fees on non-used accounts, but if you are going to use it, I will, as a courtesy to you, remove it. Because it's one of the lowest cash rates around."

Scott: "Okay sure."

Rep: "You know those balance-transfer checks they sent you, you can use them to write to yourself for cash still at the 9.9%."

Scott: "Yeah, that's what I'm actually planning on doing."
Note: Actually—not!

Rep: "And you only pay a $1 instead of a 3% transaction fee, which is kind of ridiculous if you ask me, but..."
Note: Ridiculous to who? Maybe she would like to pay the 3%.

Scott: "Right, that is one of the best things about the Bull Terrier Bank account is that the transfer fee is fixed."

Rep: "Yeah."

Scott: "Some of them are zero, some of them fluctuate 3%, but this one is $1, or it used to be 75 cents, is it $1 now?"

Rep: "Yeah."

Scott: "Same, close enough, 25 cents more. Alright so it will be waived?"

Rep: "Yep."

Scott: "Great, and what was your name?"
Note: Always be sure you note who you were speaking with for future reference.

Rep: "Mrs. Butterfly, B-U-T-T-E-R-F-L-Y. Your statement next month will have a credit of $20."

Scott: "Alright thank you very much."

Rep: "No problem, thanks for calling Bull Terrier Bank."

Scott: "Bye-bye."

Rep: "Bye-bye."

CALL #2.06: UPGRADE ACCOUNT TO AVOID FEES

Reason For Call:	Annual Fee Waived
Result:	Fees and related interest charges waived.
Difficulty Level:	Medium
Call Time:	5 minutes
Total Saved:	$51.71
$/hour to make call:	$620.52

Sometimes, banks that I've called won't waive the annual fee. They say it's their "new policy," however, they will "upgrade" the account to one that's exactly the same but has no annual fee. If they don't offer to upgrade the account (to avoid the annual fees) simply ask if you can change to another account that won't charge an annual fee.

As long as your interest rates don't change, for the worse, take this option and save the money. Ask the bank representative if it's going to change the account number. Always track that information so you don't mix up accounts with the same bank or with old account numbers.

SUMMARY

I called to have this annual fee waived last month and they told me it was taken care of. However, I received a bill this month and there was no credit.

I spoke to Ms. Bagworm who said that there were no notes from my last call. Of course Murphy's Law holds true for me here because when I went back and looked at my notes for this call, it turns out that there was too much noise on the tape to hear anything—figures! Now I can't play that for her.

The representative said that they changed their policy and don't waive annual fees anymore. They only upgrade the account to Platinum, everything stays the same, and the fees are waived.

I told her to go ahead and do that and I also asked for her supervisor's name. His name is Army Ant. This will help me prove my case the next time I have to call. At least I can say, "Hey, I called and spoke to Mrs. Bagworm whose supervisor is Army Ant."

TRANSCRIPT

Voice Menu: "Please stay on the line for customer service assistance. To ensure the quality of the service we provide, your call may be monitored or recorded."

Scott: "Yours too."
Note: That's right. I'm using this call for training—the training of all consumers!

Rep: "Briard Bank cardmember services, this is Ms. Bagworm. May I have your name please?"

Scott: "Hi, Scott Bilker. What did you say your name was?"

Rep: "Ms. Bagworm."

Scott: "Ms. Bagworm?"

Rep: "Yes. How may I help you today?"

Scott: "Let me see, if you look at my statement, you see that I have a balance on it of like $51.71."

Rep: "Right."

Scott: "There should be no balance at all. I called last month, spoke to a customer service rep. who said that my annual fee was being removed."

Rep: "Okay."

Scott: "And apparently it hasn't."

Rep: "Let me take a look for you."

Scott: "Sure."

Rep: "To maintain security on the account may I have your date of birth."

Scott: (I give her the date.)

Rep: "Thank you."

Pause...

Rep: "Did they upgrade your account or anything like that? Or did the person you talked to just say they would remove it, right?"

Scott: "I spoke to Mr. Elder Borer. And he said that..."

Rep: "They just said they would remove it, they didn't say that they would upgrade your account or anything like that?"

Scott: "He said that he did some research and found out that it has already been refunded. He spoke to his supervisor and it was taken care of on the 24th of May."

Rep: "Of last year?"

Scott: "No, of this year."
Note: I'm reading my notes from the last conversation with this bank about the fee. You'll have to follow up, as I'm doing here, if you find that the fee hasn't been waived.

Rep: "Last year on the 24th of May was taken care of. This year nothing has been taken care of."

Scott: "Hmm."

Rep: "And they changed the policy since then, that they don't waive the membership fee. So either you can upgrade to a different kind of account that has no membership fee. You have Gold Card you could..."
Note: Here we go with that the-policy-changed line again. Get used to hearing it. Try to not let it make your blood boil! Just hang in there and think of how to get them to give you your money back!

Scott: "What I don't understand is I called, I spoke to someone on May 26th this year, Mr. Elder Borer. He told me it was being taken care of, and it hasn't been."

Rep: "Well it hasn't been and there is no telling that."

Scott: "And he spoke to his supervisor at that point in time, that was a month ago."

Rep: "Yeah, I'm sorry there is no notes, I can't waive your fee, they did waive it last year. Umm, unless you want to upgrade your account..."

Scott: "Why didn't he tell me this in May? You know when I called last time."

Rep: "I'm sorry, I don't know, I can only deal with what I have. I don't see that you talked to anybody in May, or that there is any notes on the account, or that they waived the fee or anything like that."

Scott: "There are no notes from a guy named Mr. Elder Borer?"

Rep: "No. I'm sorry. You can upgrade your account to like a Briard Bank Platinum card that doesn't have a fee and we can waive the fee for this year. And you can get a new card, it wouldn't have any annual membership fee. It would be a platinum card, and basically get more benefits, and you don't have an annual membership. It would change your card number, your account number, but everything gets transferred over and I can waive your fee for you. Otherwise they changed the policy since last year they don't waive the fee."

Scott: "Okay, will it change my account number?"

Note: Although I realize now (after reading the transcript) that she already told me, you should still always ask about account number changes. If they say they're doing any account upgrades you'll need to track this new account plus be on the lookout for the new card that they should be sending you in the mail.

Rep: "Yes it would, it would change your account number. You get a new card and a new account number, and everything else would stay the same basically. You know your interest would stay the same, the..."

Scott: "That's all fine, but I mean how do I know that when I call back next month and it doesn't happen, and I say 'I spoke to Ms. Bagworm,' and they say there are no notes, nothing happens..."
Note: Yeah, what about that! I'm sick of getting the runaround! What protection do I have—how can I prove I spoke to you!

Rep: "I believe you, I believe you. I'm not saying that I don't believe, you know, that you talked to somebody. They just didn't, usually if somebody talks to the supervisor somebody would make notes on the account. Usually these things I would see, but I don't see them. But I could promise you I'll do it. I'm sorry I don't know, I'm sorry..."

Scott: "I mean, they said the same thing. I was..."

Rep: "We are also upgrading your account. So that would be something that would be processed through the system I promise you."

Scott: "Right."

Rep: "You can think about it and call me back then, alright?"

Scott: "Umm, I'll never speak to you directly again."

Rep: "We don't know that."
Note: You'll find that there is NEVER a way to contact the same people you originally spoke with. They don't have direct phone numbers plus the turnover is pretty high, I'm sure. Also, some of them eventually become adults and leave the bank rep business. Oh, yeah. I've spoken to some 15-year-old reps in the past—I'm not kidding! ☺

Scott: "Let's go ahead and do this upgrade."

Rep: "Okay, can you verify your mailing address?"

Scott: (I give her the address.)

Rep: "Okay."

Scott: "Let me get this, what's your supervisor's name?"

Rep: "Army Ant."

Scott: "Okay. Army Ant. Can you spell that?"

Rep: "A-R-M-Y A-N-T."

Scott: "And what's your first name?"

Rep: "We don't give that out."
Note: Two seconds ago you gave out your boss's first name with no problem. Go Figure.

Scott: "Okay. What's your supervisor's extension, or how can I..."

Rep: "He doesn't have one."

Scott: "He doesn't have one?"
Note: Sure he doesn't have one. That's why they "lost" my notes from the last call. Because nobody has a phone extension, they can't speak to each other. Give me a break!

Rep: "No, but you can have, I mean it's a call center sir so there is really no...It's like me giving your...it's not really going to do anything. Umm..."
Note: Many reps are easily confused. ☺

Scott: "What call center is he at, what location?"

Rep: "We are in Arizona. Anything else I can help you with sir?"

Scott: "Uh, well, will this..."

Rep: "The fee will be waived, you'll get a new card."

Scott: "Okay."

Rep: "Okay."

Scott: "We'll see. Thank you."

Rep: "Thank you for calling Briard Bank."

Scott: "Bye-bye."

Call #2.07: Leave a Program to Avoid Fees

Reason For Call:	Annual Fee Waived
Result:	Mission complete
Difficulty Level:	Medium
Call Time:	6 minutes
Total Saved:	$28.00
$/hour to make call:	$280.00

In this call I'm told that I'm in a special 1% cash-back program and that's why I'm being charged the annual fee. I don't recall ever getting 1% back on any purchases. I've even looked through my statements and I don't see any 1% bonuses. I do have other cards that truly pay 1% back, but this is not one of them.

There are many good programs that save you money when you use your credit card. However, you may not be aware of, or be able to take advantage of, these programs. There are still other times where you take advantage of the program and the credit card bank doesn't deliver on their promises.

SUMMARY

Called to have annual fee waived. I spoke to Ms. Lice. She put me on hold to look into waiving the fee. She said that I have to talk to an account specialist—she transferred me to Mr. Moth. He said that I'm getting that annual fee because I'm in a 1%-cash back program—I don't remember that. He said that if he removes that program, it will be a no-annual fee card—I did. I should see a $28 credit next month. I did get a letter saying the fee has been waived including a refund check.

TRANSCRIPT

Voice Menu: "Welcome to Cesky Bank cardmember services. Please enter your account number. Or if you are calling to apply for a new account, or check the status..."

Rep: "Thank you for calling credit card services, my name is Ms. Lice may I please have your name?"

Scott: "Scott Bilker."

Rep: "Thank you, and to better assist you, may I have your account number please?"

Scott: (I give her the number.)

Rep: "Thank you."

Scott: "Did you say your name was Ms. Lice."

Rep: "Yes."

Scott: "Oh."

Rep: "Mr. Bilker for verification purposes may I have your mother's maiden name?"

Scott: (I give her the name.)

Rep: "Thank you, how may I help you today?"

Scott: "Can you see my last statement?"

Rep: "Okay."

Scott: "Alright, now I was hoping that uh, Cesky Bank would waive this annual fee charge."

Rep: "Okay, in order to approve the mileage for the value miles."

Scott: "Excuse me."
Note: What is she talking about? I'm not in any mileage program?

Rep: "For the oh I'm sorry, for the cash, actually let me see...Let me look into that may I put you hold?"

Scott: "Sure."

On hold...

Rep: "Okay, is that annual fee for the card or for a program that you have on the card?"

Scott: "Oh, it looks like the card."
Note: The way it's showing in my statement is "annual fee." If it's a program like Auto Advantage, for example, it would be shown as a charge from another company.

Rep: "Okay, then I can transfer you to the customer center that can look into that for you, okay?"

Scott: "Okay."

Rep: "May I place you on hold while I transfer you?"

Scott: "Okay you are transferring me to who?"

Rep: "An account specialist."

Scott: "Oh, okay."

Rep: "Okay."

On hold...

Account Specialist: "Specialized services this is Mr. Moth speaking. How can I help you?"

Scott: "Hi, Mr. Moth. Do you have all my account information and everything?"

Account Specialist: "No, can I get that from you?"

Scott: "Okay..." (I give him the account number.)

Note: This really annoys me! It happens every time. I either enter the account number into the computer at the start of the call or tell all that stuff to the first rep. Then I'm transferred to the next human and have to start all over again. Just hang in there and calmly give them your information again.

Account Specialist: "Alright, one moment. And who am I speaking with?"

Scott: "Scott Bilker."

Account Specialist: "And your mother's maiden name?"

Scott: (I give him the name.)

Account Specialist: "Okay, and how can I help you?"

Scott: "Okay, can you see my account statement?"

Account Specialist: "Yes."

Scott: "Okay great. Well I was just talking to Ms. Lice and she said that I need to speak to an account specialist, that's you."

Account Specialist: "Yeah."

Scott: "Okay, umm, I was hoping Cesky Bank would waive that annual fee."

Account Specialist: "Do you know why you have that annual fee?"

Note: Yeah, because your bank wants to get me for every last dollar possible.

Scott: "It looks like an annual fee for the card."

Account Specialist: "Okay."

Scott: "If it's not from the card, then I have to look into where it is from."

Account Specialist: "Yeah, the reason why you are getting the $29, or the $28, is because you are getting 1% cash rebate back on your purchases. Is that the type of program that you would not be interested in? Because I can take you out of the program and waive the annual fee and you would have a no annual fee card."
Note: I don't remember any "cash back" from purchases.

Scott: "1% cash back. Yeah, you can take me out of that program."
Note: I'll let him save face with this lame reason to waive the annual fee.

Account Specialist: "Okay. Would you also be interested in doing a balance transfer at a lower annual percentage rate?"

Scott: "Umm, not today but you can be sure that in the future I will, that's for sure. When will I see that refund, credit? Next month?"
Note: I should have asked him about the rates when he made this offer—oh well, just be sure you always ask because you never know what kind of deal they'll have available.

Account Specialist: "Let me find that out for you, one second."

Scott: "Okay."

Account Specialist: "Yes, I will go ahead and remove the annual fee from your account. You will see a reflection on your next month's statement as well as receiving a confirmation letter confirming that I did remove it for you."

Scott: "And the only changes are the 1%. Everything else is the same on the account?"

Account Specialist: "That's correct."

Scott: "Okay. Thank you Mr. Moth."

Account Specialist: "You're welcome, have a good night Mr. Bilker."

Scott: "Bye-bye."

Account Specialist: "Bye-bye."

CALL #2.08: LISTEN TO THEIR OFFERS

Reason For Call:	Annual Fee Waived
Result:	They didn't waive the fee so I had to change card type to avoid the fee.
Difficulty Level:	Hard
Call Time:	7 minutes
Total Saved:	$28.00
$/hour to make call:	$240.00

Although I didn't get the annual fee waived, from this initial phone call, it's a great example of how to apply many of the techniques that do work 99% of the time. You'll find that, in general, most banks will waive annual fees without giving you any trouble—this example is truly the exception.

SUMMARY

They said they're standing firm on the annual fee and tracking who closes the accounts because of the fee. Mr. Housefly said he sees from my record that I can go to any other bank I want and also said, "Don't you think I would waive it if I could." I kind of believe this.

The end of this story is that I did eventually call back to take their option for the no-annual-fee card and saved the $28 annual fee.

TRANSCRIPT

Rep: "Thank you for calling Chow Chow Bank, this is Mrs. Silverfish, may I have your account number please?"

Scott: "Sure..." (I give her the number.)

Rep: "Your name please?"

Scott: "Scott Bilker."

Rep: "Mr. Bilker, your mother's maiden name?"

Scott: (I give her the name.)

Rep: "How can I help you?"

Scott: "Okay, I'm looking at my account this month and I see I have an annual fee of $28. I was wondering if that can be waived."
Note: Always start with the simple, direct, approach.

Rep: "At this time no ss...well let me just check on one thing just a minute, one second, one thing, real fast...Okay, the only thing I can offer you sir is what's called an annual fee waiver program which basically offers to remove the annual fee for a year and it gives you an interest rate of 10.65% for six months and that will waive the annual fee for one year."

Scott: "Hmm, well I have this 6.9% offer that I'm about to use but I don't think I should get this annual fee. I've got plenty of other offers from other banks to use that have no annual fees."
Note: Right away they offer me a different card that has no annual fee. I could have taken this deal right here but I wanted to push the issue to see what would happen.

Rep: "Well like I said, I can offer that fee, I mean that program for 10.65% on all transactions on the account and that will waive the annual fee for the next year. Then next year when it comes on again you can always get put back on to that program again."

Scott: "Hmmm, that's the only other thing?"
Note: Sure it is! ☺ I never believe what they initially tell me.

Rep: "That's the only thing we can offer to do at this time, yes sir."

Scott: "Hmmm, well how would I go about closing my account then?"
Note: I'm a little too jumpy here. I should have held out longer before saying that I want to close the account.

Rep: "I can go ahead and have that done for you sir and you would receive just one more billing showing a zero balance okay?"

Scott: "Hmmm."
Note: The good news is that if I close my account, I will get the annual fee refunded.

Rep: "If I did close it for you. Do you want me to close it?"

Scott: "Ummm, I'm thinking about it. Is there a manager there I could talk to?"

Rep: "I can get you in touch with a manager. Can you hold one moment for me?"

Scott: "Sure."

Rep: "Thanks."

On hold...

Manager: "Hello this is Mr. Housefly, how can I help you?"

Scott: "Ummm, I was just talking with Mrs. Silverfish about having that annual fee waived and she only gave me one option of like a 10.65% account."

Manager: "That's the lowest account, annual percentage rate we have for a no-annual fee account. It can go lower, well it can't go to 6.9. But that's a promotional offer but we can get it...the lowest we can get it...that we can lower it here is the prime rate plus zero, however, that's an annual-fee account, that's a rebate account. The lowest we can get it without an annual fee is prime rate plus 2.15% which is currently 10.65%."

Scott: "Right, well I've got that 6.9% offer that you can use by November which I'm probably going to be using, in fact, most likely, uh, very shortly. But in any case, you know the way I see it here is I've charged and repaid, on time, thousands of dollars to your Chow Chow Bank over the years. Even when, in the past, there has been erroneous information and problems with my account that have been resolved and I was hoping that the Chow Chow Bank would waive this annual fee as a courtesy."
Note: Two techniques here: (1) I said that I would use a promotional offer soon and (2) I pointed out how much business I've given them in the past. Either one of these facts have gotten my annual fee waived on many occasions from many other banks.

Manager: "Well we can uh, they have just instituted this policy, last year if you'd have called...Your scores are awesome! We'd have popped it right off. It has nothing to do with your credit history. Your credit history is great! We can see that. They made it a policy change. A conscious policy change that started in effect of June of this year that the accounts are going to be charged an annual fee and those ones that are going to be waived...see we can't even offer this waiver that we're offering you on every account. Only the ones that are in good standing. So they're very seriously at the current, at the present time, I mean, emphasizing that the annual fees are going to stay one way or the other. Either, and even, when, when they change it to a no-annual fee account in the next 12 months you have to pay $40 in finance charges, ah $28 in your case, I'm sorry. So one way or the other they're going to ah, basically ah, get the annual fee."

Scott: "Well, that's really a shame. I mean, I've got a lot of other cards that have no annual fee."
Note: I almost believe that the manager would like to waive my fee. He has acknowledged that the points I made about my history with the bank are true.

Manager: "I understand that. I can, I can see your scores and that you have no problem going anywhere you want. Unfortunately, believe me, don't you think I would remove it if I was permitted? The only way I can remove it is with a no-annual fee account and that's, that raises your rate 4 points, 3 points, in the current time, no 4%, 6.9% to 10.65%, nearly 4 points."

Scott: "Hmmm, 'cause now I have to seriously consider closing the Chow Chow Bank account."

Manager: "Yeah, that's one of the options obviously. You can see how much you can make with the, ah, no-annual-fee account. Or how much, well $28, can you save $28 by using the 6.9% that's the other way."

Scott: "Well, that's what I'll have to look at but you know it's a shame, I mean, I've always had a good relationship with Chow Chow Bank. Everything worked out fine."

Manager: "No I agree. I can see that. Trust me. We appreciate it. 'Cause I mean I see that. But unfortunately they changed their, well I don't want to say, unfortunately changed their policy, they decided to make a policy change that was effective June of this year with respect to the annual fees."

Scott: "Hmmm, is there anyone I can talk to about that policy? Or is that just set in stone?"
Note: Always try to get to the next level of authority. I didn't ask firmly enough in this case. I should have said, "I want to speak to your boss."

Manager: "Basically we sit at the bottom of the food chain."
Note: He's admitting to being a bottom-feeder.

Scott: "Right."

Manager: "I mean they make the decisions and they...it isn't...they're tracking these accounts. A lot of people there are obviously, umm, people upset with this and they're closing the accounts or something and they're tracking everyone that gets closed so you never know, they might overturn it. But at this point in time they, they're standing firm, they're going to keep it just like this."

Scott: "Alright, well then I'll, I'll, just have to think about it and make a decision. Thank you."

Manager: "You're very welcome."

Scott: "Bye-bye."

Manager: "Thanks for calling. Goodbye sir."

Note: I did call the bank later and take the option to change the card type to a no-annual fee card thus saving the $28 fee.

CALL #2.09: TEACH THEM A LESSON

Reason For Call:	Annual Fee Waived
Result:	Fee wasn't waived. Account closed to avoid fee and punish bank!
Difficulty Level:	Hard
Call Time:	5 minutes
Total Saved:	$20.00
$/hour to make call:	$240.00

Ultimately, if the banks don't do as we demand there does come a time when we need to reinforce our power as the consumer. They need to learn that we're not just blowing smoke. We are their customers and we will, and can, take our business elsewhere! They need to learn that we will follow through with our threats!

For this particular account I've called to have my annual fee waived for the last three years and haven't used the account in that time. This is certainly why they don't want to waive the fee. That's just too bad for them because now there's no chance that I'm ever going to use the account again! I guess that from their point of view I was never going to use it anyway. Since this call, I started rotating through all my credit card accounts periodically so they each get used for a couple weeks each year.

SUMMARY

I called and spoke to Mrs. Bedbug. She wouldn't waive the annual fee so I asked to speak to her supervisor. I spoke to Mrs. Stag Beetle who said that the annual fee is not negotiable because it's a cash-based account with a $1 per check fee. I asked if I could do a balance transfer by phone and get the fee waived and she said no, so I closed the account. I'll see the $20 credit on the next statement.

TRANSCRIPT

Scott: "Boxer Bank, February 4th. Calling to get the annual fee waived."
Note: Making a memo on the tape.

Voice Menu: "Welcome to Boxer Bank. We are pleased to have you as a Boxer Bank credit account member. If you are calling from a touch-tone phone please..."

Rep: "This is Ms. Bedbug speaking, may I have your account number please."

Scott: "Sure it's..." (I give her the number.)

Rep: "Okay. And name please."

Scott: "Scott Bilker. I'm sorry, what was your name again?"

Rep: "My name is Ms. Bedbug. And how can I help you today Mr. Bilker."

Scott: "I noticed that I have an annual fee on my account this month. I was hoping you could waive that fee."

Rep: "Okay, I can check for you. Just can you please verify your date of birth."

Scott: "Sure..." (I give her the date.)

Rep: "Your mother's maiden name."

Scott: (I give her the name.)

Rep: "Okay, Mr. Bilker unfortunately I will not be able to waive the annual fee because there is no waive on your fee this year."

Scott: "Hmm, why is that?"

Rep: "It is already decided not to waive."

Scott: "Hmm, let me think here. I've got like four Boxer Bank accounts with charges of probably...oh, I've charged and repaid over like $100,000 over the course of my relationship with Boxer Bank. So I'm thinking, it would be good to waive this annual fee."

Rep: "Right sir, I do understand that, but we cannot waive the fee for you."

Scott: "Okay, can I speak to your supervisor?"

Rep: "Sure, no problem."

On hold...

Supervisor: "Hello Mr. Bilker."

Scott: "Yes."

Rep: "I have Ms. Stag Beetle; she is an account supervisor who will further assist you."

Scott: "What's her name?"

Supervisor: "My name is Ms. Stag Beetle, Mr. Bilker."

Scott: "Oh, Ms. Stag Beetle. How are you doing?"

Supervisor: "I'm well thanks, and yourself?"

Scott: "Very good."

Supervisor: "I'm glad to hear that. I understand that you were requesting a supervisor."

Scott: "Yes, yes."

Supervisor: "Okay. Mr. Bilker how can I assist you today?"

Scott: "Okay, I was calling to see if you would waive the annual fee on this one account."

Supervisor: "Can you hold for a moment please Mr. Bilker?"

Scott: "Sure."

Supervisor: "Thank you just a moment...Mr. Bilker in the past we did remove the fees on this account. We are no longer removing the fees on these accounts."

Scott: "Okay, well I can understand how that can be a policy, but I have four other Boxer Bank accounts, where I have charged and repaid about a $100,000 in my relationship with your Boxer Bank. So I'm thinking it is not too much of a thing to ask to have this account fee waived."
Note: I realize at this point, that because I haven't used the card, I'm probably not going to get the fee waived. It was after this call that I began actively rotating my credit card accounts so I use them for at least two weeks each year.

Supervisor: "Right, well based on the type of account that it is, you don't get charged the fees for using the account. It's a cash-based account."

Scott: "Uh huh."

Supervisor: "You can pay cash out and not get charged a 3% transaction fee, and not get charged the rate that cash is going out right now, which is 20.55% on the account. You just get charged per check $1, that you use, and of course the rate of interest, umm, which is 16%. So we are not adjusting fees on this account that umm, the annual membership fees on this account any longer."

Scott: "Hmm. Can you do balance transfers by phone?"

Supervisor: "On this account?"

Scott: "Yes."

Supervisor: "Yes, we can do balance transfers."

Scott: "And there is only that $1 fee?"

Supervisor: "Right, it's the same as if you were to write a check, yeah. Just $1 per check."

Scott: "If I were to do a balance transfer now, would you waive the fee?"

Supervisor: "The $1?"

Scott: "No, no, would you waive the annual fee?"
Note: It's worth a shot. I'm trying to see if the lure of the balance transfer is going to give them reason to waive the annual fee.

Supervisor: "No, the fee is non-negotiable. The fee cannot be adjusted."

Scott: "Non-negotiable."

Supervisor: "Right."

Scott: "Hmm, alright then I would like to close my account."
Note: Time for them to pay for their unwillingness to satisfy a good customer!

Supervisor: "Can you verify your mailing address please?"

Scott: "Sure, it's..." (I give her the address.)

Supervisor: "Okay just a moment please."

Pause...

Supervisor: "Okay, we have closed the account and adjusted the $20 fee, your fee adjustment will be reflected on the statement that you get next."

Scott: "Okay."

Supervisor: "Okay, notification will be sent to you, you will receive it in 7 to 10 business days."

Scott: "Alright thank you."

Supervisor: "You're welcome, thank you for calling Boxer Bank."

CALL #2.10: SURE IT CAN'T BE WAIVED

Reason For Call:	Annual Fee Waived
Result:	Mission complete
Difficulty Level:	Medium
Call Time:	7 minutes
Total Saved:	$28.00
$/hour to make call:	$240.00

This card said last year that they wouldn't waive the annual fee anymore. You know, that "policy changed" routine. Instead, they changed the type of card to a non-rewards program that doesn't have an annual fee. But when the bill came this year it seems the annual fee has returned.

SUMMARY

Last year on 9/24 (call #2.07) I called to have the annual fee waived. I spoke to Ms. Lice. She put me on hold to look into waiving the fee. She said that I have to talk to an account specialist—she transferred me to Mr. Moth. He said that I'm getting that annual fee because I'm in a 1%-cash back program. He said that if he removes that program, then it would be a no-annual fee card. I did remove the program and later received a letter saying the fee has been waived.

Now, a year later, I received a bill with a charge for the annual fee. After creating a report on the account I discovered that I've charged, and repaid $60,052.00 over the life of this account. Of that, $1,901.26 is in interest paid and other bank charges. We've had the account for 10 years so that's about $200 per year in fees to the bank!

I called and spoke to Mrs. Dogtick. Of course she said that she couldn't waive the fee. She couldn't help me so she transferred me to an account specialist. After putting me on hold for a few minutes, Mrs. Dogtick came back and said that she spoke with the account specialist and explained what I said about last year's call. She told me that they, as a courtesy, removed the fee for the card. It should now be a no-fee account. We'll see.

They sent me a letter on 9/27 saying the fee was removed because of the phone call. The letter stated, "Thank you for continuing to make us your credit card of choice. We are writing to confirm that we have removed the $28.00 annual fee, as agreed during your recent telephone call."

TRANSCRIPT

Scott: "Cesky Bank, today is September 23. Calling to get my annual fee waived, they did it last year. It was never supposed to appear again."
Note: Making a memo on the tape.

Voice Menu: "Please hold while I transfer your call."

Rep: "Thank you for calling credit card services. My name is Mrs. Dogtick, may I have your name please?"

Scott: "Scott Bilker."

Rep: "Thanks. And to better assist you may I have your account number please?"

Scott: "Sure..." (I give her the number.)

Rep: "Okay, let me pull up your account. And your mother's maiden name or password for verification please?"

Scott: (I give her the name)

Rep: "Thank you so much Mr. Bilker, and how may I help you today."

Scott: "Okay well, you can see my latest account statement right?"

Rep: "Yes."

Scott: "And you see this annual charge?"

Rep: "Right."

Scott: "Well, that annual charge is not supposed to be there."

Rep: "Okay. Well, what I can do is transfer you to our specialty department. They will be able to assist you with the annual fee. I'm showing that the annual fee is billed correctly, so if you would like to have that reduced unfortunately the account would be closed."

Scott: "Okay, well, listen. A year ago I called about this and I spoke to Ms. Lice, and I spoke then again to Mr. Moth, who was an account specialist, who said I was getting the annual fee because I was in a 1% cash-back program. He said if he removed that program there would be no annual fee on the card, and he said it was taken care of. So this is supposed to be a no annual fee card."
Note: I love being able to quote from my notes, plus I do have the actual call recorded. One may say that I'm going overboard with the documentation, however, it has saved me much time and money so it does turn out to be worth the effort.

Rep: "Like I said I can transfer you. I don't, unfortunately, make the decisions concerning the annual fees. They can go ahead and speak to you concerning that. If that is something that we can remove as a courtesy, then I can. But my experience with annual fees is that we don't remove them unless you are closing the account. So I can definitely check on it for you, and you can speak to him concerning it, I'm just like I said giving you basic information that I have in front of me."

Note: She did give me a tip. She said that they would remove the charge if I were closing the account. But it's still the same story "We don't waive the fee."

Scott: "Okay."

Rep: "Is there anything else I can help you with otherwise?"

Scott: "No, that will be fine, just transfer me to the account specialist."

Rep: "You're welcome, you have a good day, thank you so much for holding."

On hold...

Rep: "Thank you so much for holding. Okay, I just went ahead and had our specialty department remove it off the account for you as a courtesy, because the program was ended and they did not remove it off the account entirely."

Note: Great! They didn't even mess with me. The rep took care of the entire situation or she was just bluffing and could have waived the fee at any time. Who knows—as long as they credit my account!

Scott: "Okay, so what happened, again?"

Rep: "Okay, previously when you called us they didn't have it completely removed. I just spoke with them and they took it off for you."

Scott: "Okay, so in other words, where was the miscommunication? They just, it wasn't done fully last year?"

Note: I'm being nice and letting them save face.

Rep: "Exactly."

Scott: "And it has been completed now? So I guess I'll see a credit by my next statement?"

Rep: "I would say so yes, within the next 30 days."

Scott: "Okay Mrs. Dogtick."

Rep: "Is there anything else I can do for you?"

Scott: "No, that will be all."

Rep: "You have a good day and thank you for calling."

CALL #2.11: "MEMBERSHIP FEE" MAY MEAN "ANNUAL FEE"

Reason For Call:	Annual Fee Waived
Result:	Mission complete
Difficulty Level:	Hard
Call Time:	6 minutes
Total Saved:	$29.00
$/hour to make call:	$290.00

This call is an excellent example of all the strategies from this chapter and a demonstration of how perseverance pays off. At this point I think it's clear that the credit card industry, independent of individual banks, has its own scripted responses designed to get us to give up, not to pursue the refunds we deserve. Well, we're not going to give up!

SUMMARY

This is a good one because the first bank representative really goes into detail as to why the membership fee is so important.

I received my statement and noticed a $29 "membership fee." I took out the photocopy of the application and it specifically said "No Annual Fee." It also said this in the letter that came with the application. However, there was a footnote that said you have to be approved for a special type of card or else there is a "membership fee."

I called and spoke to Ms. Honeybee. I asked about the annual fee and she gave me the rundown. I explained that they basically put one over on me. After listening to why they have the fee, I asked if she could waive it and she said no. I asked to speak to her supervisor and she said that the supervisor couldn't waive the fee either.

I then spoke to Ms. Bumblebee, account supervisor. She immediately waived the fee.

TRANSCRIPT

Scott: "Okay, I'm calling Rottweiler Bank to remove the annual fee."
Note: Making a memo on the tape.

Voice Menu: "Welcome to Rottweiler Bank business services..."

Rep: "Thank you for calling. This is Ms. Honeybee, can I get the account number please?"

Scott: "Hi Ms. Honeybee..." (I give her the number.)

Rep: "Okay. And your name please?"

Scott: "Scott Bilker."

Rep: "Do you have a current email address that I can update your account with?"

Scott: "It's not really important."
Note: Yeah, right! Like I really want them to start spamming me.

Rep: "Okay. And how can I help you today?"

Scott: "Okay. I'm looking at my current month's statement here, and I see this $29 membership fee."

Rep: "Okay."

Scott: "What's that all about?"
Note: I know, I know, it's about them making as much as possible but I thought I'd listen to their explanation—for our training of course. ☺

Rep: "The membership fee is for the Rottweiler Bank credit card. What that does is that it covers the 100% fraud protection on your account. It also covers the cost of Rottweiler Bank being open 24 hours a day, 7 days a week so that we can answer any questions you might have about the account. It also covers that if you ever add anybody to the account as authorized users we don't charge you to issue out a credit card to them. And if your card ever gets magnetized, lost, breaks in any way, or the magnetic strip becomes worn, we don't charge you to issue out a new credit card for that. So there's just a lot of different fees that are associated with the membership fee."
Note: Please, spare me the sob story. I can hear the violins—fraud protection, keeping the bank open 24/7, come on! The law protects me against fraud. And by the way, if they want my business, they'd better have hours when I can call. If they tried to charge me any fees for replacing a lost card or adding another user (who makes them more money by spending) I would immediately fire them and use another bank!

Scott: "Now, when I first applied for this card Ms. Honeybee, I distinctly remember, in fact, I even have the original letter here and it says. You know, no annual fee."

Rep: "Okay. There was a membership fee on the account. The first year you did not have a membership fee because it was differed for the first year. But after the first year you do have a membership fee of $29."

Scott: "I did look and I saw that when I more closely examined the paperwork that came with the account, it did say that there is a membership fee, exactly what you're telling me. However, I didn't realize that until I got this now. But when I look at my original invitation that I filled out back in March. It specifically said, you know, 'no annual fee.' So I'm..."

Rep: "On the back of the application though…"

Scott: "Right, on the application where I filled it out and sent it in."

Rep: "Right, but what I'm saying is that on the original application. When you first got it in the mail, if you would have flipped it over on the back on read all the information back there. It told you that if you went over your credit limit you would have a $29 overlimit fee."

Scott: "Right."

Rep: "There would be a $29 past-due fee."

Scott: "Um hmm."

Rep: "And a membership fee from accounts, depending on what you qualify for of $29."

Scott: "Yes, I do see that. I still have that letter."

Rep: "It wasn't a guarantee that you would not have a membership fee. It was just if you qualify for a credit card that did not have a membership fee."

Scott: "I see. And because I didn't get charged for an annual fee the first year I didn't see it then. Okay, well can we go ahead and waive that annual fee Ms. Honeybee?"
Note: They got me! They did trick me in the fine print but no matter, I'm going to have them waive that annual fee right now!

Rep: "Let's see what we can do. I'm not sure, but let's see what we can do…At this time we are not able to waive that annual membership fee for you."

Scott: "Um hmm."
Note: Yeah, yeah, that's what they all say.

Rep: "But the accounts sometimes do get reviewed for that."

Scott: "Okay. Is there someone else that I can ask about this? Like maybe your supervisor?"

Rep: "I can transfer you. I'm not sure they are going to be able to do anything, but we can certainly see. Just a moment okay?"

Scott: "Alright."
Note: Oh man, I hear that on nearly every call. It's such a catch-phrase attempt to get me to give up.

Rep: "Thank you."

On hold...

Rep: "Mr. Bilker?"

Scott: "Yes."

Rep: "Thank you so much for holding. I have Ms. Bumblebee on the other line and she is going to be able to further assist you, okay?"

Scott: "Thank you."

Rep: "You're welcome."

Supervisor: "Hi Mr. Bilker, thank you for holding. My name is Ms. Bumblebee and I'm an account supervisor here at Rottweiler Bank."

Scott: "Okay."

Supervisor: "And I understand that you wanted to discuss your annual fee."

Scott: "Yes. I was really hoping that we could go ahead and waive that fee this time."
Note: I start again at being nice.

Supervisor: "Well, I'd be happy to take a look at that for you."

Scott: "Okay great."

Supervisor: "One moment. Well the account has been opened for about a year now."

Scott: "Umm hmm."

Supervisor: "What I will do is I'll go ahead and give you a credit for the fee for this year."
Note: That's more like it.

Scott: "Ah huh."

Supervisor: "Then at this time next year it will be billed again and you can call in and we'll see if we can remove it at that point as well."
Note: So, not only are they going to waive it this year, but they'll consider waiving it next year. That's why it's so important to press on, not give in, and always ask to speak to a supervisor.

Scott: "Okay Ms. Bumblebee."

Supervisor: "I will go ahead and put a $29 credit on your account. Was there anything else I can help you with for the day?"

Scott: "No, that will be all."

Supervisor: "Okay. Well thank you for calling and have a good day."

Scott: "You too Ms. Bumblebee."

Supervisor: "Thank you. Good bye."

Scott: "Bye-bye."

CHAPTER 3

LATE PAYMENT, OVERLIMIT, AND CASH ADVANCE FEES

LATE FEES

How late do you have to be to get a late fee? Answer: One day! That's amazing! It used to be that these fees were charged on accounts that were 30 days late, but today it's a different story.

And how much are those late fees? Some are $35 or more! To me, it's analogous to getting robbed in an alley at gunpoint. Talk about an unfair fee. The punishment sure doesn't match the crime.

I've mailed in payments with plenty of time to allow for the mail to arrive but I've still been late by exactly one day.

So how is it that I was exactly one day late?

Actually, there have been many lawsuits because of this very issue. The allegations include statements like "payments received by U.S. mail that were processed by a third-party vendor failed to credit payments promptly." Another lawsuit charges that "credit card accountholders were improperly charged for, among other things, higher interest rates on balance transfers and late-payment fees." And still another states, "The use of 9:00 a.m., Eastern Time, cut-off time for crediting credit card payments received by U.S. mail is unreasonable and that the bank fails to credit payments promptly." In all these cases the banks settled out of court.

The translation is that payments weren't credited to accounts on time. Mistake? Who knows? All I know for sure is that I mail my payments in with plenty of time to spare and have been charged late fees for being one day late. I'm not going to let banks get away with charging me that ridiculous fee. There are just too many other banks that want my business. Too many other banks that are willing to treat me with respect.

The bottom line is that if you've ever been charged a late fee, then it's time to pick up the phone and get that fee credited back to your account. Don't be thinking, "Oh, well I really was late so I deserve the fee." I don't care if you were late and it was your fault. Remember that old saying, "The customer is always right." Say that late fee was $1,000.00. Would you think the same way? Absolutely not! And it's the same with a $35 penalty for being one day late.

Most banks have a policy of waiving the first late fee automatically if you call, so be sure to call. If you have more than one late fee, then you may have to spend some time convincing them that they had better remove the other late fees or you won't use their credit card anymore.

OVERLIMIT FEES

An overlimit fee is another back-alley robbery charge you get hit with if you make charges above your limit. You must be asking yourself, "How do I go over the limit if all the computers that approve my charges know my limit? How can I get approved for a charge that's above my limit?" Maybe the answer is, "So that the bank can charge me an overlimit fee." ☺

It is possible that you can go over your limit by accident. For example, say you're at your maximum charge limit and miss a payment. On the next statement the interest charges will drive you over the limit and then you'd pay an overlimit fee.

One person told me how they were at their maximum limit and the bank charged them an annual fee. Well, the annual fee caused the account to go over the limit and they were then penalized with an overlimit fee!

If you are charged an overlimit fee, be sure to call the bank and get that fee waived. You can tell them that you're going to pay down the balance below the limit on the next payment.

Also, while you have them on the phone, apply to have your credit line increased so that, if for some reason, you can't pay your balance down below the current limit, you'll be under the new limit.

If you cannot get the bank to give you a credit-line increase, then you must take other action to get your balance below the maximum. If not, they will charge you that overlimit fee month after month, and when you add that to the interest payments, you'll find that you'll never be able to get out of debt because 99% of your monthly payment goes toward paying these two fees!

One effective strategy to get your balance under the limit is to transfer some of your balance to another card. That's why it's so important to have credit options.

Say you owe $4,300 on a credit card with a maximum limit of $4,000. That means that you'd be $300 over and you'd be getting charged an overlimit fee until you can pay that off. Simply apply for another credit card, or use an existing credit card, and transfer $500 to that new card from the overlimit card. Then you'd have two credit cards with balances of $3,800 and $500 which will stop the overlimit fees (in this example).

When looking for new credit cards, be sure to make banks compete for your business before you take advantage of their offers. There's more on shopping for credit deals in chapter 6.

CASH ADVANCE FEES

Typically, there is a one-time charge to get a cash advance from your credit cards. This also includes writing yourself a check that's linked to your credit lines. It's even possible to be charged this fee when you call to make a balance transfer.

There may be cases where the bank won't charge fees under certain conditions. For example, when you're transferring a balance from another credit card or when they're running a special promotion. Just be sure that if you are charged a cash advance fee, it's something you knew about prior to getting the cash.

Many times I've accepted balance transfer offers that say there are no fees for doing transfers. Later, when my statement arrives, I find a transfer fee posted to the account!

Whenever you find a charge that's not supposed to be on your account, you must call to get that removed. Don't let them take your money—certainly not without a fight!

One last item about cash advance fees. There are many credit offers that state that you can "cash advance up to your limit," but in the fine print it says that the cash advance fee is going to be added to your balance. So in reality, the entire amount, cash advance plus fees, cannot be over that limit. Be certain that you know if you can actually use your entire credit line for a balance transfer or if you must stay under the limit, including fees.

Call #3.01: First Late Fee is Easily Waived

Reason For Call:	Late Fee Waived
Result:	Mission complete
Difficulty Level:	Easy
Call Time:	4 minutes
Total Saved:	$20.00
$/hour to make call:	$300.00

This call demonstrates that most banks have a policy of waiving the first late payment fee. And that's for being late for any reason. So don't just let them charge you that fee. Call right now!

SUMMARY

My first late, so they removed the fee—no problem!

TRANSCRIPT

Voice Menu: "Calls may be randomly monitored or recorded."

Scott: "Yours too. That's right. Yours too."

Rep: "Good afternoon. This is Katy Dids. How may I help you?"

Scott: "Hi. Um, can you see my statement?"

Rep: "No sir. I do not have your account."

Scott: "Okay, my number?"

Rep: "Yes sir."

Scott: "You don't have it?"

Rep: "No."

Scott: "I entered it."

Rep: "I'm sorry. It did not come through. I do not have it."
Note: The voice menu advised me to enter my account number with the touch-tone phone and I did. You'd think that they have you enter your account number for a reason, like to get that information to the rep so they know it when they finally speak to you. That seems never to be the case. The rep always asks for the number again.

Scott: "Okay..." (I give her the number.)

Rep: "Thank you. And for verification may I please have your name and social security number?"

Scott: "Scott Bilker..." (I tell her the information.)

Rep: "An um, you said you wanted me to look at your billing?"

Scott: "Yes."

Rep: "Okay, and how can I help you?"

Scott: "Okay, um you'll notice there is a late charge on the 14th for $20."

Rep: "Yes."

Scott: "And um, I was hoping that could be waived."

Rep: "Let's see here. Well looking at your account it looks like it's the first time you've been late so I should be able to remove that late charge for you as a courtesy because you have a good account. Okay, okay, the $20 should have been removed."

Scott: "Beautiful. Could you note, in my account, that I pay my bill as soon as I get it and I just got the latest one so I don't know why it was late, but if you could just note that somewhere for future reference."
Note: I'm setting this up so that if I'm late again there is some record that I always pay when the bill arrives, so it must be their fault.

Rep: "Okay, and I'll go ahead and adjust the account."

Scott: "Alright well thank you very much."

Rep: "Okay, well thank you for calling. We do appreciate your business."

Scott: "Oh, you know what. What is your name."

Rep: "Katy. Katy Dids."

Scott: "Alright, thank you Katy."

Rep: "Thank you for calling."

Scott: "Bye-bye."

Call #3.02: Broken Promises in Offers

Reason For Call:	Cash Advance Fees and Overlimit Fees Waived
Result:	Mission complete
Difficulty Level:	Hard
Call Time:	7 minutes
Total Saved:	$285.00
$/hour to make call:	$2,442.86

Here's a beauty. The bank offered me a deal where I transfer my balance from another bank, using one of their checks. They also said that I wouldn't be charged any fees. The letter said that I could use up to my entire credit line to do the transfer.

Well, I received my credit card statement and found that, not only have I been charged the maximum cash advance fee, but when that's added to the amount I wrote the check for, the total made my balance go over my limit!

They charged me $260 for the cash advance fee then $25 for going over my limit when using the offer as they instructed! Boy, am I mad about this one!

This incident occurred on my wife's account so she had to give the okay for my speaking on her behalf. If you have trouble being tough on the phone then have your spouse or a friend give you a hand. We all know somebody who is very assertive. That person will be happy to help.

This call is also an example of why you need to always save the original paperwork from any low-rate transfer offer. That goes for any business correspondence from credit card banks. Ultimately, it's the letter I have in my possession that convinces them to reverse all the charges.

SUMMARY

Spoke to Ms. Cockroach. I told her that the offer stated I could write checks "up to my limit." It didn't say up to my limit with cash advance fees included. I also said there was no mention of the cash advance fees in the letter.

They reversed the charges.

TRANSCRIPT

Went through the voice menu. I was just hitting any button so I could get to a human.

Rep: "Saluki Bankcard services, my name is Ms. Cockroach. May I please have your account number?"

Larissa: (Gives her the number.)

Rep: "Thank you. Your name and address."

Larissa: "Larissa Bilker..." (Gives her the address)

Rep: "Thank you. And the last four digits of your social security number?"

Larissa: (Gives her the number.)

Rep: "And how can I help you?"

Larissa: "Um, I would like my husband to speak on my behalf concerning my account."

Rep: "Alright."

Larissa: "Thank you."

Scott: "I'm here. Okay Riss..."

Rep: "Hi."

Scott: "Hi. My name is Scott."

Rep: "And how can I help you?"

Scott: "Okay, let's look at that last month's statement. You said your name is Ms. Cockroach?"

Rep: "Yes it is."

Scott: "Okay, alright. Can you see it?"

Rep: "How can I help you sir?"

Scott: "Alright, um, I see the transaction for $6,500 and this overlimit fee. What is that?"
Note: It's the bank trying to rip me off. However, I will give them a chance to explain.

Rep: "That is over...for being over the credit limit. Wait a minute, one moment. Okay sir, your credit limit, um, at that time...you had a credit limit increase that came through on June 3rd."

Scott: "Right."

Rep: "So, before that...what the limit was. You had exceeded the limit at that time. That's why you had a $25 overlimit fee."

Scott: "Well, the limit before that was $6,500."

Rep: "$6,500 was the credit limit."

Scott: "Umm hmm."

Rep: "And that fee..."

Scott: "Yeah."

Rep: "You know that um, 4% transaction fee."

Scott: "Uh huh, whoa."

Rep: "That promo check fee."

Scott: "There shouldn't be any, ah, percent transaction fee. Well you know that..."

Rep: "Well, okay, yeah, that was why that it was showing it was over the limit when that fee was added. So if you wrote out one of the checks to transfer that balance from Boxer Bank."

Scott: "Emm hmm. Um, um, it says, in the PS of this letter from Saluki Bank."
Note: Keep all paperwork. In this case I'm looking right at the original letter with the credit offer.

Rep: "Uh huh."

Scott: "You can 'write your checks for any amount up to your available credit limit.' It seems like it's saying the available credit limit is $6,500."

Rep: "Right, that was the credit limit. But it, what it doesn't say is that fee, that fee actually took you over in this case."
Note: It's nice that she agrees that the letter "doesn't say" what it should.

Scott: "It doesn't say up to your limit..."

Rep: "Well."

Scott: "With fees included. (small laugh, more like a giggle.) In fact it doesn't even say there's going to be a 4% check fee anywhere in this little promotion. It says 'see terms and conditions herein' but it doesn't mention that fee. It said 'save money on the Winter Sale Checks' but it doesn't seem like I'm saving anything

here. It seems like it cost three hundred and something dollars for nothing. So, I'm hoping you can help me, and reverse those fees."
Note: Case made, then ask for refund.

Rep: "Okay, Mr. Bilker. I'm not able to reverse the fees but I will speak to a supervisor. Can you hold please?"

Scott: "Sure."

Rep: "Thank you."

On hold...

Rep: "Okay, I've had a supervisor adjust the $25 overlimit fee as well as the $260 purchase check fee."

Scott: "It's been adjusted?"
Note: Boy they changed their tune quickly as soon as I started reading their original credit offer letter.

Rep: "Yes it has. And the minimum payment now will just reflect $136."

Scott: "Okay, $136, so..."

Rep: "Yeah."

Scott: "All that's been adjusted."

Rep: "Yes it has."

Scott: "So what's the balance now?"

Rep: "One moment. The balance is just $6,500 sir without those fees."

Scott: "Wow, that restores my confidence in Saluki Bank completely."

Rep: "Okay."

Scott: "And you're, can you just spell your name for my records."
Note: I want to make sure I have the name of this rep just in case the fees are not removed when I get the next statement. Well, in my case, I have the recordings to prove what was said.

Rep: "Sure, it's C-O-C-K-R-O-A-C-H."

Scott: "Alright, and I guess this will appear on next month's statement?"

Rep: "It sure will."

Scott: "Alright, well thank you very much."

Rep: "Sure, was there anything else I could help you about?"

Scott: "Um, no, that will be all for today."

Rep: "Okay, thank you for calling."

Scott: "Bye-bye."

Rep: "Bye."

CALL #3.03: ONE CALL, TWO FEES WAIVED

Reason For Call:	Overlimit and Late Fees Waived
Result:	Mission complete
Difficulty Level:	Easy
Call Time:	3 minutes
Total Saved:	$50.00
$/hour to make call:	$1,000.00

In this call I'm speaking on behalf of my friends Kelly and Tom Mayer (names changed). Kelly and Tom asked me to speak on their behalf as Tom, to make the call easier. There's a late fee and overlimit fee and I want to get them both removed.

SUMMARY

I spoke to the rep, Luna Moth, who waived both fees no problem. $50 saved in a few minutes.

TRANSCRIPT

Rep: "This is Luna Moth. May I have your name please?"

Kelly: "Yes, Kelly Mayer."

Rep: "And Ms. Mayer, may I have your social security number please?"

Kelly: (Gives her the number.)

Rep: "And your home phone number, with area code first."

Kelly: (Gives her the number.)

Rep: "And how may I help you today?"

Kelly: "Um, I'd like my husband to speak with you about my account."

Rep: "And this is about your Standard Card account?"

Kelly: "Yes."

Rep: "And your husband's name?"

Kelly: "Tom."

Rep: "Um, actually, Mr. Mayer is on the account with you."

Scott: "Oh, okay. So I can talk on the account too?"

Rep: "Yes sir."

Scott: "Okay, great. Okay, um can you look at my last statement please?"

Rep: "Your July billing statement?"

Scott: "Yes."

Rep: "Yes, sir."

Scott: "Okay great um, I was really hoping you could help me here. I see there's this past-due fee and overlimit fee and I was hoping that based on my account standing those could be waived."

Rep: "Past-due fee and overlimit...oh, you're looking on your August billing statement. Your most recent billing statement."

Scott: "That's correct."

Rep: "Okay. Now I am showing that there was a past-due fee and an overlimit fee placed on the account when the payment that was due on the 1st of July wasn't received."

Scott: "I know, but it was, we mailed it on time. It was only off by a day."

Rep: "I'm showing we received the payment on the 8th of July and the payment was due by the 1st..."
Note: Oops, oh well, I'm still going to argue and get those fees removed anyway. Don't be scared off by the truth. ☺

Scott: "I know..."

Rep: "...of July."

Scott: "I don't know what could have held it up, but I was hoping that Mexican Hairless Bank could do something."

Rep: "Well as a courtesy to you, Mr. Mayer, I can remove the fees on the account. But anytime a payment comes in after the past-due date..."
Note: Courtesy-shmertesy! They don't deserve $50 for doing nothing!

Scott: "Okay."

Rep: "A past-due fee will automatically be assessed on the account. And if your account is, at the time, um, over its limit, an account...the past-due fee, will draw behind that overlimit fee. And I would not be able to guarantee in the future that those fees will be able to be removed. But I can go ahead, and as a courtesy to you, remove the fees on the account."

Scott: "Okay, so both those fees: the past-due fee and the overlimit fee?"

Rep: "Yes, sir. I can remove those fees for you as a courtesy to you."

Scott: "Wow, thank you very much. What's your name again?"

Rep: "Luna Moth."

Scott: "Could you spell that for me?"

Rep: "L-U-N-A M-O-T-H."

Scott: "Well thank you very much Luna Moth."

Rep: "You're welcome. Is there anything else I can assist you with today?"

Scott: "What statement will that show up on? Those credits?"

Rep: "It will show up on your next billing statement."

Scott: "Great. Well, that's all you can help me with today."

Rep: "Alright. Well thank you for calling Mexican Hairless Bank."

Scott: "Thank you very much."

CALL #3.04: WINNING HALF THE ARGUMENT

Reason For Call:	Transfer Fee Waived
Result:	Mission complete
Difficulty Level:	Hard
Call Time:	11 minutes
Total Saved:	$10.00
$/hour to make call:	$54.55

It's not always possible to get everything you want, but be sure to try to walk away with something. Bargain for cash! In this next call, I couldn't get them to waive the entire fee however; they gave me some money, which makes the call worthwhile and the bank knows that I'm not going to simply allow them to take advantage of me!

SUMMARY

I called to make a simple transfer on their 5.9% offer. They said there is a transfer fee with a minimum of $2 or 2%, but not greater than $20. I told them I didn't want to pay the fee. I ended up getting transferred to someone who I had to threaten to use another card before she agreed to cut the fee in half to $10 instead of $20.

TRANSCRIPT

Rep: "This is Spittlebug. How may I help you?"

Scott: "Hi Spittlebug. I'd like to do a balance transfer."

Rep: "Okay, can I get your name please?"

Scott: "Scott Bilker."

Rep: "And could I get your mother's maiden name for security?"

Scott: (I give him the name.)

Rep: "Thank you, just one moment...Okay, um, let me just go ahead and get this form ready. How many were you going to transfer today?"

Scott: "One."

Rep: "Okay, and what is the name of the credit card?"

Scott: "Okay, before we go any further, I just want to verify all my terms here. Still 5.9% until like July, correct?"
Note: Always, always, always, ask how much they're going to charge for a balance transfer before you do it!

Rep: "5.9% variable. Yeah, it's based on the London Inner Bank Rate plus 0.3%. The London Inner Bank Rate, we actually review that during a year period, we review it quarterly so we review it four times during that period. Um, at the time that you received the notification looks like it's 5.6%. Which is plus 0.3% which is the 5.9%."

Scott: "Right."
Note: Yeah, whatever guy. Just give me the bottom line. Don't be confused with tech-speak. Get the APR.

Rep: "It can go up to, it went up to 5.7% and then from what I understand it just went back down to 5.5%. So it does vary a little bit."

Scott: "Hmmm. Uh, let me see. Alright let me go ahead and we'll do this transfer first."

Rep: "Okay, and you're aware of the transaction fee, right?"

Scott: "There's a transaction fee?"
Note: You should always ask directly if there's going to be a transfer fee.

Rep: "Um, hmm. 2% of the amount with a $2 minimum, $20 maximum."

Scott: "Hmmm, and that's going to count for the balance transfer--even if I do it by phone?"
Note: Many banks will waive balance transfer fees if done by phone rather than by sending checks.

Rep: "Yeah."

Scott: "There's no way they can waive that?"
Note: It would have been better to say something like, "I really want to do this transfer now but I don't want to pay that transfer fee."

Rep: "Uh, uh, no."

Scott: "Well, I might have to use a different card then. Alright, there's nothing they can do about that?"

Rep: "Not about the balance, uh the transfer fee, no."

Scott: "Cause I've got to tell you, I have other cards I can do this with, and they're not going to charge a balance transfer fee. But I got the Greenland Dog Bank Platinum card recently and I figured I'd let them have a little profit, but if they don't want it, then I'll just use a different card. Is there anyone there I can speak with?"

Note: That wasn't a strong enough or a very clear statement. I should have said, "Is there anyone there that I can speak with to discuss this matter of the balance transfer fee."

Rep: "Yeah."

Scott: "Who might be able to waive..."

Rep: "I don't know if they'll be able to do it. You can speak to uh, a supervisor, and then it's their decision if they decide to do it, that's fine."

Scott: "Okay."

Rep: "Okay, just one moment."

On hold...

Rep: "Thanks for holding. I have Mrs. Tarantulae on line and she's going to further assist you."

Scott: "Okay."

Supervisor: "Hello this is Mrs. Tarantulae. How may I help you?"

Scott: "Hi Mrs. Tarantulae. I'm a new customer of your Greenland Dog Bank. And I called and was going to do a balance transfer, and then I found out about the transfer fee and it's $2, 2%, or $20 max, if I do it over the phone. I was hoping it could be waived on my first transfer."

Supervisor: "Actually, um, the reason why we charge the 2% transaction fees..."

Scott: "Uh, huh."

Supervisor: "...is because we offer our low rate for 12 months instead of just 6 months, what other companies do."

Note: Actually they charge the transfer fee to make as much money as possible. She just happened to leave that out of her response.

Scott: "Right."

Supervisor: "Um, it depends upon how much you're transferring anyway. If you're transferring over $1,000, that's $1,000 at the 2% fee and then of course, everything above that, that percentage goes down. But like if you're transferring

$2,000 then it's only a 1%, if you're transferring $4,000 then it's half a percent. You know it just depends on how much you're transferring. But we don't adjust that, they're, they're not waiving them."

Scott: "They're not going to waive it. I got to tell you. I mean quite honestly, I've got like at least a few other cards that have a 5.9% rate that I could transfer to with no transfer fee. But since I got the Greenland Dog Bank Platinum Card, and I've been using this card only for purchases, as you probably can tell if you're looking at my account. I was hoping I could do this transfer and you know, let Greenland Dog Bank, get a little profit going (snicker). You know but I'll just use a different card. I mean it's really up to Greenland Dog Bank if they want to take it. I mean if they waive the $20 fee, I'll transfer $3,800 right now."
Note: Specifying how much I want to transfer is the key. This way I could argue that the interest on this amount, over the 12-month period, makes their waiving the fee worth it for them. That's why it's so important to be able to do the math.

Supervisor: "Um, I'll adjust half of it. Technically, we're not supposed to adjust those at all but since you want to do $3,800 I'll adjust half of it. I'll adjust $10."
Note: Okay, I'll take that $10. At least it's something. This shows that they are willing to negotiate.

Scott: "Fair enough. Fair enough. Can you do the transfer?"

Supervisor: "Sure."

Scott: "Okay, um, can you just tell me your name again so I can..."

Supervisor: "Sure, it's Mrs. Tarantulae.

Scott: "Okay, Mrs. Tarantulae, alright. It's going to go to Samoyed Bankcard services. You have an address for them?"

Supervisor: "Is that the PO Box 5648."

Scott: "I've got a different one PO Box 8547."
Note: Always be prepared with the statement from the bank that you want to send the transfer to. You'll need to give that information to the transferring bank and you want it to be accurate. You should highlight the important info that's on the statement. That includes mailing address, toll-free telephone number, account number, and the dollar amount you want to transfer.

Supervisor: "Account number please."

Scott: (I give her the number.)

Supervisor: "Dollar amount is $3,800?"

Scott: "Correct."

Supervisor: "I just need to verify everything." (She reads back the transfer information to me to make sure that it's correct.)
Note: You must be very careful to ensure that this information is correct or you could be sending money to someone else's account! Boy, that would be a pain to fix!

Scott: "How long before that goes out?"
Note: You want to make sure that the transfer payment arrives on time, before the due date. If it won't, then you'll have to make sure that you make at least one payment by the due date or you could face late charges—no big deal anyway. You'd just call and get those waived too if that happens. ☺

Supervisor: "It does take approximately two to three weeks, now if it's electronic funds transfer there's a possibility they could get it in three days. If they don't take electronic funds transfer, then a physical check will be mailed and that can take the two to three weeks."

Scott: "Okay, when would I be able to know if it's one way or the other?"

Supervisor: "Well, you could always call back and it would be noted on the account. Probably about four to five days. As far as when they post it (the receiving bank) you would have to check with them. We would send a letter to you the day we either electronic-funds transfer it or mail it. We send the letter about the same time they would receive it if it was mailed."

Scott: "Okay, great. Alright and thank you very much."

Supervisor: "Well you're welcome. Anything else I can help you with?"

Scott: "No, that will be all."

Supervisor: "Okay, thanks for calling."

Scott: "Of course the fee is only $10 for the transfer."
Note: Just checking.

Supervisor: "That's correct. It will show as $20 and as $10 adjusted."

Scott: "Okay, cool. Thank you."

Supervisor: "Thank you for calling Greenland Dog Bank. Bye"

Scott: "Bye-bye."

CALL #3.05: SPARE ME THE LECTURE

Reason For Call:	Late Fee Waived
Result:	Mission complete
Difficulty Level:	Easy
Call Time:	11 minutes
Total Saved:	$35.00
$/hour to make call:	$190.91

Calling here for my friend, Norris Zimel (name changed), to remove a late fee. During the call, the rep is going to try and up-sell me on a credit report program. Be careful not to end up spending more money by purchasing programs when you're really calling to save money!

Since I'm already on the phone, I also try to get Norris a credit line increase, which is denied.

SUMMARY

I called for Norris and spoke to Ms. Flea. She waived the fee and gave me a lecture about paying on time. I spoke to Ms. Wasp about raising Norris's limit. They didn't raise the limit—declined! She said Norris could try again in one year.

TRANSCRIPT

Scott: "Today is March 22nd."
Note: Making a voice memo on my tape about the call.

Voice Menu: "Welcome to Landseer Bank. Please enter your 16-digit account number."

On hold...

Rep: "Good day. This is Ms. Flea. May I get your name please?"

Scott: "My name is Norris Zimel. Your name is Ms. Flea?"

Rep: "Yes, my name is Ms. Flea."

Scott: "Hi Ms. Flea."

Rep: "Hi there Mr. Zimel, can I get your home telephone number and the last 4 digits of your social security number."

Scott: "Sure..." (I give her the numbers.)

Rep: "Alright, how can I help you today?"

Scott: "Okay, can you see my most recent statement?"

Rep: "Yes, I can."

Scott: "Do you see that late fee there?"

Rep: "Actually those are on transactions. Okay, yes I see it."

Scott: "Alright, well this is my first time being late and uh, it was sent but apparently it didn't arrive so I took care of it online, immediately."
Note: It's been my experience that 100% of all first-time late fees get removed.

Rep: "Okay."

Scott: "So I am hoping you can waive that late fee."

Rep: "Okay, let me check on that for you."

Pause...

Rep: "Okay I can waive it this one time, umm, I am required to go over some things with you. Number one, when you do mail your payment we do ask that you mail it 5 to 7 business days before the due date. And then if you are going to make online payments, which certainly you can make online payment anytime, not just because the payment didn't arrive, if you want to do it every month just to make sure that your payment gets here, you know if you are not trusting the postal service for example..."
Note: Spare me the lecture.

Scott: "Umm hmm."

Rep: "You can make payments every month. The only criteria is that you do it a banking day prior to your due date. So you would definitely want to do it by midnight of the 16th each month, unless that is on a Friday, Saturday, or Sunday. Because it is not going to post until the next banking day."

Scott: "Okay."

Rep: "But that will save you postage and also let you know that your payment has been immediately posted to your account."

Scott: "Alright."

Rep: "I did credit that fee off for you, it will show as a credit at midnight tonight, and then be a part of your available credit tomorrow."

Scott: "Okay."
Note: In other words, go spend it—it's available to use!

Rep: "Alright?"

Scott: "Alright, well thank you."

Rep: "I did want to ask you a question Mr. Zimel."

Scott: "Go ahead."

Rep: "When was the last time you had a chance to look at your credit bureau report?"

Scott: "Hmm, not too recently, why?"
Note: Here comes the up-sell.

Rep: "Okay, we have a program called Private Shield that makes it very simple for you to get access to your credit bureau reports from all three major agencies..."

Scott: "I wouldn't be interested in that. How about a credit line increase, what's my credit line, about $200, something like that?"
Note: That ended her spiel.

Rep: "Your credit limit is currently, I have to get back over there. Have a balance around $200."

Scott: "That's kind of ridiculous."

Rep: "Not necessarily. Landseer Bank is very, very conservative in lending. We start..."
Note: Please! That's why the bank sends me letters saying I should use my credit line to buy a new wardrobe.

Scott: "That's conservative, the late fee is uh, 10% of the entire limit."

Rep: "Do you have any other credit cards besides Landseer Bank?"

Scott: "I think I have maybe one other."

Rep: "Who is it through?"

Scott: "I can't recall offhand."

Rep: (Laughs.)

Scott: "Pug Bank."
Note: Norris shows me his other card.

Rep: "Check their late fees. I have a Pug Bankcard."

Scott: "Uh huh."

Rep: "Their late fees are I think $35."

Scott: "Umm."

Rep: "I mean, I've never been late but I know that I've read it, like I read everything that I get. Umm they have in there that if they charge you for check by phone, we charge $10 for a check by phone, they charge $15. I know that because I tried to make a check payment by phone and when she told me $15. I'm like wait a minute. 'Cause I had already mailed one and it was my due date, and it hadn't been posted and I didn't want that late fee. But umm, I had always paid more than my minimum and my account was set-up so I could pay in advance, so I technically didn't have a payment due. But when she said $15 I'm like 'no way, no way, not gonna happen.' But then she said $35 for my late fee, and I'm like 'oh wait a minute let's re-think this.' But then it you know...I know $25 sounds like a lot but..."
Note: Just listening to her story.

Scott: "But when you've got a $200 credit limit, it is a lot."

Rep: "Well it's $25 whether you have $200 or $20,000."

Scott: "Right."

Rep: "So it's not really based on what your limit is, but I can check on a credit limit increase for you."

Scott: "Let's do that."

Rep: "But you just opened in January though, well let's see what happens. Normally we ask that you maintain your account for at least 6 months, but your account is coming up that if you need additional purchasing power I can send you to our credit services department. Umm, was that why you wanted a credit limit increase, for additional purchasing power?"

Scott: "Yeah, it would be nice."

Rep: "Alright, let me put you on hold just one second, okay?"

Scott: "Sure."

Rep: "Thanks."

On hold...

Scott: "Yes I'm here."

Rep: "Thanks for holding, I do have Ms. Wasp on the line. She is going to assist you further."

Scott: "Okay, thank you."

Rep: "And you were calling to check on a credit line increase?"

Scott: "Yes."

Rep: "Okay, let me just take a look at that for you real quickly."

Scott: "I gotta tell you Ms. Wasp, $200 is nothing. I'm sure you know that."

Rep: "I completely understand."

Scott: "You can't buy anything. I'm in college and I can't even buy like 2 school books for $200. However, I did get another credit card recently that has a limit on it, might be uh, like $300 it's not much, but I would rather use the Landseer Bankcard if I could."

Rep: "I did submit that request for you at this time however it is coming up declined, and the reason for that is your account is just too new. Umm, generally the way it works is that once your account has been opened for one year you are going to be eligible for periodic reviews for an increase. If you are found eligible for an increase you are going to be notified by statement. So that is something we will automatically look at for you."

Note: This particular bank is quite tight about credit line increases. I have a few of their cards and it does take some time before they raise the limit. However, it's always good to ask. I've found that I can usually get some type of credit line increase 50% of the time by just calling and asking.

Scott: "I guess I'll have to use the other credit card. I mean uh, eventually, I just don't get it. I mean $200, it's just not so reasonable. I mean is my credit report that lousy?"

Rep: "Not necessarily saying that anything is wrong with your credit. It could be maybe you just don't have enough credit."

Scott: "Hmm."

Rep: "But a letter is going to be coming out to you within 7 to 10 business days regarding that."

Scott: "Okay. Alright well I wish I could use Landseer Bank."

Rep: "Okay, sorry about that sir."

Scott: "Well I know you don't make the policies, but someone who does make the policies should really take a hard look, I mean what's the use of even giving someone a credit card if they can't use it really."
Note: Don't blame the person you're speaking with at the moment. Always let them know, that you know, that they don't make the policy.

Rep: "Umm hmm."

Scott: "You know, so. Okay well that's good for today."

Rep: "Alright and just keep in mind also, have you had a chance to look at your credit reports to make sure that everything is accurate?"

Scott: "Yes, well I will be looking now anyway since I was just declined credit by you right now. So I will take a look at it when I get my report."
Note: Because Norris was declined the credit line increase he is now entitled to free copy of his credit report from the agency that supplied the information to this bank.

Rep: "Okay, well just keep in mind that we do offer a service called Private Shield."

Scott: "Uh huh."

Rep: "What they do is send you a free copy of your credit reports from the 3 major credit bureaus. If you do happen to find mistakes, the correction papers are included in the package."
Note: They are relentless at trying to sell me this credit-report package.

Scott: "Alright, well I can look at my credit report for free. I was just declined for credit. Thank you."

Rep: "Thanks for calling Landseer Bank and have a nice day bye-bye."

Scott: "Bye-bye."

CALL #3.06: SO I WAS LATE BEFORE

Reason For Call:	Late Fee Waived
Result:	Mission complete
Difficulty Level:	Medium
Call Time:	4 minutes
Total Saved:	$25.00
$/hour to make call:	$375.00

For some reason this bank says I've been late a few times. I don't recall that fact. And believe me; I'm on top of this stuff! Sometimes the bank mails account statements very close to the time the payment is due. You'll need to act quickly to allow 10 business days for your payment to arrive! ☺

SUMMARY

Apparently I was late the previous month, but I still got them to waive the fee!

TRANSCRIPT

Went through the voice menu.

Rep: "Thank you for calling cardmember services. This is Ms. Horsefly. May I have your account number please?"

Scott: "Hi Ms. Horsefly..." (I give her the number.)

Rep: "The name on the account is?"

Scott: "Scott Bilker."

Rep: "Okay, and who's the primary?"

Scott: "Me. Scott."

Rep: "Okay, maybe I think it's a newer one."

Scott: "What, this one? Oh, maybe it is. Yeah, Larissa, okay, she's the primary."

Rep: "Okay, and what is her mother's maiden name?"

Scott: "Her mother's maiden name?" (I give her the name.)

Rep: "Okay, and how may I help you today Mr. Bilker?"

Scott: "Okay, umm, well there's a late fee on the statement and I double-checked and I see the statement posted it at 11, on the 11th and the bill's due on the 9th and it certainly looks like it is late. But it was mailed with plenty of time. I just, I don't get it."

Note: It pays to admit to the truth (sometimes) and ask what they can do to help. If you're late, admit it, and ask if they can make an exception.

Rep: "Actually, when did you send it in?"

Scott: "I don't know when I sent it in, but plenty of time. I mean, just look at the past records. You'd see that none of them were ever late."

Rep: "Hmmm, actually, in May you were late…"

Scott: "May!"

Rep: "Correct umm…"

Scott: "How late was I in May?"

Note: I don't recall being late, in fact, when I looked at my statements I couldn't find any late payments and certainly there were no late fees!

Rep: "Octob…May you were, 6, 7, 8, 9, three days late. Ummm, October you were 7, 8, 9, 10, 11, 12, five days late. November you were two days late. Okay, that's the only time. And this time, March 9, 10, 11, you were two days late. Okay, you do need to mail it off 7 to 10 business days in advance. I'll go ahead and issue a courtesy credit."

Note: Even though I've been late before they still waived the fee.

Scott: "Okay."

Rep: "Can you hold on a few moments."

Scott: "Sure."

Rep: "Thank you."

On hold…

Rep: "Okay, hello sir."

Scott: "Yes."

Rep: "Okay, what I went ahead and did is I went ahead and issued you a credit for $25."

Scott: "Okay."

Rep: "And it will take one billing cycle."

Scott: "Okay."

Rep: "Okay, was there anything else I could help you with?"

Scott: "No that was, that was very helpful."

Rep: "Okay."

Scott: "And umm, okay, so now, what, what day are they usually mailed, these statements?"

Rep: "Mmmm, let me see."

Scott: "Cause I don't want to be late, even a couple days. But I mean, if I get it, I, I want like at least a couple of days to have like some coffee and sit down and write the check."
Note: They're sending me the bill too close to the payment date so even when they're paid right away it's not enough time to get it there by the due-date.

Rep: "We sent that out to you from the 11th to the 15th. You should get it by the 20th of every month."

Scott: "And then it's..."

Rep: "Or the 23rd and then it's due anywhere from the 6th to the 9th."

Scott: "Okay, alright. I'll note that and I'll ah, keep a closer eye, on the timing. Alright, well thank you Ms. Horsefly."

Rep: "Is there anything else I can help you with?"

Scott: "No that will be fine."

Rep: "Thank you for calling cardmember services. Goodbye."

Scott: "Bye-bye."

Call #3.07: Never Ending Overlimit Fees

Reason For Call:	Transfer Fee Waived
Result:	Fee waived but they wouldn't lower the interest rate.
Difficulty Level:	Medium
Call Time:	8 minutes
Total Saved:	$41.24
$/hour to make call:	$309.30

Always review your account to make sure that you're not being charged for some type of credit protection or insurance program that you don't want. Sometimes you may be coerced into trying these programs and forget to cancel them when the trial period ends. Then the cost of the program, plus interest fees, and other fees, can drive you over your limit so you get charged even more fees!

SUMMARY

I made this call for my friend Tony Bryer (name changed). The card is really hurting him with crazy fees! They're charging him an annual fee of $4 per month, $16.24 for Account Protection Plus (an insurance policy for them so if Tony dies, they get paid), $25 overlimit fee (each month), and 22.7% APR! He's really going to have to work to get out of this one. The balance on this card is actually increasing each month because of all the fees.

I spoke to Carrion Beetle. I had her cancel the Account Protection Plus, and she waived one of the overlimit fees. She transferred me to account specialist, Carpenter Ant, so I could bargain for the interest rate. Carpenter Ant told me that the rate is non-negotiable. The fact that Tony has been having trouble paying on this account has certainly affected the power he has to negotiate a better rate, but he'll still need to call back later and try again.

TRANSCRIPT

Voice Menu: "Thank you for calling the Gordon Setter Bank cardholder service center."

Scott: "Yeah, you're welcome."

Rep: "Thank you for calling cardholder services. This is Carrion Beetle speaking, may I have your account number please."

Scott: (I give her the number.)

Rep: "And your name."

Scott: (I give her the name.)

Rep: "Mr. Bryer for security purposes I need you to verify your mother's maiden name and your social security number."

Scott: (I give her the information.)

Rep: "And your address is..."

Scott: "That's me."

Rep: "Home phone number is..."

Scott: "That's correct."

Rep: "How can I help you Mr. Bryer?"

Scott: "Can you look at my last statement please?"

Rep: "Yes, I am."

Scott: "Okay, great. Well let's start with that Account Protection Plus."

Rep: "Okay."

Scott: "What is that again?"

Rep: "Okay, if you die then it will pay the balance up to the credit limit. If you are unemployed or disabled, then it will freeze interest from accruing on the account so you don't have to make monthly payments."
Note: Yeah right, of course Tony wants to make sure the bank gets paid if he dies. That's his main concern in life. ☺ Credit protection is simply very expensive life insurance.

Scott: "Okay. Alright, I'd like to cancel that."

Rep: "Okay."

Scott: "Effective immediately and have that..."

Rep: "One moment please."

Scott: "Sure."

On hold...

Scott talking to Tony: "Yeah great, if you die they get paid. And you pay for it in advance. I don't think so. If I die, tough on them! Send me a bill, tombstone 25."

Tony: "It takes this long to get rid of it?"

Scott talking to Tony: "It's some kind of...I don't know how they got you on that one. That's alright."

Rep: "Mr. Bryer, thanks for holding. I have just cancelled the card protection plus for you. Is there anything else I can help you with?"

Scott: "Sure, umm, next thing is this overlimit fee. This is going crazy here, $25 every single month. I can see I'm over the limit. Can we raise the limit, or can we do something here?"

Rep: "Okay, no sir. As soon as you're under your credit limit then request for an increase, but as long as you carry an overlimit balance I cannot put the request in for an increase. I can tell you what you need to send in, in order to be under the limit and to stay under the limit to stop having an overlimit fee."
Note: Tony will never get under the credit limit as long as they keep charging him overlimit fees. Talk about a catch-22. It's not even a catch-22; it's a way to keep him in debt forever. A way to continue charging him fees for eternity!

Scott: "I didn't realize this overlimit fee is billed every single month. Don't you think..."

Rep: "Yes sir, it is. Every month that you carry an overlimit balance you will be assessed a $25 overlimit fee. Until you are under your credit limit."

Scott: "Okay, alright. Okay, next thing we gotta talk about here. I realize this isn't all your policy, but I'm hoping you can help me Carrion. This 22.7% is there anything we can do about that? Because that is just not competitive and I'll tell you what..."

Rep: "I can transfer you to the department that can discuss the annual percentage rate with you."

Scott: "Okay."

Rep: "And is there anything else I can help you with before I transfer you?"

Scott: "Uh, let me see here. Umm, no that's good for now. Thank you Carrion Beetle."

Rep: "Okay and I'll...you know that in order for you to be under the limit you need to send in at least about $659.33."

Scott: "$659? Okay."

Rep: "Yes sir, or you can just say $660."

Scott: "Okay, I certainly will. I'll make it $690 just to be sure."

Rep: "Okay. And sir, umm, as soon as...well I can just go ahead and adjust one of the overlimit fees for you as a one time courtesy."
Note: This demonstrates that no matter how bad things may seem you should always call and get as many fees waived as possible.

Scott: "Oh, wow I'd really appreciate that Carrion."

Rep: "Okay, I have just removed it for you and I'll just go ahead and transfer you to that department that can discuss that with you. You have a nice day and thank you for calling."

Scott: "You too, and thank you so much."

Rep: "You're welcome."

On hold...

Scott talking to Tony: "Okay so, so far that's $41 off your bill."

Tony: "I haven't called in that second card they sent me. The first card was expired."

Scott talking to Tony: "Hmm, haven't called it in eh?"

Tony: "Nope. Because I don't want to, haven't even bothered."

Scott talking to Tony: "Okay, good. Thanks for telling me that. That's good."

Tony: "Yeah and they sent you the new card. I didn't even bother like, you know the sticker comes on the back."

Scott talking to Tony: "Right, you didn't activate it."

Tony: "No."

Scott talking to Tony: "Great."

Scott: "Yes."

Account Specialist: "Hi. My name is Carpenter Ant. I'm an account specialist. Your call has been directed to me today sir, and I do understand that you have requested a lower percentage rate."

Scott: "Yes."

Account Specialist: "Okay and at this time sir the bank is not negotiating a percentage rate. It does change about every 2 to 3 months."

Scott: "Well maybe this will change something here. I've got a nice 6.9% transfer offer from Mexican Hairless Bank, and also I have not activated this card. Because this rate is, it's just unfair. And I'd like to use this card, and I'm just not going to anymore unless some kind of fair rate is established. 22.7% is just out of hand. I'm sure there is something you can do for me so I don't have to close my account out here and transfer my balance."

Account Specialist: "There is not. There's not, and again I tell you, about every 2 to 3 months if you want to try back then you could. If not, I could just send you back letters saying that you close the account. But as of right now the APR is non-negotiable."

Scott: "Hmm, is there anyone else there I could talk to."

Account Specialist: "No sir."

Scott: "You're the final word on this Mr. Ant."

Account Specialist: "Yes sir."

Scott: "Alright well then, I'll guess I'll just have to transfer my balance out of there. Alright, well thank you anyway for your time."

Account Specialist: "Sir, did you want me to close the account, or did you want to leave the account open."

Scott: "It's going to have to stay open until it's paid off, but I won't be using it."

Account Specialist: "Okay."

Scott: "Alright, thank you Carpenter Ant."

Account Specialist: "You're welcome sir. Bye-bye."

Scott: "Bye-bye."

Call #3.08: BANK TRIES TO PULL A FAST ONE

Reason For Call:	Cash Advance Fee Waived
Result:	Mission completed
Difficulty Level:	Easy
Call Time:	5 minutes
Total Saved:	$29.00
$/hour to make call:	$348.00

Here's another call where the bank doesn't uphold its promises. I wanted to take advantage of a 0% APR offer, good for one year, with a one-time fee for each transfer. The fee is 4% of the amount transferred up to a $50 maximum. According to the bank's letter, "These checks may be used for any amount, up to your available credit line." I went ahead and wrote myself a check for $12,500 (the entire credit line) and deposited it into my money market account.

This situation is similar to that of call #3.02. However, in this case the bank did say there was a transfer fee involved, but they didn't say it would affect the amount of my credit line that was available for the offer. When the bill arrived I noticed an overlimit fee of $29 assessed on my account.

The bottom line for this call is that, as mentioned before, you must retain all the details of the original offer for future reference. Also, don't give in to arguments by the bank representatives!

SUMMARY

I called and asked bank rep, Ms. Centipede, why I was charged the $29 overlimit fee. She told me it's because I was over the account limit since the $50 transfer charge, plus the $12,500 check, makes my balance $12,550.00. As soon as I mentioned that the overlimit fee was on my statement, she removed it instantly! I didn't even have to ask!

I explained that the credit offer letter stated that I could write the check up to my limit and Ms. Centipede started arguing with me. If she really believed that I was completely at fault she would not have waived that fee so quickly.

I originally thought the rep would just waive the fee and apologize for the confusion. I thought she would say something like, "Mr. Bilker, we're sorry that the wording of the letter was confusing. I can understand how you feel. I will certainly bring this to the attention of my supervisors and management so we can review these details. Thank you so much for calling!" Keep dreaming Scott. ☺

TRANSCRIPT

Voice Menu: "We are pleased to have you as a Hound Dog Bank Member."

Scott: "Right."

Voice Menu: "Save over $10 when you send a teddy bear. Choose from over 100 bears at..."
Note: Wow! Now the voice menus are trying to sell me stuff!

Scott: "Right." (I press "0" in hopes of getting a human.)

Voice Menu: "...and type in coupon code 'honey' or..."

Scott: "Yeah, bear this..."

Voice Menu: "If you are calling from a touch tone phone please press one now."

Scott: (I say the number.)

Voice Menu: "Please clearly speak your 5-digit zip code."

Scott: (I say the number.)

Voice Menu: "As of January 31ˢᵗ your outstanding balance is $12,579. Please be aware that you have exceeded your credit limit by $79. Please send a payment of at least $251 as soon as possible so you can continue to use your account."
Note: That's exactly what I'm calling to take care of.

Voice Menu: "Please stay on the line for customer service assistance. To ensure the quality of the service we provide, your call may be monitored or recorded."

Scott: "Yours too."

Rep: "Cardmember services. Ms. Centipede, how may I help you?"

Scott: "Hi, what is your name again?"

Rep: "Ms. Centipede. How can I help you today?"

Scott: "Alright. Well I've got a question about my account."

Rep: "Okay, let me have your name."

Scott: "Scott Bilker."

Rep: "Okay Mr. Bilker, how can I help you today?"

Scott: "Okay, umm, why do I have this overlimit fee?"

Rep: "Okay. Mr. Bilker, let me also have your date of birth for verification."

Scott: "Sure." (I give her the date.)

Rep: "Because you are over your limit."

Scott: "Okay. How did that happen?"

Rep: "You did a balance transfer for $12,500."

Scott: "Yeah."

Rep: "Also there is a balance transfer fee of $50."

Scott: "Umm hmm."

Rep: "And that took you over your credit line. Your credit line is only $12,500."

Scott: "Right. Okay well, you see I think that's an error because I have the letter from Hound Dog Bank. It says, you know I used one of these balance transfer checks Ms. Centipede. It says these checks 'may be used for any amount up to your available credit line.' What was my available credit line before I wrote that check?"

Rep: "Up to. Your credit line is only $12,500 sir."

Scott: "Yes, but these checks may be used for any amount up to your available credit line. My available credit line was $12,500, I wrote the check for $12,500."

Rep: "That's the credit line sir, and of course you know you are going to go over your credit line. You can't take it all off of there, you've got to leave something there for the fee..."

Scott: "Uh, listen..."

Rep: "Also for the finance charge. I did give you back the $29 overlimit fee."
Note: She took it off before I even asked! She knew I would ask. I have to venture to say that she knows the letter was deceptive and has already received a few complaint calls.

Scott: "Okay."

Rep: "It's already been deleted. But you should have left a little room there for finance charges and also for the fee."
Note: Now she's trying to blame me for their deceptive letter!

Scott: "Don't you think the letter should say 'You should leave a little room there. You shouldn't write the checks up to your credit limit, maybe up to your credit limit minus the fee.'"

Rep: "Okay, but the fees are in the letter also."

Scott: "Yes, but it says these checks may be used for any amount up to your credit line. You know, it does give you the impression that you can write the check, well, up to your available credit line."

Pause...

Scott: "Hello?"

Rep: "Sir, it's in the letter. Okay, again you used your whole credit line, of course you are going to go over your credit line if..."

Scott: "I know, but I am just concerned about the wording. I mean, if it said..."

Rep: "Mr. Bilker, if you weren't sure about how much you should use on the checks you can always call us, 24 hours."

Scott: "Right. Well, I was very clear, I mean it said up to the credit line. I know you removed it and I appreciate that, but I just want a little clarification of the writing there. Because, you know, I don't know what to believe anymore. I mean, it said..."

Rep: "Sir, you wouldn't take your whole credit line. If you know your credit line is $12,500 and you go over that, and you take that whole amount it is going to go over."

Scott: "It doesn't..."

Rep: "You can go up to, and you should never take the whole credit line because, yes you will go over and receive the $29 fee on that."

Scott: "I just don't see where it says that. Like even in the fine print here it says 'balance transfer check amounts may not exceed your available credit line.' It doesn't say valid balance transfer check amounts and charges may not exceed. It says the check amounts."

Rep: "It told you not to exceed the whole credit line Mr. Bilker."

Scott: "Well, no. It says the check amounts, the check amounts, not the..."

Rep: "You go over the $12,500..."

Scott: "I didn't. I wrote it for $12,500."

Rep: "Well, it's $12,500, you took your whole credit line. That's going to take you over the credit line."

Scott: "But it said I can use up to my available credit line."

Rep: "It says up to sir, it doesn't say take the whole $12,500."

Scott: "Up to means...Well you know what, I know you waived the fee and that's great, but I'd like to talk to a supervisor about this."

Rep: "Not a problem, hold on."

Scott: "Thank you."

Note: I did speak to a supervisor and she continued to argue. It's not worth making you read their ridiculous comments. Suffice to say that I saved the money, made my point, and moved on. Just remember to never let them push you around or blame you for their problems!

CHAPTER 4

HOW THE BANK BEGGED FOR ME TO
COME BACK

THE STORY

This next series of four phone calls demonstrates the fact that the banks need us more than we need them! We, the consumers, have power over the banks! The calls in this chapter are a related series. They need to be read in order so you can follow the entire story.

In summary, I end up having to close an account because the bank doesn't waive a late fee. Then, one month later, the bank calls me back to ask me why I closed my account, waive the fee, and beg for me to return—I love it!

Calling to have a late fee waived kicks off this series of calls. At this point in time I was using online checking. I wanted to pay my bills online to "simplify" my life but it ended up causing many problems.

The biggest problem was that my checking account bank didn't directly wire the funds to payees. The bank basically moved the money from my individual checking account to a large in-house checking account that they used to write physical checks and mail them to the indicated addresses.

The problem with that system is that the money is taken out of the account the day the information is submitted online. This made it appear like the check had been cashed on the submission day when in reality the check hadn't even been sent! The bank sends the checks out within a couple days and there is no way of knowing when, for example, the phone company actually cashed the check or if they even received it!

Consequently, the payments the bank had been sending to my creditors would sometimes not get cashed for a variety of reasons, like the account number wasn't written on the check! This was also the problem with utility company payments. My cable TV provider sent me a notice that I hadn't paid the bill, but when I looked online it showed that they already cashed the check.

Anyway, one of those checks that didn't make it through was to a credit card that I had been using for 10 years. In fact, it's the very first major credit card for which I got accepted. Of course, the credit card bank immediately charged me a late fee.

I knew that I did the online bill payment within plenty of time for the bank to receive it prior to the due date. When I first discovered that my check didn't arrive on time from the online payment system, I called the credit card bank and they waived the late fee. I continued using the online checking because this was one of the first problems I had with the system.

In a couple months I had the same problem with the same credit card bank. My online check did not arrive on time. This time, when I called the credit card bank, they didn't waive the late fee so I closed the account. Well, one month later they called me back and begged for me to come back—and I have the entire story on tape for you to enjoy!

As you may have guessed, I have long since stopped using online checking with my bank for this reason. Also, it turned out to be more work then just writing the check and mailing it.

However, online payments can work well when you set up electronic payment with each creditor individually. When you set this up, the creditor will take the money directly out of your checking account. The bank will usually give you an option to make one-time payments or automatic payments. I prefer one-time payments because I don't want to have the bank taking money from my account without specific authorization.

This method of payment is easily tracked because you can see the transaction in your checking account. When you see it there, it really happened, so you know that the creditor has actually received the money.

Of course, this is more work to set up because you need to register with each and every company that you need to pay. I do suggest that you use a different username and password for each bill to reduce the chance of fraud. If you use the same information on all accounts, and someone gets a hold of that information, then they'll have the keys to your financial castle.

Looking back I am glad that I had that original problem with online checking because it showed me how far the banks would go to beg for my business. You need to keep that in the back of your mind when you call.

The only downside is that you may, as is usually the case, have to ask for a supervisor to finally get someone that really cares about making money for the bank instead of going home at 5:00 PM.

CALL #4.01: LATE FEE WAIVED

Reason For Call:	Late Fee Waived and Finance Charges Refunded
Result:	Mission completed
Difficulty Level:	Easy
Call Time:	4 minutes
Total Saved:	$37.59
$/hour to make call:	$563.85

In the first of this four-part series, I call to have my late fee waived. My check was late because I was using an online check payment system, which failed.

SUMMARY

The cat kept interrupting my phone call by jumping on the computer. Sheepdog Bank waived the fee and asked if I want to be enrolled in their automatic payment program.

TRANSCRIPT

Scott: "Just start pressing buttons till you get a rep."

Rep: "Sheepdog Bank customer service. My name is Ms. Wolf Spider, may I have your account number please."

Scott: (I give her the number.)

Rep: "Thank you. And what is your name?"

Scott: "Scott Bilker."

Rep: "And your mother's maiden name please."

Scott: (I give her the name.) "I'm sorry, I didn't catch your name."

Rep: "Mrs. Wolf Spider. W-O-L-F S-P-I-D-E-R."

Scott: "Okay, I'm sorry. Mrs. Wolf Spider."

Rep: "How may I help you this evening?"

Scott: "Okay, can you see my statement? My most recent one?"

Rep: "Okay, just one moment. Let me go ahead and access that information."

Scott: "Okay."

Rep: "Okay, sir. I do have that in front of me."

Scott: "Okay, well um, I'm looking at the transaction on the 23rd, there's a $25 late fee and the finance charge of $12.59."

Rep: "Emm hmm."

Scott: "And I see there that it is certainly late, July 17th was the date that you got the payment but it was certainly sent with plenty of time...I don't know why it was delayed. I was using an electronic pay system with my bank, like an online one, maybe it got delayed then. But I was hoping Sheepdog Bank would be able to waive those fees. Since I'm..."
Note: I was about to give the spiel about how long I've been with the bank and how I've paid on time, yada, yada, but she knew where I was going.

Rep: "Okay, just one moment. I'll go ahead and review the account and see if we can do that for you. Can I put you on hold please?"

Scott: "Sure."

Rep: "Thank you."

On hold...

Rep: "Okay sir, thank you for holding. Now, I have gone ahead and waived those late fees and the finance charges on the account."

Scott: "I'm sorry. I couldn't hear you." (My cat just knocked some stuff off my desk.)
Note: I keep notes on the silliest things sometimes.

Rep: "I have gone ahead and waived the late fee and the finance charges on the account for you. Those will credit to your account in the next few business days. And also I wanted to take the opportunity to tell you about a free program that we have called SheepdogPay. Where you can set up to make your payments out of your checking account each month but it's done through Sheepdog Bank. Okay, and it's done by the due date. You don't have that problem of it being posted late to your account."

Scott: "Oh really, is..."

Rep: "Yes, and if you'd like some information, I'd be happy to send you a packet. There's no obligation but you can review it. If you decide to enroll, just send it back to Sheepdog Bank."

Scott: "Is it free to enroll?"
Note: I bet it's free. Wouldn't they love to just have my permission to pull funds from my checking account at will!

Rep: "Yes, it's free. There's no charge to you whatsoever. You can set it up to take the entire balance in full each month or a set payment or the minimum payment due. Whichever you prefer."

Scott: "That sounds interesting. I certainly wouldn't mind checking it out."

Rep: "Okay, I've gone ahead and um, ordered a copy of the packet for you. Can you just verify your mailing address please?"

Scott: (I give her the address.)

Rep: "Okay, great. That is what we have on file. You should have that within about 7 days, okay."

Scott: "Alright, well thank you for everything Ms. Wolf Spider."

Rep: "You're welcome. Bye-bye."

Scott: "Bye-bye."
Note: Seems easy enough so far, right?

Call #4.02: LATE AGAIN AND NO WAIVING

Reason For Call:	Late Fee Waived
Result:	They didn't waive the fee.
Difficulty Level:	Hard
Call Time:	9 minutes
Total Saved:	$0.00
$/hour to make call:	$0.00

It's two months later and I'm late again because of that online checking payment system. This time my credit card bank does not waive the late fee.

SUMMARY

Sheepdog Bank wouldn't waive my late fee because they already waived my first late fee. I really tried and threatened on this one but they wouldn't budge so I'm going to transfer my balance out of there and call back and cancel my accounts—all four of my accounts!

TRANSCRIPT

Rep: "Hello this is Ms. Crab Spider of Sheepdog Bank customer service, may I have your name please."

Scott: "Scott Bilker."

Rep: "Thank you Mr. Bilker. May I have your full account number."

Scott: (I give her the number.)

Rep: "Thank you. Mother's maiden name?"

Scott: (I give her the name.)

Rep: "Thanks, how can I help you today?"

Scott: "Okay, can you look up my last statement?"

Rep: "No problem, give me a moment to pull it up."

Scott: "Okay."

Rep: "Okay, and I brought it up and it was the one in August right? Or did you want the most recent one?"

Scott: "The most recent statement."

Rep: "Okay, and was it because of a late fee on it, or what was your question?"

Scott: "That's what I'm getting to, the late fee on this."

Rep: "And give me a moment."

Pause...

Rep: "Okay, and the reason you received a late fee. Okay you had a payment of $41 due on September 10th, and we did receive a payment of $41 but we received it on September 14th."

Scott: "Yeah. So I see. Umm, I sent that the 4th. Six business days should do it."

Rep: "Unfortunately there is nothing that I can do. Umm, the 14th is the day that we received it. Umm, your account does not qualify for a late-fee credit, you already received yours."

Scott: "Yeah I know, umm, I just, I'm trying to figure out what is going on. I mean I sent one today, can you write that down on my account? When is this one due? It is due..."

Rep: "October 16th."

Scott: "Today is the 2nd. I have sent it now. It is there, it should be going. I guess, you know, I'm using an electronic pay, with my bank. Maybe they are messing up, but either way I want to ask you if I could qualify and get this waived."

Note: Basically, I don't care about their policies. I have my own policy which why is I won't be robbed in an alley by the bank! That's $25 for what? How much did it really cost them for my being late? Why do they have all the rights? How about a law that gives us the right to charge the bank fees when they make a mistake! "Got my interest rate wrong...that's $50 please." Everyone reading this please write to your Congressperson today! ☺

Rep: "Unfortunately no, I cannot take it off."

Scott: "Is there anyone there I can speak with that might be able to?"

Rep: "You can speak with my supervisor, but I wouldn't be able to guarantee it. Let me put you on a brief hold, okay?"

Scott: "Sure."

On hold...

Rep: "Mr. Bilker."

Scott: "Yes."

Rep: "I have my supervisor on the line and she will be able to assist you further."

Scott: "Thank you Ms. Crab Spider."

Supervisor: "Good evening, this is Ms. Black Widow at Sheepdog Bank, how can I help you today?"

Scott: "I guess Ms. Crab Spider didn't fill you in?"

Supervisor: "Umm, you are requesting another late fee credit, even though you just had one?"

Scott: "That's correct."

Supervisor: "It's a one time courtesy credit we gave you just a month ago sir."

Scott: "I'm very, very familiar with that. On this particular one I sent this on the 4th it was due on the 10th. I sent one today for this month, today is the 2nd, I mean I don't know why it's getting there late. I mean once I send it, it is out of my hands. Unless I send it by courier, or Airborne Express or something. I'm hoping..."

Supervisor: "Probably the September payment if you send it on the 4th the 7th was a holiday. That's probably what caused the problem."

Scott: "Not that much of a problem, I mean according to the post here it's the 14th that's 10 days. That's a lot of days in transit."
Note: And I'm supposed to pay $25 because of holidays! Give me a break.

Supervisor: "I'm sorry sir, it's a one time courtesy credit that we gave you. You need to be mailing a payment 5 to 7 business days before the due date."

Scott: "That was 6 days, I know, but okay a holiday."

Supervisor: "Not at all, the 4th was a Friday it was the following Thursday that's 1-2-3-4 mail days."

Scott: "But it didn't get there until the 14th."

Supervisor: "That's right it was received..."

Scott: "I know you're not the mail, and I know you don't make the policies, I'm hoping you're going to be able to do something."
Note: I'm trying to be nice here by letting the supervisor know that I'm not holding her responsible for the bad policy of her bank.

Supervisor: "I cannot, you've had a one time courtesy credit of the late fee just a little over a month ago. We sent you the SheepdogPay enrollment form, did you look at that?"
Note: So, they won't waive the late fee, yet they're still trying to sell me on the plan to allow them to suck money out of my checking account so they can guarantee their own payment.

Scott: "Yes, I looked at that."

Supervisor: "Have you considered doing that program so that you wouldn't have to worry about this."

Scott: "This should be electronic. Doesn't Sheepdog Bank accept electronic payments?"

Supervisor: "If you wired it through your bank, yes."

Scott: "It's supposed to be."

Supervisor: "You wired the payment through your bank?"

Scott: "I think so, yeah. It was all done through the computer."
Note: Okay, so I may not know for sure if it was really wired or a check that was sent. So what. This bank has extracted money from me for years without my complaining now it's time they do as I say.

Supervisor: "You said you mailed it."

Scott: "Well, I didn't mail it, I told the bank with my computer to pay it, and that day was the 4th."

Supervisor: "So you didn't mail it on the 4th?"

Scott: "Well it was supposed to be taken care of on the 4th. I mean that's the day the transaction occurred. Either they mailed it, or they electronically wired it on that day."

Supervisor: "You would have to follow up with whomever you set that payment up with."

Scott: "I certainly will, you can bet on that."

Supervisor: "We gave you the one time credit. We gave you the finance charge credit, we gave the..."

Scott: "How long have I had my account with Sheepdog Bank? I'm just curious."
Note: Time to start playing hardball!

Supervisor: "Just a moment. About 10 years."

Scott: "Wow, that's a lot of years. You think they made more than 25 bucks in all those years?"

Supervisor: "Probably. That's really not the point sir. The point is that we gave you a credit and two months in a row the payment was late."

Scott: "Okay."

Supervisor: "Unfortunately we gave you the one time credit, I'm sorry that it came in late again, but the fee is valid. We have to receive the payment by the due date."

Scott: "Okay well..."

Supervisor: "Your bank is responsible for the payment being late because you asked them to do it electronically. You may have your bank, you know, make the request in writing. If it's your bank's fault that it was late, then you can make that request to your bank."

Scott: "Alright, well, this is what I'm going to do, I'm going to transfer my balance right out of Sheepdog Bank to another card, and I'll be done with Sheepdog Bank, over this."
Note: I'm really starting to get mad about this situation!

Supervisor: "I'm sorry that you feel that way, but the policies are in effect for a reason. The payment is due by the due date."
Note: The reason is to gouge people for $25!

Scott: "Okay, well."

Supervisor: "And everybody has to abide by the same rules. We are, we give the one-time courtesy credit, but we expect that it is not going to happen again."

Scott: "Alright so, in other words, it is definitely worth losing someone who has paid on time for many years, over this thing. I just want to clarify that."

Supervisor: "I don't think it is."

Scott: "But Sheepdog Bank does. You might not, but Sheepdog Bank does, certainly they do. I mean uh, they made thousands of bucks off of me, probably in all that time."

Supervisor: "For us to have people who can make the payments on time. Everybody has the same opportunity to make the payments on time, for the people that don't, they are going to pay the late fees."

Scott: "Let's see, I had like 144 payments or whatever in the last ten years, with two late in a row because of technical difficulties. Either mail or a single holiday."

Supervisor: "Why was your payment late in August?"

Scott: "I don't know. I called then. It was some other kind of delay of some sort. I don't know. I'm trying to work this out. I'm not stiffing Sheepdog Bank here. I will get to the bottom of this. That's for sure, in some manner."

Supervisor: "If you requested your bank to do the electronic transfer, you know this looks like a payment that was mailed to us, it wasn't electronic."

Scott: "Well, from my end it's electronic, whether, I don't know how they are connecting with Sheepdog Bank, and I will certainly look into it."

Supervisor: "If your bank will admit that they are the ones that caused it to be late, then have your bank write us a letter with an explanation and we can certainly review it. If it is due to your banks error, if they make the request in writing we might be able to make an adjustment. But you would need to follow up with the bank and find out what happened."

Scott: "Well, I will be following up with the bank, but there is no way it's going to be adjusted now you're saying."

Supervisor: "Not tonight, no."

Scott: "Okay. Alright. Tell them one customer down, and like three accounts to go. 'Cause I have like 1-2-3-4 actually total. 4 accounts to zero. Alright thanks for the customer service."
Note: I'm threatening to close all accounts with this bank.

Supervisor: "You're welcome."

Scott: "Yeah bye-bye."

CALL #4.03: LAST CHANCE FOR THE BANK

Reason For Call:	Late Fee Waived
Result:	They didn't waive the fee.
Difficulty Level:	Hard
Call Time:	5 minutes
Total Saved:	$0.00
$/hour to make call:	$0.00

It's now one month after the last call (#4.02). I'm ready to close my accounts if they don't waive that late fee. I have already transferred my balance from this card to another so it has a near-zero balance.

SUMMARY

Spoke with Ms. Brown Recluse Spider. She wouldn't waive the fee from September 22nd so I closed the account. She said there weren't any supervisors available to speak with. We'll have to wait and see if they call back but the account is officially closed.

TRANSCRIPT

Voice Menu: "Sheepdog Bank, our menu options have changed."

Rep: "Sheepdog Bank customer service this is Ms. Brown Recluse Spider, may I have the account number please."

Scott: "Sure..." (I give her the number.)

Rep: "Mr. Bilker for security your mother's maiden name."

Scott: (I give her the name.)

Rep: "Okay, and how can I help you today?"

Scott: "What's your name again?"

Rep: "It's Ms. Brown Recluse Spider."

Scott: "Ms. Brown Recluse Spider. Hi Ms. Brown Recluse Spider. Umm, can you, well first of all what's my balance?"

Rep: "Sure let me bring that up, just a moment. You have a credit balance of $2.68."

Scott: "Okay. Alright, can you see my last few statements?"

Rep: "Let me bring that up, it will be just a moment. Okay."

Scott: "Back in my statement from closing date September 22nd I was charged a $25 past due fee. I was hoping Sheepdog Bank would waive that fee."
Note: I'll give them one more chance to waive the fee.

Rep: "Let me check and see if I can go back that far, can you hold for me?"

Scott: "Sure."

On hold...

Rep: "Thanks very much for your patience in holding. At this time I am not able to waive that one, because we credited a late fee a month before."

Scott: "I know I, there must have been some mail problem, or a electronic pay problem, or some difficulty. I called previously I was hoping Sheepdog Bank would take care of it."

Rep: "No sir, at this time we are not able to waive that one."

Scott: "Hmm, okay, umm, is there anyone I speak to about closing my account."
Note: Time for them to pay for treating me this way!

Rep: "I'm sure I can take care of that for you here it'll be just a moment."

Pause...

Scott: "I've got 4 Sheepdog Bank accounts with a total of $18,500 worth of credit, and I'm going to have to close them all over this $25."

Rep: "Sir I can't waive the fee again because we just waived, we just credited your account the month before."

Scott: "Is there anyone else I can speak to, maybe a supervisor?"

Rep: "Sure."

On hold...

Rep: "Thanks so much for your patience in holding, I wasn't able to reach a supervisor at this time. You can call back and ask the next available representative to transfer you to a supervisor, or I can have somebody give you a call back within 24 to 48 hours."

Scott: "Hmm, or I could just close my account right now."

Rep: "Did you want to do that?"

Scott: "Alright, let's close it."

Rep: "One second, sir."

Scott: "It's just so strange, you know, 10 years with Sheepdog Bank, charged and repaid thousands of dollars, on time, and because of $25 late fee it's..."

Rep: "I'm doing my job, this is what I'm told to do, this is our policy and I'm going by the rules here."
Note: Just following orders, blah, blah, blah.

Scott: "Okay."

Rep: "I'll go ahead and get you a confirmation letter in the mail. Is there anything else I can assist you with today?"

Scott: "No, that will be it. It's officially closed?"

Rep: "Yes it is."

Scott: "Alright, thank you."

Rep: "Thank you."

Call #4.04: Bank Calls Me to Beg

Reason For Call:	They called me to beg!
Result:	Late fee waived, interest rate reduced from 17.99% to 9.99%, and 6.9% transfer offer!
Difficulty Level:	Easy
Call Time:	12 minutes
Total Saved:	$25.00
$/hour to make call:	$125.00

If you've been following the story so far, then here is the moment you've been waiting for—the call where the bank apologizes, finally waives the late fee, and offers me a better deal to come back. The neat thing about this one is that they called me!

SUMMARY

Ladybug called from Sheepdog Bank to ask, "Why I closed my account? What was the problem? Could they do anything?"

I explained that on my 9/22 statement I was charged a $25 late fee and they wouldn't waive the fee. Ladybug said she could waive the fee and asked if I wanted to open my account again. I said sure but I want some more stuff. She then gave me a 6.9% transfer offer that lasts for 6 months, and I have until 2/17 to use that offer.

And what about my regular 17.9% rate? She lowered it to 9.9% on purchases for 6 months then after that it goes to 13.9% and stays there forever. I explained that she saved Sheepdog Bank because I was going to close my other 3 accounts next, after the New Year, because of that $25 late fee.

TRANSCRIPT

The first few seconds of conversation are missing because I had to set up the recording device. Since I wasn't initiating the call I wasn't prepared to record it.

Scott: "I just want to get my paperwork out on this, okay."

Rep: "Oh, okay."

Scott: "What's your name again?"

Rep: "My name is Ladybug."

Scott: "Ladybug."

Rep: "I was just curious. I noticed here that you closed it. I was wondering if there was something here we could do better for you."

Scott: "I think there certainly is. Umm, just got to find, umm, I'm just getting my statement here."

Rep: "Okay."

Scott: "Okay, Ladybug, this is what happened."

Rep: "Okay."

Scott: "I had a...Well first of all you know how long I've had my account, right? Do you see that?"

Rep: "Right yeah, 10 years. Yes."

Scott: "In good standing the whole time."

Rep: "Yep, very good."

Scott: "I'm really glad Sheepdog Bank is calling back to, you know, see. But this is what happened. I had a late fee assessed on my account on my statement closing date 9/22."

Rep: "Okay."

Scott: "And it was $25, and I was doing like electronic banking. I don't know how but the times got messed up, and I called Sheepdog Bank and they wouldn't refund that to my account."

Rep: "The $25."

Scott: "Yeah."

Rep: "Okay, let me just double-check on that here for ya. Let me find where the late fees are here. Umm, okay, 9/22, they were not able to credit that. Hmm, I don't know why not. I know I can take that off here for you. Was that the only reason?"

Scott: "That was the only reason."

Note: Notice how one department's "policy" isn't the same as another's. They wouldn't waive the fee the first time because they waived it once before. Now, since they're not making any money, they want to waive the fee. That's the other "policy." It must read "If we're not making a profit, then do whatever the customer wants so we can start earning money!"

Rep: "Okay, the $25 fee. Well, I know I can take that off for you, and put the credit back on the account. I'm really sorry that they weren't able to handle that the first time."
Note: You'd better be sorry, real sorry!

Scott: "I couldn't believe it either. I mean uh, I said, when I spoke to the rep, I said you know I can't believe Sheepdog Bank is going to throw away a customer that has been with them for more than 10 years over $25."

Rep: "Over, yeah exactly."

Scott: "I mean umm..."

Rep: "Exactly."

Scott: "I mean I spent thousands of dollars in interest payments with Sheepdog Bank for ten years and I've gotten services in return and that was fine, but..."
Note: Now I just want to rub it in.

Rep: "Yeah, you're right, you're right. Actually I will go ahead and remove that fee, put a credit back on the account. If you want to reopen it we can certainly look at some other options here that might make it better for you. Um, as far as the late fee I can right away get a credit on that."

Scott: "Okay I would definitely want to get my card back, you know with that, and that sounds like a...It's just sad that it had to come to all this. I mean I had to call and cancel, and..."

Rep: "I know it, I know. I wish we could have been there the first time for you. You had just called the customer service number."

Scott: "Yes."

Rep: "Yeah, I'm surprised, sometimes I don't know what their criteria is, or what happens there, but I can certainly, certainly get the account reopened there for you and there is no cost. So it's not a..."

Scott: "Would the account, I guess the account number would be different."

Rep: "No, actually you will keep the same account number. We'll just, I'm sure you cut up your cards right?"

Scott: "Umm, I might have, I might not have. I'm going to have to look, I might have thrown them in the file; I might have cut them up. I don't really know."

Rep: "Well it doesn't cost for us to send you a new card either so I can certainly drop one of those in the mail for you tomorrow. And that way you would have a card if you need it. Umm, okay I just need to verify a few things here. How was your name as it appeared on the card?"

Scott: "Umm, as it appeared on the card?"

Rep: "Yeah."

Scott: "Well, I guess it would be the same as it appeared on my account: Scott L. Bilker."

Rep: "Okay, and then as far as your address, that still verified everything updated."

Scott: "Yes. Everything is the same."

Rep: "Okay, and, umm, what was your social security number?"

Scott: (I give her the number.) "See what happened, I had a really good rate too, at the time. I think the rate was, uh, like 6.9% and I had a balance on there of, the whole thing maxed out. Yep, $2,000 at 6.9%, and I was so mad I just paid it off, even though the rate was great, because of that $25 fee."
Note: Now I'm starting to drop the hint that I want something for coming back.

Rep: "Right, right."

Scott: "Can Sheepdog Bank...First of all what would my limit be when I come back, will it be increased?"
Note: No more hints. It's time to start demanding changes to the account.

Rep: "Okay, here just a second I'm getting that $25 off. And I did see there was a 14 cents finance charge because of that. I'm removing that for you as well."

Scott: "I appreciate that Ladybug."

Rep: "Oh, not a problem. Okay, let me go back and check here on the interest rate. Oh, wait we'll look at the limits here. Uh, $2,100 and you might need an increase on that?"

Scott: "If I qualify for one I'll take it. If they give a really nice welcome back rate I think I might actually forget the whole thing ever happened."
Note: This is the direct approach.

Rep: "Okay, as far as the credit line increase what we could do here is certainly send up a request to our new business department, and they go over and review the accounts for that reason. They just, you know, ask for some information here and we can certainly look into that. They would give you a response within 7 to 10 days on what they did with that. Umm, you want to try for that we can certainly, you know, go ahead and put a request in."

Scott: "I don't know if it is really necessary then."

Rep: "At this point."

Scott: "If there is like an automatic one, that maybe I'm entitled to, I'll take it, if not, then I'm not going to apply for one at this moment."

Rep: "At this moment, okay, that's not a problem. I didn't see an automatic one, readily available here, but at any time, you know, in the future, if you need it, give us a call and see if we can at that time. And let's see, as far as your interest rates, what have we got? Oh, okay, you were on a 6.9% balance transfer rate. That's how that was. Let me just double-check. Yep, accepted 6.9%, you actually would still qualify for that. Through the middle of February of next year to bring in a balance at that rate, and then 6 months from that day to pay it off."

Scott: "Hmm, okay, so..."

Rep: "That is just, you know, on the balance transfers there."

Scott: "Okay, so 6.9% transfer until February?"

Rep: "Yep, you have until February 17th to bring in the transfer and it would be, you know, 6.9% is good on the transfer from the date you bring it in for 6 months. As far as your regular interest rate, you know concerning new purchase and cash advance, that is currently at a 17.9% variable. What I can do on that is drop down to a 9.9% fixed rate for 6 months and after that it is only 13.9% variable. So you would not be looking at another 4% higher on the 17.9%. We can make everything 13.9% on the long haul there. A variable rate, would that sound okay for you?"

Scott: "I'll take that."

Note: It seems that since Ladybug couldn't get me that credit line increase she compensated by lowering the interest rate. It's probably a standard offer to get historically good customers to return. Too bad they didn't treat me nice when I was using the card but that's okay because I'm getting a much better deal now!

Rep: "Okay, I'll get that in effect here immediately for you."

Scott: "So the 9.9% would be in effect immediately?"

Rep: "In effect immediately, yeah. It is good for 6 months on all new purchases and cash advances. And then your 6.9%, you know, that's good on balance transfers. So you might, you know, you'll have actually 2 different rates on the card, if you were to transfer a balance."

Scott: "You know what, let me look and see in my file here, if I have a card. I am very happy Sheepdog Bank called, it restores my faith."

Rep: "I was glad I was able to help you here."

Scott: "Well you certainly were. I mean it was just sad for me, cause I had such a long relationship with Sheepdog Bank. I would just think, from a marketing standpoint, it must cost $500 to find a good customer, and then to let one go would be just crazy business, you know. Let me see. Yep, I still have the card."

Rep: "Okay."

Scott: "Yeah, and I have...I'm very glad you called, Sheepdog Bank should be very happy that you called, you can tell them it was very smart because I have 3 other Sheepdog Bank accounts, that I was really considering closing over this whole thing."

Rep: "Hopefully, we won't do that."
Note: You'd better hope for that! ☺

Scott: "Well I won't do that now, but I was gonna. I was thinking about it. And after the New Year I might've. And the total credit line is like over 20 something thousand dollars. That has all been in good standing for 10 years. So this phone call saved Sheepdog Bank a lot of money."

Rep: "Did, I mean, were you interested in keeping three separate accounts, or did you want to put them all together or..."

Scott: "Well, you know, two of them are my wife's. And the other one is my Gold Card and um, in fact the last time I spoke with a rep I believe they were telling me I could combine both my accounts into say the Standard Card and get the same rates on the Standard Card account."

Rep: "Yep, you're right, you're right. We can take your Gold Card and move it right over here into your Standard Card and you would have all those rates here that I mentioned to you that would be available. And then, you know, just basically consolidate just to the one card."

Scott: "How fast could that happen?"
Note: Always investigate all your options while you have a human on the phone.

Rep: "Actually I can do it right now."

Scott: "Hmm, alright well, I can do it at anytime that quickly?"

Rep: "Yeah, yeah, you actually call in and tell them you want to consolidate everything to your Standard Card. Your wife's cards now they wouldn't be able to, basically you're not the primary?"

Scott: "No, but she could do it to hers?"

Rep: "Yeah, she could take her 2 cards and put them together, and you can pull your 2 together. That's fine."

Scott: "Okay."

Rep: "Yep, yep, it's just a matter of a few minutes, not a big project. See I know it does take 3 to 5 days for the actual credit line and balance to set up, but you're still able to, you know, use your cards, everything would go to the one that you're keeping. So it's not a big deal at all, you wouldn't even ever know it happened, basically it happens pretty quick."

Scott: "Wow. Okay well you know what. Now that I have this new option available to me I will, I'll have to think about it. But since I can call back and do it, I think you can pretty much bet that I might."

Rep: "Okay, well, we'll be here 24 hours, we'll be glad to help you if we can."

Scott: "Okay Ladybug, well I appreciate your calling."

Rep: "Oh, not a problem. I'll get a confirmation letter out there on your new interest rate in about 7 to 10 days."

Scott: "Okay."

Rep: "Okay, and umm, what else was I supposed to tell you? Oh, if you were going to do cash advances just be aware that there is a 3% or $5 minimum transaction fee."

Scott: "Right."

Note: Let's do some math real fast. A 3% transfer fee for a 6-month offer is like 6% (2 x 3%) for a 1-year period. So, with an APR of 6.9% plus the 6% transfer rate, the cost really feels like 12.9% APR. Not the greatest cash-advance deal but I'll keep it around as an option.

Rep: "Which most banks, you know, do, but that's what our rates are on cash advance. Well, did you have any other questions?"

Scott: "No, but there is no fee for transfers of course?"

Rep: "No, no sir not at all."

Scott: "Okay, well that answers all my questions Ladybug."

Rep: "I think I did send a new card out. Umm, no I haven't sent a new card out."

Scott: "Well there's no need to."

Rep: "Okay, just wanted to double-check."

Scott: "Alright."

Rep: "Okay well thank you so much, Scott, for your time and I'm glad I was able to help you."

Scott: "Okay, good I appreciate that."

Rep: "Oh, not a problem, you have a good evening."

Scott: "You too, Ladybug."

Rep: "Thank you, bye-bye."

Scott: "Bye-bye."

CHAPTER 5

LOWERING YOUR INTEREST RATES

IT'S THE COST OF DEBT

This is the most important chapter when it comes to saving money by negotiating with your bank. That's because it's not the debt that's the main problem, it's the cost of that debt! If you can borrow $10,000 today, not make any payments, then 10 years in the future still owe $10,000, you'd be fine. However, that's not the way it works.

When you "borrow" money you're really "buying" that money. When you pay it back there are interest charges and other fees that the bank receives from you in return for lending that money. These fees are what keep you in debt!

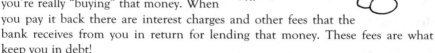

As you probably know, paying back your loans too slowly will result in your paying the maximum fee for the borrowed dollars. Consider this: if you borrow $5,000 at 19.8% APR, and make minimum payments, it will take nearly 46 years to repay and cost $24,000 when it's over! If you do the math, you'll find that you repay $96 for every $20 borrowed! That's a $76 fee for a $20 bill!

The key to repaying your debt efficiently, and I mean cheaply, is to keep your finance charges as low as possible. And to do this you must focus on the APR, the interest rate. Many people don't even look at their interest rates. I'm sure you do since you're interested in saving money. However, even when you're diligent at reviewing your credit card statements, it can be easy to overlook some interest costs. The main point here is to watch the cost of purchase interest rates versus cash advance interest rates. Usually, the cost for cash advance rates is much greater than that for purchases. Your credit card statement will break your balance up into these two categories and show the associated rates.

The good news is that you will be able to negotiate better rates with many of your current credit card banks. I've found that, by using the techniques I present in this book, more than 70% of the banks that I negotiate with for lower rates have agreed. If they don't, I punish them by transferring my balance to another bank. After that, it's only a few weeks before they send me a new low-rate offer! In reality, they all have to lower their rates eventually!

CALL #5.01: $13,673 SAVED WITH ONE CALL

Reason For Call:	Interest Rate Lowered
Result:	Rate lowered from 22.55% to 8.75% plus $40 refund!
Difficulty Level:	Easy
Call Time:	11 minutes
Total Saved:	$13,673.00
$/hour to make call:	$74,580.00

This is a classic story that I'm always asked about during media interviews. It happens to be my first experience with lowering my rate—and I have the entire conversation on tape for you to enjoy!

SUMMARY

The bank raised my rate to 22.55% up from the 6-month 6.9% promotion rate. I spoke with the Account Retention Department and they immediately lowered my rate to 8.75% and gave me a $40 refund for finance charges that occurred when the rate changed. This new deal will last for another 6 months. My balance on that statement is $7700.07.

To understand the magnitude of the rate dropping from 22.55% to 8.75% we need to look at the payments and payoff times associated with those rates. Under the conditions that I paid today's minimum payment of $154 until the balance is paid off, it will take 12.6 years and $23,223 to pay off my balance at 22.55%.

A rate of 8.75% would allow me to pay off that $7700.07 balance, at $154 a month, in only 5.2 years, costing only $9,550. The savings generated by this one phone call are $13,673 as long as I continue to call back and keep the rate at 8.75%!

Actually, I did eventually transfer my balance to far lower rates and thus saved much more than $13,673.00.

TRANSCRIPT

Note: This is the VERY FIRST recording I ever did! I don't have the beginning of the conversation when I asked to be transferred to the "account retention department." It was during the beginning of the conversation that I got the idea to record this and maybe, someday, write a book about the results!

Rep: "Special Services this is Mud Wasp speaking. May I have your account number?"

Scott: "Sure my account number is..." (I give him the number.)

Rep: "Your name?"

Scott: "Scott Bilker."

Rep: "Your mother's maiden name?"

Scott: (I give him the name.)

Rep: "Alright, how can I help you today Mr. Bilker?"

Scott: "Okay, I just got my statement this month and I noticed the rather large jump in the interest rate. I know that promotional period is probably over..."

Rep: "Right, I can probably extend that same rate, you had an 8-7-5 variable rate, for another six months, uh, the eight and three quarter, or the prime rate itself, whichever is greater for uh, six months...If you're interested in that."

Scott: "Um, what's the rate?"

Rep: "Eight and three quarters."

Scott: "For six months?"

Rep: "Right...That is the uh lowest rate we have, but you know if you're interested I could extend that on the entire balance ah, and on the cash and retail transactions."

Scott: "Hmmm." (Tapping my fingers on the table.)

Rep: "Would you be interested in that?"

Scott: "Would it um, would that also take care of this month's 22.55%, will I get a refund for the difference in rate for this month's statement?"
Note: Try to get a refund for anything you can! In this case I'm asking for a refund of the month's interest charges on top of the reduction of the APR.

Rep: "Actually, ah, January's...February's statement would go on at the first six months at that new rate...so ah, I could enter that rate, put a $40 credit toward the difference in the finance charges."

Scott: "You could do that?"

Rep: "Right...now did you want me to do that then?"

Scott: "That sounds fine."

Rep: "Okay, I'll enter that in the, ah, computer system and send out a letter to verify the terms..."

Scott: "Okay."

Rep: "...and um and we do appreciate your business and we encourage you to use the card and take advantage of the lower interest rate on the account."

Scott: "Okay, so that's eight and three quarters (8.75% APR), a $40 credit, and what's your name?"

Note: I'm just summarizing what we talked about so I can be sure what I'm going to be receiving. Plus I want to double-check this rep's full name just in case what we discussed doesn't actually happen.

Rep: "Um, Mud Wasp."

Scott: "Alright, well that sounds fine. And it's for six months you say."

Rep: "That's correct."

Scott: "Okay, six months."

Rep: "Alright, thank you for calling."

Scott: "Okay. Bye-bye."

CALL #5.02: STOP GOUGING MY FRIENDS!

Reason For Call:	Interest Rate Lowered
Result:	Rate Lowered from 21.4% to 15.9%
Difficulty Level:	Medium
Call Time:	8 minutes
Total Saved:	$77.00
$/hour to make call:	$577.50

A good friend of ours, Kathy Boyd (name changed), called to say hi. We ended up getting into the subject of credit cards. She mentioned that one of her credit card banks has been charging her rates as high as 21.4%! I suggested that she call to lower her rates but she didn't know exactly what to say.

I suggested to Kathy that I speak on her behalf as her fiancé. Then we can call right now using the conference call function on my new phone. She liked the idea! We went on to save her some money!

SUMMARY

Kathy called to say hi and was asking about her debt. She was saying that Whippet Bank is charging her 21.4% (for purchases before 5/8) and 17.9% (for purchases after 5/8). I called Whippet Bank and put us all on conference call with Kathy. She told the rep that I am her fiancé and that she wanted me to talk for her.

I asked for the rate to be lowered and they did from 17.9% to 15.9% but the rep said that not even a supervisor could lower the 21.4%. I still asked to speak to a supervisor and the result was that they lowered her rate all the way down to 15.9% for both. Kathy's balance is $931 and she is paying $45 toward the debt so her total savings $77! Kathy called me "The Credit King."

TRANSCRIPT

Note: The first part of this transcript is just prior to calling the bank. I'm getting the facts from Kathy.

Kathy: "I was late in the past."

Scott: "You were late. How many times?"

Kathy: "In the past."

Scott: "How late?"

Kathy: "Well, when I first started acquiring amounts on my card I was a couple months late. 'Cause I didn't have a job."

Scott: "How long ago."

Kathy: "That was 4 years ago."

Scott: "Oh, okay, that's fine. All right, it's July 31st. I'm here with Kathy Boyd who says hi. Say hi Kathy."
Note: Just making notes on the tape.

Kathy: "Hi."

Scott: "Okay, Whippet Bank is gouging her for 21.4% and 17.9% and we're going to see what we can do about it. Hopefully we can do something."

I make the call...

Rep: "Whippet Bank, this is Isabella Moth may I have your name please?"

Kathy: "Kathy Boyd."

Rep: "I can barely here you, hello."
Note: The rep is having a hard time hearing Kathy because of the 3-way call function on my phone.

Kathy: "Hello, ah, Kathy Boyd."

Rep: "Your mother's maiden name?"

Kathy: (Gives her the name.)

Rep: "And how can I help you?"

Kathy: "Um, I was looking over my bill with my fiancé and um, and I wanted him to talk on my behalf."
Note: Simple phrase to pass the phone, "...speak (talk) on my behalf."

Rep: "You want to talk to what?"

Kathy: "I wanted my ah fiancé to talk on my behalf of my..."

Rep: "Okay."

Scott: "Okay, hi, hi I'm, I'm here on the other line."

Rep: "I'm sorry, okay."

Scott: (Giggle, giggle.)

Rep: "Yeah, I can barely, barley hear her."

Scott: "Okay, you can hear me fine?"

Rep: "Yeah."

Scott: "Okay, great. Alright, I'm looking at one of her last statements here."
Note: Not really, but it sounds believable.

Rep: "Emm hmm."

Scott: "And I'm looking at the interest rates and they're, they seem a little high and I was hoping Whippet Bank could do something about that."

Rep: "Ah, which interest were you talking about? The 17.9%?"

Scott: "Well, the 21.4%."

Rep: "The 21.4% I cannot touch until that rate is paid off, until that amount is paid off."
Note: Don't believe everything the first rep tells you. You must always continue to push for the lower rate!

Scott: "It will be paid off by this low-rate offer I have here in front of me in about ten minutes. I mean I was hoping that I wouldn't have to do one of these 5.9% deals but there's a big difference. Isn't there anything they can do? I mean she's been a good customer and she's paid Whippet Bank..."
Note: Okay, I was bluffing. I did have a 5.9% deal in front of me but it was my offer, not Kathy's. Now I've made the threat so they're going to have to starting thinking about plan "B" to keep Kathy's business.

Rep: "Let me check. Hold on please."

Scott: "Sure."

Rep: "Okay."

On hold...

Rep: "Hello sir?"

Scott: "Yes."

Rep: "Thank you very much for holding. 21.4% I cannot adjust but on the 17.9%."

Scott: "Okay."

Rep: "I can lower it to 15.9%, as your permanent rate."
Note: This is a good start.

Scott: "Okay, is there any balance on that rate right now?"

Rep: "Yes, your new purchase and cash advance coming are all on that rate."

Scott: "Okay, and it's going to be lowered to 15.9%?"

Rep: "Yeah, if you want."
Note: Obviously I want it. I actually should have pushed a little further.

Scott: "Well of course, we'll take that."

Rep: (Giggles.)

Scott: "And um, when can we find, is there anyone else there that might be able to do something about the 21.4%?"

Rep: "Ah, you can talk to a manager but um, to tell you honestly, um, a manager won't lower that rate either."
Note: That's what they all say. Don't believe it! Keep being persistent because if you have a good history with your credit card bank, they want to keep your business!

Scott: "Okay, well I still think that it will be pretty cool to talk to one."

Rep: "Sure."

Scott: "But you can do the 15.9% now..."

Rep: "Yeah."

Scott: "...and I can talk to someone now too?"

Rep: "Yep."

Scott: "Okay, great."

Rep: "Okay, let me ah..."

Scott: "Let's lower the rate first."

Rep: "Yeah, now it's 15.9% and effective immediately and it will show on your next statement."

Scott: "Beautiful."

Rep: "Okay."

Kathy: "Great."

Rep: "So you want to talk to a manager?"

Scott: "Uh huh."

Rep: "Hold on."

On hold...

Rep: "Hello sir?"

Scott: "Yes."

Rep: "Thank you for holding. I do have a manager on the line to assist you further, go ahead."

Scott: "Great."

Manager: "Hi sir, my name is Mrs. Fruitfly. How may I help you?"

Scott: "Hi Mrs. Fruitfly. I'm helping my fiancée here with her finances, and I'm looking over the Whippet Bank statement and this 21.4% I feel is a little unfair. She has been very good with her account and um, and we've got a whole bunch of these low-rate offers and, ya know..."
Note: Always be prepared to tell your story several times during the call.

Manager: "Sure, um and the representative lowered the APR on the new purchases I see so as kind of an FYIB only reason for the 21.4% balance that was when she had gone two payments past due."

Scott: "Emm hmm."

Manager: "Um, but she's had six months of on-time payments, at least now so um, typically what happens when we lower the interest rate, it's kind of a, okay, that'll be, on the balance going forward. But I'll just go ahead and move everything into that lower rate for you right now."
Note: That didn't take too long. See that. The manager certainly could, and did, lower the rate, contrary to what the first rep said.

Scott: "Oh wow. That would really be super."

Manager: "Well it's not a problem."

Scott: "Okay, now and that will be effective immediately?"

Manager: "Yeah, you'll see that right on the next statement then."

Scott: "Great. Thank you very much."

Manager: "You're welcome. Thanks for calling in."

Scott: "Okay."

Manager: "Bye."

Scott: "Bye-bye."

Note: After I hung up with the bank, Larissa picked up another line to chat. Below is some more of my conversation with Kathy, and my wife.

Kathy: "Wow."

Larissa: "What did they agree upon?"

Scott: "15.9%..."

Scott: "I hate when people get gouged for no reason, I can't stand it! I gotta tell ya that."

Kathy: "That was very impressive. I think saying that you had these offers in front of you that are offering 5.9% or whatever, helped a lot. You're the Credit King!"

Scott: "Thanks. It's always been my experience, when I call the banks, that having an offer from another bank, helps convince them to lower the rate."

CALL #5.03: "NOW THAT YOU SAID THAT..."

Reason For Call:	Interest Rate Lowered
Result:	Rate lowered from 16.71% to 11.9%
Difficulty Level:	Hard
Call Time:	12 minutes
Total Saved:	$864.00
$/hour to make call:	$4,320.00

This call was made on my wife's credit card. Initially she had to be on the phone to give me authorization to speak for her. We had a low-rate promotional deal at 4.9% that just ended and they raised her rate. I'm calling to see if the bank will lower the rate.

SUMMARY

I called and found that they raised Larissa's rate to 16.71%. The bank representative wouldn't lower the rate and said nothing could be done. Then I said I would just transfer the balance. All of the sudden a lower rate became available. She said, "now that you said that" and transferred me to another rep who offered me 11.9% until the balance is paid off, if I transferred at least $100.

My previous month's balance was $4,700 with $120 in payments. At 16.71% it takes $6,854.40 to pay off the loan. At 11.9% it takes $5,990.40 to pay off the loan. Total savings is $864.00!

TRANSCRIPT

Voice Menu: "This call may be monitored or recorded."

Scott: "Yours too."

Rep: "Thank you for calling card services. May I have your name please?"

Larissa: "Larissa Bilker."

Rep: "Hi Ms. Bilker, my name is June Bug. May I have your account number please?"

Larissa: (Gives her the number.)

Rep: "Okay, one moment while your account comes up. Okay Ms. Bilker, for security purposes, may I please verify your Social Security Number?"

Larissa: (Gives her the number.)

Rep: "Okay, how can I help you?"

Larissa: "Actually, I'd like my husband to speak about my account with you?"

Rep: "Okay."

Larissa: "Thank you."

Scott: "Hi, what's your name?"

Rep: "My name is June Bug."

Scott: "Hi June. I guess you can see the latest statement?"

Rep: "I will...once you told me you want me to look at your latest statement."

Scott: "Okay."

Rep: "Slowly but surely it's coming...it says it's creating it."

Scott: "Okay."

Rep: "Okay, what are we looking at?"

Scott: "Alright, um, I guess the last one, the closing date is July 13th."

Rep: "Right."

Scott: "The APR at that time was 4.9%."

Rep: "Um, hmm."

Scott: "And I think as of like recently, it changed."

Rep: "Right."

Scott: "What is it now?"

Rep: "Okay, hang on."

Scott: "Sure."

Rep: "It's...let's see, on purchases it's 16.71% and on cash advances it's 19.61%."

Scott: "And on the balance right now?"

Rep: "Um, it would have gone to 16.71%."

Scott: "Okay, it's 16.71%."
Note: They are out of their minds if they think we're going to carry a balance at that ridiculous rate!

Rep: "Um hmm."

Scott: "Okay, I wanted to ask if that can be lowered or changed or dropped, is there something..."

Rep: "Um, I'm not showing there's anything available right now. Although we just had some promotions sent out in massive millions of quantities."
Note: Okay, then give me one of those "mass million" offers. ☺

Scott: "Um hmm."

Rep: "Um, but I'm not showing that it's available on your account right now."

Scott: "Well, is there any way they can just lower it?"

Rep: "No."
Note: Most of the time the first response is going to be "no," but you should never give up!

Scott: "Okay, well I'm gonna transfer that balance out."

Rep: "Okay."

Scott: "I mean, to another, a different card."

Rep: "Well now that you've said that, hang on a second."
Note: Looks like I hit on the magic phrase. That would be the one that threatens the bank with losing some profit!

Scott: "Sure."

Rep: "Okay, we have to go through all these checks, okay?"
Note: What does she mean by "checks"? I'm thinking it's an actual checklist of things that the cardholder must say before getting the best deal.

Scott: "Sure."

Rep: "Hang on."

On hold...

Account Specialist: "Thank you for calling card services. May I have your name please?"
Note: They should really know this by now.

Scott: "My name is Scott Bilker."

Account Specialist: "Thank you Mr. Bilker. My name is Hornbeetle, and how may I assist you tonight?"

Scott: "Well I was speaking to June a moment ago."

Account Specialist: "Okay, oh, I'm sorry, she transferred you to me. Is there something I can do for you?"

Scott: "I, I don't know. Are you another rep just like her?"

Account Specialist: "No, I'm an account specialist, sir. And how may I help you?"

Scott: "Oh, okay, well I was calling um, and talking to June about my account. The promotional 4.9% offer."
Note: Most of the time you will need to tell your story, in its entirety, again to each manager or supervisor.

Account Specialist: "Um hmm."

Scott: "And now the rate was moved to 16.7% and June told me that you'd be able to do something with that."
Note: Well, that's not exactly what June said, but it sure sounds pretty good!

Account Specialist: "Okay, I'll do my best to try and help you. Um, may I have that account number? 'Cause the number that I keep pulling up is not a valid number."

Scott: "Okay." (I give her the number.)

Account Specialist: "Okay, just one moment."

Scott: "Sure."

Account Specialist: "Okay, Mr. Bilker the promotional rate has expired."
Note: Thanks for the tip genius! That's the reason I'm calling!

Scott: "Okay."

Account Specialist: "And that is for...that it went to the regular rate on the card. But let me just see. I don't know if we have anything to offer right now but I can check it for you."

Scott: "Okay."

Account Specialist: "Okay, I do have something for you here. Did you have a balance transfer that you want to do tonight? 'Cause if you do I could lower that down to 11.9% for you."
Note: Notice how the, "no, there's nothing that can be done" has quickly changed to "yes" we do have something.

Scott: "Gee, 11.9% is still not that great."
Note: That's a good start but I'm not about to jump on their first offer. Especially when I have dozens of other banks I can call to find out what they can do for me right now.

Account Specialist: "But that would be the overall rate on the card. That's not a promotional rate that will expire. That would be the rate on the card. Right now your rate is at 16.7% and that is the rate that it went to after the promotional rate expired but this would be the rate on the card that would replace the account rate."

Scott: "And it would be that rate forever?"

Account Specialist: "Yes."

Scott: "For eternity?"
Note: It's a little hard to believe so I'm going to repeat myself a few times to make sure I'm clear on this.

Account Specialist: "Until we got some promotional rates or something like that."

Scott: "Okay, and that rate was what? 11.9%?

Account Specialist: "Uh huh."

Scott: "That rate is still a little high. I mean I can transfer it right now to another card for 6.9%."
Note: I really want to push to make sure that I'm getting their best deal.

Account Specialist: "Right, but it would expire 'cause that's a promotional rate."

Scott: "I know but it doesn't matter. It will expire in six months."

Account Specialist: "Uh huh."

Scott: "Instead of paying, you know, 11.9% for six months I'll pay 6.9%. I mean is there, I mean can you get it closer, can you, you know?"

Account Specialist: "No. That is, we don't have another, see the promotional rate that you had has expired so we don't have another promotional rate to offer you right now. But that we be, offer you a lower rate which is a very good rate overall on the card. Because most credit card rates goes higher than that. They're like 16%, 18%, and 21%."

Scott: "Right, most might, but mine don't."

Account Specialist: "Hmm."

Scott: "Uh, let's see. Um, available credit $1,194."

Account Specialist: "It would only take $100 to get that rate."

Scott: "I, I think I'll have to think about that, and call you back. Would that be available when I call back?"

Note: Two mistakes on my part here. First, I should have made the transfer on the spot to lock in the 11.9% just in case I had trouble finding another bank to do a transfer with. Second, I asked if I could get that deal when I call back. That gave her the opportunity to pressure me. She could have said something like "if you don't do it now you won't be able to get that rate so you have to decide right now while you're on the phone with me."

Account Specialist: "Yes, I can, yeah."

Scott: "Would I have to contact you again? Would I have to go through this whole conversation or would I just explain..."

Account Specialist: "Well, just contact me. My name is Hornbeetle. My extension is 4026."

Note: Now that's rare! A person that you can contact again, someone with an actual phone. I'm guessing that there may be some type of commission involved with her being the person that does the transfer or some other type of point system.

Scott: "Okay Hornbeetle, I will sleep on this and get back to you."

Account Specialist: "Okay. Well thank you for calling and have a good night."

Scott: "You too."

Account Specialist: "Bye-bye."

Scott: "Bye-bye."

Note: I did call back and get the 11.9% rate but soon thereafter found another, better, deal and transferred the balance to a rate lower than 11.9%.

Call #5.04: "Don't tell them I told you..."

Reason For Call:	Interest Rate Lowered
Result:	Rate Lowered from 23.99% to 19.8%
Difficulty Level:	Hard
Call Time:	12 minutes
Total Saved:	$128.00
$/hour to make call:	$640.00

I made this call for our very close friends, Kelly and Tom Mayer (names changed). We were talking about credit cards and rates over dinner a previous evening and I said that we should give the bank a call and see if they'll lower Kelly's interest. They're charging her 23.99%, which is absolutely insane!

During this call I play the role of Tom (Kelly's husband). When it came time to negotiate the rate, the manager said she had to speak with Kelly because Kelly is the account owner. That wasn't a problem because I was on the other line and could talk to her while she was talking to the account manager.

SUMMARY

The bank is charging them 23.99% on their balance of $1,422.81. Their payments are $60 per month. The first rep I spoke with said there was nothing at all she could do about the rate. I told her I would transfer the balance then she asked if I would close the account and I said, "I may." Then I asked to speak to a supervisor and she transferred me to another department. The rep then said she'd "Tell me a secret, but don't tell them I told you. If you threaten to close your account they'll be more willing to work with you." The next rep I spoke to said they would lower the rate to 19.8%. Kelly's savings are $128.00. At 23.99% it takes $1,947.60 to pay off the accounts, at 19.8% it takes $1,819.80.

TRANSCRIPT

Voice Menu: "All calls may be monitored or taped for quality purposes."

Scott: "Yeah, yours too."

Rep: "Thank you for calling account services. My name is Carolina Mantis, can I please have the account number?"

Kelly: (Gives her the number.)

Rep: "Can I get your name and social security number please?"

Kelly: (Gives her the information.)

Rep: "Okay. Can you also give me your home telephone number?"

Kelly: (Gives her the number.)

Rep: "Okay, and what can I do for you today?"

Kelly: "Umm, I'd like my husband to speak about my account with you."

Rep: "Okay. Before we do that let's just go ahead...now Kelly, I'm going to need to put him down as an authorized inquirer. Okay, so I'll quickly do that. Sir, what's your name?"

Note: It's usually not the case that someone has to be an "authorized inquirer" on the account to speak on your behalf. Tell the rep that your friend/spouse/parent/sibling is handling your bills for you and that you would like them to speak on your behalf right now.

Scott: "Tom Mayer. I'm right here on line number 2."

Rep: "Okay, now we've gone ahead and done that. So from this point on Tom, you would be able to call in and inquire about anything on the account."

Scott: "Okay great."

Rep: "Now is that alright with you Kelly?"

Kelly: "Yes."

Rep: "Okay, now what can I do for you?"

Scott: "Okay, what's your name again?"

Rep: "My name is Carolina Mantis."

Scott: "Okay, can you see my last statement there?"

Rep: "Let's see. Let me pull that one up. I do have it."

Scott: "Okay."

Rep: "Now what were you looking for on the statement?"

Scott: "Okay, um, I've been looking at the last few statements and I'm looking at this interest rate, 23.99%."

Rep: "Right."

Scott: "I've been paying that high rate for a while now, and on time, and I think it would be a little fair to reduce that rate."

Note: That was a weak request. I should have been more firm with something like, "This rate is too high and it would only be fair, at this point, to lower it as a courtesy for my being a good customer."

Rep: "Okay, well, to be completely honest with you, I don't have that ability. Let's see what we can do here...let me, can I get you to hold for one moment?"

Note: Yeah, yeah. That's what they all say.

Scott: "Sure."

Rep: "One moment please."

On hold...

Rep: "Tom? Kelly?"

Scott: "Yes."

Rep: "I just wanted to let you know, um, I'm still looking into that to see if there is something we can do on that."

Scott: "Okay."

Rep: "Um, if I can just get you to hold for a minute longer."

Scott: "Okay."

Rep: "I just wanted to let you know I hadn't forgotten about you."

Scott: "Alright, thank you."

Rep: "One moment."

On hold...

Rep: "Tom?"

Scott: "Yes."

Rep: "Thank you for holding. Um, in looking at this, it doesn't look like actually there's any way at this point that we can change the APR. The 23.9% is the set APR. Um, I do want to tell you though however, periodically, sometimes they'll send out a mailing..."

Scott: "Umm, hmmm."

Rep: "...for an invitation, for basically the same thing at a lower APR..."

Scott: "Umm, hmm."

Rep: "...a lower interest rate. And those are just totally at random."
Note: At random? I don't think so. Those computers are churning up the best way for the bank to make the most money. If they can continue to gouge Kelly and Tom for 23.99% then they'll keep going. Kelly and Tom won't be getting any of those offers.

Scott: "Right, well here's the situation. I've got like three transfer offers here at 6.9% and I'm going to use them because 23.99% is just absolutely crazy."

Rep: "Sure, I understand."

Scott: "And I was hoping that since I've been doing business with Saint Bernard Bank they'd have some flexibility. I mean, you figure they're making 30 bucks a month or $300 a year at this point, in finance charges, and it's going to go to zero. So is there anyone I can talk to that might be able to do this?"

Rep: "Okay, so basically you're saying it's either lower the APR or cancel the card."
Note: That's not exactly what I said but it sure sounds right.

Scott: "No, not cancel the card. I would just transfer the balance off and maybe at sometime in the future use it or cancel it if it never, ever drops. But I don't think right now I'd cancel it."

Rep: "Ummm."

Scott: "But I certainly would transfer the balance off of there because, 23.99%, that's ridiculous, I shouldn't be paying that. Is there a supervisor there I could talk to?"
Note: I should have probably given her a chance to say more. Leave some silence, some time for her to respond. She may have given me a tip on getting the rate lowered. It seemed she was driving at that "lower the rate or cancel the card" magic sentence.

Rep: "Sure, let me see if he's available. Can you hold one more moment?"

Scott: "Sure."

Rep: "One moment."

On hold...

Rep: "Okay sir?"

Scott: "Yes."

Rep: "Thank you for holding. I'm going to do something else for you."

Scott: "Okay."

Rep: "Were going to transfer you to another department that does have some leeway where this issue's concerned."

Scott: "Okay."

Rep: "I'm going to let you know a little secret though."
Note: I love secrets! That's why you shouldn't be nasty to the reps. Let them know that you know that they don't make the policies. Ask for their help and advice on how you can best go about getting the bank to lower your interest rates.

Scott: "Okay."

Rep: "You want to tell them that you're going to trans, err that you are looking to close your card. They'll be more willing to work with you that way."
Note: Thanks for the tip.

Scott: "I appreciate your help."

Rep: "So, let me go ahead and transfer you, don't tell them I told you that."

Scott: "I won't say a word."

Rep: (Giggle) "Just one moment please."

On hold...

Manager: "Mrs. Mayer?"

Scott: "This is Mr. Mayer."

Manager: "Okay, requiring closing the account I have to speak to Kelly."

Scott: "Well the account's not getting closed just yet. I want to talk to someone about the account."

Manager: "Okay, well if we're talking about the annual percentage rate because this is not, you're not financially responsible for it."

Scott: "Umm, hmm."

Manager: "I happen to have to talk to Kelly."

Scott: "Okay, umm, can you hold on?"
Note: I thought I was just made an authorized inquirer on this account of this credit card. This demonstrates, yet again, how disconnected these banks are between their departments.

Manager: "I can."

Scott: "Stand by."

Manager: "Okay."

I put them on hold because I had to call Kelly back on my other phone line with a conference call.

Scott: "Hello."

Manager: "Hi."

Scott: "Okay, my wife is on the other end of the phone now."

Kelly: "Hello."

Manager: "Kelly?"

Kelly: "Yes."

Manager: "Hi, this is Chinch Bug of the credit department."
Note: Isn't everyone at the credit card bank in the credit department? ☺

Kelly: "Hi."

Manager: "I understand that you had an inquiry about your annual percentage rate. Is that correct?"

Kelly: "Yes."

Manager: "Okay, now what is the problem?"

Scott: "I'll tell you the problem. The problem is 23.99%, which we've been paying for a while, just isn't fair. We've got all kinds of offers here at 6.9% and um, I'm going to take advantage of them if I can't work something out with Saint Bernard Bank, I mean..."

Manager: "Okay, Mr. Mayer um, I'd have to let you know something really quick on the account. You are an authorized inquirer on the account but you are not financially responsible, so legally I cannot discuss any of this with you."

Scott: "Umm, hmmm."

Note: What a bunch of bull. This manager is just trying to get us to quit asking about the account's interest rate.

Manager: "I can tell you what the percentage rate is, and what the payments are and things like that on the account. But when it comes to actually changing things or making negotiations for this. You are not somebody I can legally talk to about that."

Scott: "Well Kelly's right here. You can talk to her."

Manager: "Okay."

Scott: "Go ahead Kelly."

Manager: "Okay."

Kelly: "I just wanted to know if there's anything you can do to lower the rate for us."

Manager: "You know. Because you have had the account for a little over two years."

Kelly: "Uh, huh."

Manager: "We actually can reduce your annual percentage rate."

Note: Well you don't say. See how they're going to make you jump through hoops. It's worth it because of the money you save right away. In this call's case it's $128 for a 10 minute phone call, that's $768 per hour for making the call plus future savings by having the lower rate.

Kelly: "Okay."

Manager: "Unfortunately the lowest we go is 19.8% so we would not be able to match the 6.9% that you're getting from other offers. This card is designed to help you reestablish credit and it sounds like that's what it's done for you."

Note: Actually, the card is "designed" to get as much money as possible from people who have had trouble in the past!

Kelly: "Right."

Manager: "So if you want it to go down to 19.8% that would not be a problem but it is the lowest that we offer."

Kelly: "You can't go any lower than that at this time?"

Manager: "That's the lowest that we offer. We cannot go any lower than that, no."

Scott: "You know what Kelly. Why don't we take the 19.8% for now and we'll look at those offers more carefully and then decide."
Note: I can see that they're not going to budge any further on this secured card.

Kelly: "Okay."

Manager: "Okay, so what I can do is go ahead and lower that for you right now. Okay?"

Kelly: "Uh, huh."

Manager: "And them um, if you decide to close in the future then all you'd have to do is call back."

Scott: "Okay. Will that be effective immediately?"

Manager: "And that actually takes effect with your next statement and your next statement will be printed on the 3rd of September so a week from Thursday that will be in effect."

Kelly: "That's 19.9%?"

Scott: "19.8%."

Manager: "19.8%, correct."

Kelly: "Okay."

Manager: "Okay? Is there anything else I can do for you?"

Kelly: "No, that's it."

Manager: "Okay, that's all taken care of."

Kelly: "Thank you."

Scott: "Bye-bye."

Manager: "Thanks for calling Saint Bernard Bank and have a good day."

CALL #5.05: 21.08%, I DON'T THINK SO

Reason For Call:	Interest Rate Lowered
Result:	Rate Lowered from 21.08% to 15.9%
Difficulty Level:	Hard
Call Time:	5 minutes
Total Saved:	$160.00
$/hour to make call:	$1,920.00

Here's another call for Kelly and Tom Mayer (names changed). The bank has been gouging the life out of them for 21.08% and we're on a crusade to lower these rates.

SUMMARY

Kelly and I called and spoke with Hornet who told me that she couldn't lower the rate. I asked to speak with a supervisor and spoke to Deer Tick. After I told her about the transfer offers I have, she agreed to lower the rate to 15.9% and it will show on the next billing statement. She also mentioned that we could call back in 6 months to have the account reviewed for another rate reduction. With a balance of $1,745 at 21.08% and payments of $80, it's repaid in 28 months and costing $2,240. With the new rate of 15.9% the payoff time is 26 months, so we save two months or $160.

TRANSCRIPT

Scott: "I'm with Kelly, today is the 14th of March, calling Bearded Collie Bank."
Note: Making a voice memo on the tape.

Voice Menu: "Welcome to Bearded Collie Bank. Please enter your 16-digit account number."

Scott: "Alright." (I enter the numbers.)

Voice Menu: "Enter your 5 digit zip code."

Scott: "What's your zip?"

Kelly: (Gives me the zip code.)

Voice Menu: "To ensure the highest quality of service your call may be recorded."

Scott: "Yours too."

Rep: "Customer relations, this is Hornet, may I have your name please?"

Kelly: "Yes, Kelly Mayer."

Rep: "Hi, and can I have the last 4 digits of you social security number."

Kelly: (Gives her the number.)

Rep: "Okay, can I have your whole social security number?"

Kelly: (Gives her the number.)

Rep: "Okay, can you verify your home address please?"

Kelly: (Gives her the address.)

Rep: "Okay and can you verify your home phone number please?"

Kelly: (Gives her the number.)

Rep: "Okay and can you verify your date of birth for me please."

Kelly: (Gives her the date.)

Rep: "Okay, thank you for verifying that for me. We have a different last four digits of your security number. We have..."

Kelly: "I'm sorry that's right. I'm thinking of my husband's."

Rep: "Alright, and how can I help you today?"

Kelly: "I just want to talk to you about my account."

Rep: "I'd be happy to assist you."

Kelly: "Actually my husband is going to talk for me."

Scott: "I'm here."

Rep: "Hi sir."

Scott: "Yes."

Rep: "How may I help you?"

Scott: "Okay, well I'm taking a look at this Bearded Collie Bank account, which we have had for awhile, how long have we had this account?"
Note: You always want to point out how long you've been doing business with the bank.

Kelly: "I guess about 4 years."

Scott: "Oh, what's your name?"

Rep: "My name is Hornet."

Scott: "Hi Hornet."

Rep: "Hi."

Scott: "4 years we have had this Kelly?"

Kelly: "4 or 5."

Scott: "Okay, and uh, I'm looking at this interest rate, 21%. That is absolutely way too high, and I'm hoping that Bearded Collie Bank can lower that a little."

Rep: "Unfortunately, we wouldn't be able to lower that at this time."
Note: Every time! That's what they all say! Get used to hearing it. You must be persistent! Never give up!

Scott: "Okay, I'll tell you what I have here. I have got a Greenland Dog Bankcard that is offering me 7.99% to transfer the balance, and uh, I already have the card, I'm thinking about doing it. Now I have had a good relationship with Bearded Collie Bank, but 21% is out of hand. If you can't do better than that I'm just going to have to transfer that whole balance, like today."
Note: There's the threat, well, in this case it is a bluff because I'm really looking at one of my personal offers. Kelly doesn't have any other offers at this time.

Rep: "Unfortunately we won't be able to lower the interest rate right now."

Scott: "Can I speak to your supervisor about this?"

Rep: "Sure, can you hold for one moment?"

Scott: "Sure."

Rep: "Okay, thank you."

On hold...

Kelly: "How come they won't lower it? They won't say why."

Scott: "Hmm."

Rep: "Mrs. Deer Tick is on the line, she's an account supervisor, she will further assist you."

Scott: "Did you say Mrs. Deer Tick?"

Rep: "Yes."

Scott: "Okay."

Supervisor: "Hi Mr. Mayer, my name is Deer Tick, I'm an account supervisor here at Bearded Collie Bank."

Scott: "Hi Mrs. Tick."

Supervisor: "Hi. She was explaining to me that you were calling in to see if I could get your annual percentage rate lowered on your account, is that correct?"

Scott: "Right, basically the way I'm looking at it is I'm going to give Bearded Collie Bank a chance to still do business with me because I've just got too many offers on other cards at much better rates. I mean if this was even reasonable, but 21% is just unreasonable when I have an offer here from Greenland Dog Bank for 7.9%, an offer here from Whippet Bank for 2.9%, and an offer from my Hound Dog Bankcard at 9.9%. Now I mean, 21% is just ridiculous, if it was like 15%, something even reasonable, then I would consider sticking around. But you know I just want to see, since I've had a good relationship with Bearded Collie Bank, to see if you are going to do anything for me, or if I'm going to be leaving."
Note: I have to go through my story again but this time it's a little more concise and to the point.

Supervisor: "Right, I am showing that you have been with us for 5 years, and we definitely do appreciate your business. What I can do is go ahead and make an exception, and go ahead and look over the account and I can go ahead and lower your annual percentage rate down to 15.9%, now that would be LIBOR. And on your cash it would be 19.8%-LIBOR."
Note: That's pretty good. They'll drop the rate on the balance to 15.9% and for cash advances to 19.8%. Since all the charges are from purchases the total drop is 5.18%, which translates into a minimum savings of $160.

Scott: "Okay."

Supervisor: "That would be taking in some money there, because right now it does look like it is that 19.87%."

Scott: "Umm hmm."

Supervisor: "You want to go ahead and accept that then?"

Scott: "I accept that."
Note: I should have pushed harder for a lower rate.

Supervisor: "Okay, we will go ahead and put that in the system. Umm, that should update, let's see when does your statement close? Your statement closes on the 13th, so you should see that reflected on your next statement when you receive that. Umm, do keep in mind continue making your payments on time, staying under your limit, and no returned check fees and then in six months you will be eligible where you can be reviewed again, to see if you can get that lowered again."
Note: You bet we'll be calling back in six months! I'm marking my calendar right now! When I do call back I'll be sure to mention that I was told by Deer Tick to call back and get the rate reduced.

Scott: "Great."

Supervisor: "Alright, is there anything else I can do for you today?"

Scott: "No, no, that will be fine, I'm very glad Bearded Collie Bank cares about keeping me as a customer."

Supervisor: "Yeah, we definitely do. You have been with us for 5 years, and we do appreciate your business."
Note: That's more like it.

Scott: "Alright, thank you."

Supervisor: "You're welcome, you have a good day."

Scott: "Bye-bye."

Supervisor: "Bye-bye."

Call #5.06: What's That Charge For?

Reason For Call:	Interest Rate Lowered and Refund
Result:	Rate Lowered from 19.8% to 16.9% and $199 refund
Difficulty Level:	Hard
Call Time:	13 minutes
Total Saved:	$479.00
$/hour to make call:	$2,210.77

Another call for our good friends Kelly and Tom Mayer (names changed). This time we're calling to get the interest rate reduced plus get a charge removed that Kelly doesn't recognize. What happens sometimes is that you decide to try a program offer and they give a few months free. After that period they'll charge your card in perpetuity! If you don't use the program, you should stop them from charging you for it!

We also get them to lower the APR. This is a card on which we previously had the rate reduced in the past (call #5.04) and now we're calling back to make them go lower!

SUMMARY

Kelly and I called and spoke to a rep that transferred us to the account maintenance department. We spoke to Click Beetle who lowered the rate to 16.9% effective 3/19. I told him that we would be calling back periodically to get the rate reduced. With a balance of $4,942.93, payments of $180, and rate of 19.8% the payback time is 37 months costing $6,660. At 16.9% the payback time is 35 months or a savings of $360. Also, we removed the $119 fee for their "buy-smart" program.

TRANSCRIPT

Scott: "Okay, we are calling Saint Bernard Bank, Kelly and Tom, it is the 14th of March."
Note: Making a memo on the tape.

Voice Menu: "Thank you for calling Saint Bernard Bank. Please enter your account number..."

Scott: (I enter the numbers.)

Voice Menu: "Please hold while we access the account. Please enter the last 4 digits of your social security number."

Scott: (I enter the numbers.)

Voice Menu: "Thank you. Continue to hold while we access the account."

Scott: "Uh huh."
Note: I wonder if they make us jump through hoops so we simply hang up and give up. You can't let the voice-menu-torture stop you from getting to a human!

Voice Menu: "The current balance on your credit card is..." (The computer generated voice continues with more account information.)

Kelly: "I thought I had no credit available."

Voice Menu: (Continues going through the card information.)

Scott: "Right, I know this." (I push random buttons.)

Voice Menu: "Please hold for assistance from a representative. This call may be monitored for quality assurance."

Scott: "Yeah, yeah, yours too."

Rep: "This is Mole Cricket, how can I help you today Mrs. Mayer?"

Kelly: "Yes, umm, I would like to speak to someone about my account please."

Rep: "Okay, how can I assist you?"

Kelly: "Umm, my husband is on the line and he is going to be taking over for me."

Rep: "Okay."

Scott: "Hi, I'm here too."

Rep: "Hello Mr. Mayer, how may I assist you sir?"

Scott: "Okay, well I'm looking at this credit card statement, and umm, first of all tell me, how long have we had this account?"
Note: I want this rep to know that Kelly and Tom have been good customers for a while!

Rep: "Okay, I'm showing that the account was, hold on one second. I'm showing that you had the account for 5 years."

Scott: "Okay, 5 years. I thought we had this one for a long time. Well I'm looking at this rate 19.8%, and I got to tell you it's just too high. I've got too many other credit cards offering me good deals, but I've had good experiences with Saint

Bernard Bank in the past, so I'm calling to see if you want to lower that rate to keep my business."

Rep: "Okay, are you wanting to cancel the card?"

Scott: "Am I willing to cancel the card?"
Note: That type of response always throws me off a little. I'm wondering if they're just trying to mess with me or they're just used to people closing accounts because the rates are too high.

Rep: "No, are you wanting to cancel the card?"

Scott: "Umm, I probably wouldn't cancel, I would probably just transfer my balance to a low-rate on another card."
Note: It would have been better to say, "If I cannot get a better rate, then I'll be forced to cancel my account—it's up to you." I should have remembered this from call #5.04.

Rep: "Okay, because I am showing that you started off with the card at a 23.9%."

Scott: "Right, which is totally insane, by the way."

Rep: "Well that's 23.9%..."

Scott: "Unless you guys are the Mafia, or something."
Note: Umm, if you're reading this, and you're in the Mafia, I was just kidding. I know you have really good rates. ☺

Rep: "Well no that's 23.9% annually, that's not every month."
Note: No kidding genius! If it was 23.9% per month that would be 286.8% APR. A rate that I'm sure they'd love to charge if they could get away with it.

Scott: "Right, if it was 23.9% every month I'm sure there would be a lawsuit involved."

Rep: "Okay, then it was lowered to 19.8%."
Note: Kelly and I got that rate lowered from 23.9% a while ago (call #5.04).

Scott: "Yeah, when was that?"

Rep: "Umm, that was back a ways. I'm not sure when it was actually lowered. I only have access to something that shows on the account."

Scott: "Okay."

Rep: "What I can do is transfer you to our account maintenance department."

Scott: "Okay."

Rep: "They are the ones that will be able to assist you further, umm with the APR. Is that okay?"

Scott: "Sure."

Rep: "Okay. Please hold while I transfer you."

On hold...

Voice Menu: "Did you know that your account could qualify for Saint Bernard Bank health advantage?" (Continues running ads.)
Note: They're always trying to sell you on something, even when you're on hold.

Scott: "Uh huh."

Kelly: "What the hell is Saint Bernard Bank Buy-Smart fee for $119? I don't even see that."

Scott: "We'll take care of that while we are at it."

Kelly: "Whatever it is, we don't want it."

Scott: "Oh that's for sure. I'm just gonna..."

Rep: "This is Click Beetle, may I have your name please?"

Scott: "Hi, Click this is Tom Mayer and I am here with my wife Kelly. Say hi Kelly."

Kelly: "Hi."

Rep: "And could you verify your social security number, Mrs. Mayer."

Kelly: "Yes..." (Gives him the number.)

Rep: "And how can I help you?"

Scott: "Okay, well I'm looking here at my account and umm, we have been with Saint Bernard Bank for 5 years, and I'm just telling you that 19.9% is just too high. It's just insanely high. And I am hoping that Saint Bernard Bank will lower that rate. I tell ya, I just got 2 great offers in the mail, one from Hound Dog Bank, 2.99%, and one..."
Note: I make the threat.

Rep: "Introductory, yeah."
Note: He's trying to imply that low, introductory rates are somehow inferior to their wonderful 19.8% rate.

Scott: "Yeah, introductory, okay in six months. You know that's six months that Saint Bernard Bank is not going to be making anything by the way. Hound Dog Bank, 9.9% and one from Cattle Dog Bank. Now I'm happy with Saint Bernard Bank service, but I am not happy with that rate, so give me a reason to stay. That's what I'm saying."

Rep: "Well, what I can do right now is I can drop the rate to 16.9% for you at this time."
Note: That's better. Lower the rate now!

Scott: "You can't do better than 16.9?"

Rep: "No."

Scott: "Well you know what I'll take it for now, and uh, when will that be effective?"
Note: I should have been more demanding.

Rep: "That will go into effect as of, one moment...It will go into effect as of March 19th, and it will include all balances as well."

Scott: "Okay, all existing balances, alright. I'll tell you though I am going to be calling back periodically to see if you can do better than that."

Rep: "Okay."

Scott: "And uh, it's going to be real important to keeping me as a customer. Alright?"
Note: I'm wasting my breath at this point since the rep already told me that they're not going to reduce the rate further. It would have been better to say nothing about "keeping me as a customer" because it sounds like I'm whining.

Rep: "Alright, Mr. Mayer."

Scott: "I got another question for you while we're here. Can you see my account information?"

Rep: "Yes."

Scott: "This Saint Bernard Bank Buy-Smart fee, what exactly is that?"

Rep: "It's for a product on there that was, let's see that's a renewal fee, one moment...That's for a membership product, discounts to uh, for shopping uh..."

Kelly: "Yeah they doubled it, I don't want it."

Scott: "We don't want that."

Rep: "Okay, we can get that cancelled for you."

Scott: "Okay."
Note: Not only did they charge Kelly for a service she doesn't use, they doubled the price of the non-used service and charged her without first letting her know about the price increase!

Kelly: "Will that be taken off the balance?"

Rep: "Yes."

Scott: "Oh yeah, that will come right off."

Rep: "Okay that will be off the account in 3 to 5 business days."

Scott: "Okay great."

Rep: "Is there anything else I can help you with today?"

Scott: "No that will be all."

Rep: "Well, my goal is customer satisfaction, have I answered all of your questions today?"

Scott: "Yes you have."

Rep: "Alright, thank you for calling Saint Bernard Bank Mr. Mayer."

Scott: "Bye-bye."

Rep: "Bye-bye."

CALL #5.07: THEY DON'T ALWAYS LOWER RATES

Reason For Call:	Interest Rate Lowered
Result:	Waived a Late Fee but did not lower the rate
Difficulty Level:	Hard
Call Time:	7 minutes
Total Saved:	$25.00
$/hour to make call:	$214.29

The most important aspect of your being able to negotiate a better rate with your bank is that you've been good with your credit card and debt management in the past. Also, if you've had a long and positive relationship with the bank.

This call was made for my good friend Tony Bryer. He has had some payment difficulties in the past. The problem here is that he was close to his limit, then he was late, subsequently, the late fee caused him to go over his limit. Then he started to get zapped with overlimit fees repeatedly month after month.

This domino effect created many unnecessary and expensive fees on his account. We're going to do our best here but it's a tough situation.

To get the rate lowered in the future, Tony is going to need to transfer this balance to other cards then call back after a few months of paying on time.

SUMMARY

This bank is charging a $25 overlimit fee, each month, plus has an APR of 25.9%. I spoke to Robber Fly who said I would have to speak to an account specialist to get the overlimit fee waived. I then spoke to Ms. Lice, who waived the $25 overlimit fee. She said the account was $94 over, I said, "Yeah, and $75 of that are overlimit fees." She also said I couldn't bargain on the interest rate because the account is in "collections" which means it's over the limit. I said I would send in $100 to get it under the limit.

TRANSCRIPT

Voice Menu: "Welcome to Bullmastiff Bank."

Tony talking to Scott: "I'm sure I've been late."
Note: Tony's on another line listening in.

Rep: "Customer relations, this is Robber Fly. May I please have your name please."

Scott: "Hi Robber Fly. Tony Bryer."

Rep: "And Mr. Bryer could I please have your social security number so I can bring up your account."

Scott: (I give her the number.)

Rep: "One moment. Okay Mr. Bryer, could you please verify your home telephone number with the area code first."

Scott: "Okay..." (I give her the numbers.)

Rep: "How may I help you?"

Scott: "Alright, can you see my last statement?"

Rep: "Yes sir."

Scott: "Okay, I've got this $25 overlimit fee, and I've been paying this for months and I'm hoping that one of these can be removed as a courtesy, at least one of these overlimit fees."

Rep: "Why, did you receive one last month also?"

Scott: "For the last, at least three months."

Rep: "What I can go ahead and do right now is go ahead and connect you with an account specialist who can assist you with your request. Okay?"

Note: At least this rep didn't play games. She immediately said she couldn't "assist" and would transfer to someone who could. Now that's something to say to reps in future calls, "Can you assist me with lowering my rate...can you assist me with waiving that fee or do I need to speak to someone else."

Scott: "Okay."

Rep: "Okay, one moment.

On hold...

Rep: "Thank you so much for holding. I have Ms. Lice on the line she has your account information and will assist you further."

Scott: "Great, thank you Robber Fly."

Rep: "Thank you."

Account Specialist: "Mr. Bryer?"

Scott: "Yes."

Account Specialist: "Okay, you are aware that you are currently $94.23 over your credit limit, right?"

Scott: "Right, I'm definitely aware of that."

Account Specialist: "So what can I do for you today?"

Scott: "I'm hoping one of those overlimit fees can be adjusted off my account. I mean I'm over $94 and 75 of the dollars are the last three months in overlimit fees. Of which I've paid all of them so far. I'm hoping at least one of them can be adjusted as a courtesy."
Note: I should have asked for more than one fee to be waived.

Account Specialist: "I'll take care of it for you."
Note: Even with all the difficulty Tony has with his account they still gave him a $25 credit—just for asking!

Scott: "Oh, you're going to take care of it?"

Account Specialist: "Already done."

Scott: "Okay great. Also Ms. Lice, while I have you here. I've just got to talk to you about this 25.9% APR. It's just a little out of hand."
Note: That rate is INSANE!

Account Specialist: "You've got to get yourself out of collections before we can do anything about that."

Scott: "Out of collections?"

Account Specialist: "That's right."

Scott: "What do you mean collections?"

Account Specialist: "Your account is in collections."

Scott: "I didn't know that, did I receive a letter about that?"

Account Specialist: "Yes sir. Hold on just one second okay."

On hold...

Scott: "Well that sounds to me like you haven't been paying or something. You still have the physical card right?"

Tony: "Yeah."

Scott: "Okay. Well let's find out what that's about."

Tony: "I don't remember a letter. I haven't used that card even."

Scott: "Okay. We are at $101 today. It's a good day, it's a good start. You like my little argument there. You're $94 over, and I'm like, 'yeah $75 of them are overlimit fees.'"

Tony: "Yeah. I was like holy cow that was cool."

Account Specialist: "You there."

Scott: "Yes I am, Ms. Lice."

Account Specialist: "Sorry about that my computer knocked me out and I had to get back in real quick."

Scott: "Okay."

Account Specialist: "As far as lowering your APR that is exactly what you are going to have to do. You are gonna have to get yourself out of collections."
Note: This demonstrates that you may actually need to ask what you can do to get what you want. In this case the rep is telling me that the account has to get out of collections. If a rep says, "We cannot lower your rate," then ask, "What do I need to do to get my rate reduced?"

Scott: "Why am I in collections? What is collections?"

Account Specialist: "Because your account is over its credit limit."

Scott: "Okay."

Account Specialist: "Okay, that's the reason you are in overlimit collections. It's sent automatically through the system, it wouldn't have made a difference if you were $10 or $2. You were over the credit limit."

Scott: "Can we raise the limit, I mean a $500 limit. Every time I get my statement there is this little box that says, 'Is this enough credit for you?' and I always say no, let's raise the limit. Is there some reason why my limit has never been raised?"

Account Specialist: "Okay, it's because you have continuously been in overlimit collection status since August 12th."

Scott: "August 12th this year?"

Account Specialist: "Uh huh. So anything that you have done recently it's not going to do for you. And the only thing I can really recommend at the moment to get your credit limit raised, take care of what you still owe over your credit limit, which is $69.23."

Note: We have to try to get the limit increased so the current balance is not over the limit. Here's a simple question: Does that bank: (a) want to increase his limit so they don't charge him that overlimit fee each month or (b) not raise the limit and gouge Tony forever, or longer, with that overlimit fee? You know the answer.

Scott: "Okay."

Account Specialist: "Okay. Umm, plus a minimum payment of $17.83."

Scott: "Okay."

Account Specialist: "And that'll bring you completely current."

Scott: "Alright, and then I can call you back and talk about the rate?"

Account Specialist: "And actually call and speak with somebody."

Scott: "Okay."

Account Specialist: "Okay, 'cause a lot of times if you check a box or if you write a letter, you really don't get a big response back."

Scott: "Right."

Account Specialist: "Call customer relations and they'll go from there with you. So do you think that you'll be able to make a payment of, umm, like $87."

Scott: "Sure."

Account Specialist: "Okay."

Scott: "Would I call you back directly Ms. Lice?"

Account Specialist: "No, you sure wouldn't. You can speak to anybody, but I'll leave the information on the account."

Note: Always be sure that the account rep you speak with leaves those notes in your account file. The reason I started recording these conversations with reps is because often those "notes" weren't available when I called back.

Scott: "Okay, great."

Account Specialist: "Okay, as long as you make that payment as soon as it posts to the account, umm, what we'll do is we can go in at that point and try and lower your rate, lower your APR and see if we can get you a credit limit increase."

Scott: "Sounds good."

Account Specialist: "Okay."

Scott: "Alright, well thank you very much for that help and waiving that fee for me today Ms. Lice."

Account Specialist: "No problem. You have a great day sir."

Scott: "You too Ms. Lice."

Account Specialist: "Bye-bye."

Scott: "Bye-bye."

Call #5.08: INTEREST FEES WAIVED FOR NO REASON

Reason For Call:	To check balance
Result:	Interest charges waived
Difficulty Level:	Easy
Call Time:	2 minutes
Total Saved:	$6.43
$/hour to make call:	$192.90

This is a strange call. I'm just asking for my balance and then, for no apparent reason, the bank representative waived my interest charges. No negotiation needed—hey, that's not even why I called! This call is included as an example of how making the call can pay in ways you sometimes cannot anticipate.

SUMMARY

I called to check my balance because I did a balance transfer before the bill arrived. I need to know if the transfer had been credited before I sent in my payment, otherwise they would have to send me a check for the overpayment. I called just to ask the bank rep my balance and he said that it's $6.43 so I knew the transfer payment arrived. Then, for no reason at all, he said he'd "take care of the balance" then he credited me the interest charges for the month. I didn't even ask!

TRANSCRIPT

Rep: "Thank you for calling Komondor Bank. My name is Cankerworm, how can I help you?"

Scott: "Hi, I've got a question about my balance."

Rep: "Okay, can I have your account number?"

Scott: "Sure..." (I give him the number.)

Rep: "Okay sir, for the protection of the account, can you verify the last four digits of your social security number?"

Scott: (I give him the numbers.)

Rep: "Okay, thank you for verifying this information, and umm, okay how may I help you?"

Scott: "Okay, what's my balance?"

Rep: "$6.43."

Scott: "Okay beautiful, do I have a payment due?"

Rep: "Okay on the 13th."

Scott: "Okay, I have to pay..."

Rep: "This is strange, no payment due. We must have received, you must have made a payment somewhere."

Note: That's because I paid by doing a balance transfer with another bank. When they receive the payment it's credited as a regular payment and therefore makes the amount due $0.

Scott: "Okay, so I don't need to pay anything. I would imagine the payment you got was the payment."

Rep: "Okay, I see what happened. Yeah, I see what happened, $6.43. Okay, no payments due."

Scott: "I'll just get a bill next time for 6 bucks."

Rep: "Yeah, well I am going to take care of that though."

Scott: "Oh, you are going to take care of that?"

Rep: "Yeah."

Scott: "Cool."

Note: Now that's customer service! Sure, some may say, "it's only $6.43," and that may be true, however, that's one free ticket to the movies (matinee) just for calling to check my balance—and I'll take it!

Rep: "Is there anything else I can help you with?"

Scott: "No, no. So what's my balance now, zero?"

Rep: "Yeah."

Scott: "Great, well thank you very much."

Rep: "Thank you for calling Komondor Bank sir."

Scott: "Bye-bye."

CALL #5.09: $7K SAVED TODAY

Reason For Call:	Lower the interest rate
Result:	Rate reduced from 16.99% to 9.99% and promotional rate reduced from 8.9% to 6.9%!
Difficulty Level:	Easy
Call Time:	7 minutes
Total Saved:	$7,098.00
$/hour to make call:	$60,840.00

I did this call for my friend Lewis Wilson (name changed). He's got great credit, and high balances, from school-related charges. This makes it very easy when trying to negotiate good deals!

SUMMARY

I called to attempt to get his rate reduced. I spoke to bank representative, Ms. Caterpillar, who verified that the APR is 16.99%. There's also a balance transfer offer at 8.9%. I asked about lowering the APR and was transferred to account specialist Mr. Monarch Butterfly. He dropped the rate from 16.99% to 9.99% and also dropped the balance transfer rate from the 8.9% to 6.9%. The new 9.99% will be effective next month.

Savings based on paying a constant $318 (2% of today's balance of $15,856.15) and are as follows: At 16.99% it takes $27,704.00 to pay off the loan and at 9.99% it takes $20,606.00. This phone called saved Lewis $7,098.00.

TRANSCRIPT

Scott: "Lewis Wilson."

Voice Menu: "Welcome to Wetterhoun Bank. For faster service…"

Rep: "Ms. Caterpillar speaking. May I have your account number?"

Scott: "Sure, account number is…" (I give her the number.)

Rep: "And your name?"

Scott: "Lewis Wilson."

Rep: "And Mr. Wilson, how can I help you?"

Scott: "Okay. Can you just verify for me what my annual percentage rate is?"

Rep: "You have a 16.99%."

Scott: "Yeah, that's what I thought it was."

Rep: "You have a promotional rate for balance transfers and checks at an 8.9%."

Scott: "Hmm, well that's definitely useful to know Ms. Caterpillar. I'll tell you what though, I'd like to have that current balance reduced to like an 8.9%."
Note: Sometimes you won't even know about any deals until you call. The rep immediately wanted to make me aware of a great transfer rate.

Rep: "Let me transfer you to an account manager so he can give you the options that are available to you for that. Okay?"

Scott: "Alright, thank you."
Note: At least she didn't play games. She knew that she couldn't lower the rate and is transferring me to someone who can help.

Rep: "I'll connect you, okay?"

Scott: "Alright, thank you Ms. Caterpillar."

Rep: "Do you have any other questions I can help you with?"

Scott: "No, that'll be all."

Rep: "Okay. One moment, have a great day."

Scott: "You too."

On hold...

Manager: "Mr. Monarch Butterfly speaking, how may I help you?"

Scott: "Hi Monarch. Do you have all my account info and stuff there?"

Manager: "Is this Mr. Wilson?"

Scott: "Yes it is."

Manager: "All I need sir is your date of birth."

Scott: "Okay." (I give him the date.)

Manager: "Happy belated birthday."
Note: How sweet. Aren't all birthdays either: (1) right on your birthday or (2) belated?

Scott: "Thank you."

Manager: "How can I help you?"

Scott: "Alright. I'm just looking at my account here. It's at 16.99%. I've got to tell you, that's extremely high. Now, I know there is a transfer offer around 8.9%, I think that we can lower this rate down to like an 8.9%."
Note: I'm very firm here because I know I have power. That's because Lewis has many other credit options and if this bank doesn't lower the rate I'll punish them by paying them off with another card.

Manager: "Let's take a look at this card here. You've been with us for years."

Scott: "Yes indeed."

Manager: "Okay. And when you use the account Mr. Wilson you primarily use a lot of check transactions, balance transfer type things?"

Scott: "Well, you know a mixture of everything."

Manager: "Okay."

Scott: "If we can get this thing into a good rate zone maybe I'd use it more. I've got plenty of available credit."
Note: Tell them that you'll use the card more if the rate is more reasonable.

Manager: "Alright, now on this particular...I've got two rates, actually, that I can offer you. You tell me which one you want. I have, I can bring the balance to 10.99%. And what that would do is it would still keep promotions coming on the account periodically, so that you can take advantage of those. Or, I can knock it down to a 9.99%. Which basically means that when the current promotion is offered it will be at the 9.99%, and you probably will not see a lot of promotions after that. Okay?"
Note: Like sure they'll not be sending any more promotional—offers. Please, spare me.

Scott: "You know, for now I think I'll take the 9.99%."
Note: It would be a very rare situation in which you would not choose the lower rate.

Manager: "Okay, alright. That will take effect the 1st day of your next billing statement. Which for your particular account would be February the 3rd."

Scott: "Okay."

Manager: "That's when the $15,000 will go to the 9.99%."

Scott: "Okay."

Manager: "Then you also have other options. Right now on your account you have the 8.9%. And if you want to do any balance transfers of off that, that could be negotiated down to a 6.99% through to July."

Note: Listen to that! He's now offering to reduce the APR for the promotional transfer from 8.9% to 6.99%.

Scott: "Hmm. 6.99%."

Manager: "Basically what that would do for you is it would take the money that you wanted to transfer, plus the $1,900 that's sitting at 8.9% and carry that at the 6.9% through July."

Scott: "Would that take my current balance down too?"

Manager: "No, it would just take the $1,900. The other $10,700 would stay at the 9.9%."

Scott: "Okay, well right now I have like, okay. But there is like a $15,000 balance. That whole thing would go to 9.9%?"

Manager: "Except for that small balance that is at 8.9%, yes sir."

Scott: "Okay, alright, so I've got it. Okay, but now the new balances would be 6.9%, until July when I took advantage of the transfers. I'll keep that in mind, because I've got some other banks to talk to. And if, with that 6.9% it looks like Wetterhoun Bank might be the winner here."

Note: I want to let him know that they're not the only game in town. Sometimes they'll offer you a better deal. In this case I do really need to call more banks.

Manager: "Alright Mr. Wilson."

Scott: "Thank you Monarch."

Manager: "Thank you sir, have a great day."

Scott: "You too."

Manager: "Thank you."

Scott: "Bye-bye."

CALL #5.10: SAVINGS FOR DAD

Reason For Call:	Lower the interest rate
Result:	Rate dropped from 22.99% to 13.99%
Difficulty Level:	Easy
Call Time:	8 minutes
Total Saved:	$0.00 (will save money when card is used)
$/hour to make call:	$0.00

This one is for my father, Harvey L. Bilker. He has perfect credit. This bank is really taking advantage of him. I help my father with his finances all the time but I hear from other friends that their parents are paying too much on their credit cards and nothing is being done about it.

My parents' generation grew up without credit and avoided debt. They may be good at saving and financial planning; however, things are changing today. They're starting to turn to their credit lines to fill the gap between declining savings and social security. The result is that more senior citizens are experiencing debt for the first time.

SUMMARY

I just noticed that my dad's APR on this account is 22.99%. They're out of their minds! I also need to change the mailing address.

I called and spoke to Mayfly who transferred me to Damselfly. I asked Damselfly to lower the rate. I said, "I might be old but 22.9% is a big number." She asked me about my rates and balances on other cards so I told her I was getting 9.99% on the Landseer Bankcard. She came back with 16.9% and asked if that was okay. I said, "You can't do better than 16.9%?" She put me on hold and came back with 13.9%.

TRANSCRIPT

Voice Menu: "Welcome to Whippet Bank..."

Scott: "Calling to get my Dad's rate lowered."
Note: Making a memo on the tape of the reason for the call.

Rep: "Thank you for calling credit card services. My name is Mayfly. Can I have your name please."

Scott: "Hi Mayfly. It's Harvey L. Bilker."

Rep: "Can I get your account number, Harvey?"

Scott: (I give her the number.)

Rep: "Thank you. How can I help you today?"

Scott: "Okay, a couple of things. First of all, I just realized that my rate here is 22.99%. And that's just out of hand. I'll never carry a balance with a rate like that."

Rep: "Okay."

Scott: "Now this account has been in good standing for a long time, I think you guys can do better than that."

Rep: "I will be able to transfer you to the APR specialist. What else do you have a question about?"
Note: At least she doesn't waste my time.

Scott: "I want to make sure that the bills...I want to have my bills sent to a different address."
Note: I'm having my father's bill sent to my home address so I can help him with his finances more easily.

Rep: "Okay. Let me go ahead and change the address for you. Do you have the card there. Your platinum card."

Scott: "Umm, do I have it on me."

Rep: "Yeah, I need to get an expiration date, and I need to check the number on the back."

Scott: "Okay, let me see. I have to look in my wallet. I'm just moving and it could be in the files, you know. Let me see. You know what...Oh wait. Yeah, I have a card."

Rep: "Is it Whippet Bank Select Platinum?"

Scott: "Got an expiration of..." (I give her the number.)

Rep: "And on the back..."

Scott: (I give her the number.)

Rep: "What's the new zip code that you want it to go to?"

Scott: (I give her the zip.)

Rep: "And the address?"

Scott: (I give her the address).

Rep: "Is there a new phone number?"

Scott: (I give her the phone number.)

Rep: "Okay let me go ahead, is there any other questions that you had?"

Scott: "No, I'll just talk to that APR specialist."

Rep: "Alright, just a moment. Have a nice day."

Scott: "Thank you."

On hold...

APR Specialist: "Thank you for calling specialized services. My name is Damselfly. May I have your name please?"

Scott: "Harvey L. Bilker."

APR Specialist: "For security purposes can I have your mother's maiden name?"

Scott: (I give her the name.)

APR Specialist: "And how can I help you sir?"

Scott: "Okay, well I was just noticing on my statement here that I've got a rate of 22.99%, and I might be old, but that's an awfully large number for what I should be paying. I mean I've got a perfect record, and there is no way I'd carry a balance on this card, ever, or use it for any major purchase. That's just an unjust rate. Now, I know you can do better than that for your good customers."
Note: Again, retelling the story...

APR Specialist: "Okay. So you want to know if there is a lower rate available?"

Scott: "Yeah."

APR Specialist: "I'll be happy to check on that for you. Can you, umm, so we can better understand your credit cards needs, what is your interest rate on your other credit cards?"
Note: Yeah, right, "better understand." She wants to know the competition so they can offer the highest rate possible after learning the details of my other options.

Scott: "Let me see here. I've got, my Landseer Bankcard is at 9.9%. And I have an offer from them, 3.9% for 6 months."
Note: I'm just making these up.

APR Specialist: "Okay."

Scott: "That's the only other card I have."

APR Specialist: "Do you have a balance on that credit card?"

Scott: "Sure do. $1,000."
Note: Actually he doesn't. I just want the rep to think there's a possibility that I would transfer my balance with them if the rep gives me a better rate.

APR Specialist: "$1,000."

Scott: "A little over, maybe a $1,010."

APR Specialist: "Okay. I'm showing that we can reduce your interest rate to 16.99%. How does that sound to you?"

Scott: "That's a good start."

APR Specialist: "Okay."

Scott: "You can't do better than 16.99%?"
Note: I should have been a little more firm and said, "You'll need to do better than that."

APR Specialist: "Let me place you on hold just for one moment and check."

Scott: "Sure."

On hold...

APR Specialist: "I'm showing 13.9%. I can reduce that to sir."

Scott: "I'm sorry can you say that again Damselfly?"

APR Specialist: "13.99%."

Scott: "13.99%?"
Note: So why didn't she give me this option before? You know the answer. Their goal is gouge as much as possible from us. We cannot allow that to happen!

APR Specialist: "Yeah."

Scott: "Oh, that's even better. Okay that sounds fine. And will that become effective immediately? I'll see that on my next statement?"
Note: I should have kept pressing for a lower rate. Lesson learned.

APR Specialist: "Actually it'll update tonight. So it will show up on your next statement that prints after today."

Scott: "Okay."

APR Specialist: "Your new annual percentage rate will be reduced to prime plus 9.24%. Currently 13.99% based on a prime rate of 4.75%. This annual percentage rate will apply to current and future non-cash advance balances. It will not be less than 13.99%."

APR Specialist: "Please make sure you pay on time or your interest may be increased."
Note: If you're late they'll raise your rate! Many banks will even raise your rate if you're late paying other creditors! Don't pay late.

Scott: "Oh, how much? I've never been late but I'm just curious, what would happen?"

APR Specialist: "It may go up to like 19.99%."
Note: Think about this. My father's rate was 22.99% and he has never been late. The penalty rate for being late is actually less than when he was paying on time!

Scott: "Oh okay. I don't plan to be late."

APR Specialist: "You're welcome. Is there anything else you need help with today?"

Scott: "No, that'll be fine."

APR Specialist: "You have a good day, and we appreciate doing business with you."

Scott: "Thank you Damselfly."

APR Specialist: "Thank you. Bye."

Scott: "Bye."

CALL #5.11: LOWER THE RATE AND GET A REFUND!

Reason For Call:	Lower the interest rate
Result:	Rate reduced from 13.99% to 9.99% and $26.59 interest charge refund!
Difficulty Level:	Easy
Call Time:	8 minutes
Total Saved:	$1,632.00
$/hour to make call:	$12,240.00

This call demonstrates that you need to: (1) be nice to the reps; (2) don't be hasty in closing the account because you'll need a long history with the bank to get the good deals; and (3) always ask for interest rate charges to be waived.

SUMMARY

This is my wife, Larissa's, card. I had a low rate offer on this card for 3.99%. The low rate has expired and I'm calling to see if they can reduce the rate from 13.99%. I see that there is a balance transfer rate of 5.7% shown right on this month's statement but they're probably going to tell me that it's for new transfers only.

I also want to get them to refund the finance charges for this current statement! It shows as $90.08 for the balance of $7,567.00.

I spoke with Acrea Butterfly who transferred me to an account manager, Angy Cricket, in the rate department to see what they can offer me.

Angy Cricket said that the lower rate is 9.99% fixed. The new 5.7%-to-March offer still stands. I also asked for her to credit the account for the difference between the 13.99% and the 9.99% fixed. This credit turned out to be $26.59.

With a balance of $7,612 at 13.99% it takes 75.72 months to repay with a payment of $152 per month. At 9.99% it takes 65.16 months and saves $1,605 plus $27 interest credit for a total of $1,632.

TRANSCRIPT

Voice Menu: "Thank for calling Billy Grand Bank card service. The next available representative will be with you shortly."

Scott: "Okay, great. I love shortly."

Rep: "Good morning. My name is Acrea Butterfly, can I please have your name?"

Scott: "Hi my name is Scott Bilker."

Rep: "Mr. Bilker, can I please have your full account number."

Scott: "This account number changed so I don't know which to give you. So I'll try the latest one." (I give her the number.)

Rep: "Mr. Bilker your home phone number?"

Scott: (I give her the number.)

Rep: "Okay, what is Mrs. Bilker's date of birth?"

Scott: "Mrs. Bilker's?"

Rep: "Umm hmm."

Scott: (I give her the date.)

Rep: "Along with her mother's maiden name."

Scott: (I give her the name.)

Rep: "And how can I help you?"

Scott: "Okay, let me just make sure it's the right account. This one used to be 9293, it's got a balance of $7,612."

Rep: "That's correct."

Scott: "Okay good. Alright, I'm looking at the statement here Acrea and I see the interest rate is 13.99%."

Rep: "Umm hmm."

Scott: "And I'm hoping that you can reduce that rate for me."

Rep: "I don't have another rate to offer you, but I can have you speak with an account manager in our rate department to see if they have any other rates available for you at this time."

Scott: "Sure, transfer me."

Rep: "Alright, thank you for your business and stay on the line."

Scott: "Okay."

Pause...

Manager: "Billy Grand Bank at your service this is Angy Cricket, how may I help you?"

Scott: "Hi Angy. I wanted to ask you about the rate on my account here."

Manager: "Okay, may I have that account number please?"

Scott: "Sure, account number is..." (I give her the number.)

Manager: "Okay, thank you. And also may I have your name please."

Scott: "My name is Scott Bilker, this is my wife's account, Larissa."

Manager: "Okay, and may I have Larissa Bilker's date of birth?"

Scott: "Sure..." (I give her the date.)

Manager: "Okay, and..."

Scott: (I give her Larissa's mother's maiden name.)

Manager: "Thank you." (Laughs) "You must have done this already."
Note: I get a lot of practice. ☺

Scott: (Laughs) "I'm familiar with the procedure."

Manager: "Okay."

Scott: "I'm calling because that rate of 13.99% is just too high and uh, in fact I see here (on the statement) that there is a low balance transfer rate of 5.7% just offered as a standard."

Manager: "Oh yeah, that's 'til March of next year, yes."

Scott: "Okay, so uh, now I am hoping that you can offer me a lower rate right now Angy."
Note: Directly asking for the rate to be lowered.

Manager: "Let's see. On the existing balance?"

Scott: "That's correct."

Manager: "Because it looks like you had the 3.99% on that, and then that expired. I see."

Scott: "Umm hmm."

Manager: "Now what we are looking at is the fixed rate reduction because, I know you had the 3.9% before, and we are not going to have anything comparable to that now that you are at the contract rate."

Scott: "Uh huh."

Manager: "So I don't know if you are comparing to, you know, another promotion or another fixed rate, but that's what we are looking at so it's going to take a minute or so to pull through the lowest rate available, fixed rate available. Because you have had this account for over 8 years so, okay, the lowest fixed rate is 9.99%."
Note: Look at that—a nice rate reduction just for calling. Think of how much money the bank makes because people don't call to get the best deals.

Scott: "Uh huh."

Manager: "And that would include the current balance and any other balance of purchases and cash advances. That rate will take effect on the 4th of January, since you are in the middle of that December cycle right now, so. Except for that APR change all the other terms and conditions of your credit card will remain in effect, nothing else would change."

Scott: "Okay, so basically it can be reduced to 9.99% from this 13.99?"
Note: Summarize the rate change so everyone is clear.

Manager: "Yes correct, and that would be a fixed rate, so, and you would also still carry with it that promotion, the one you have that has the 5.7% 'til March. That still stands too, so if you did any transfers they would be 5.7% 'til March. And then 9.9% thereafter."

Scott: "You know that sounds worth keeping. Again, I want to keep doing business with Billy Grand Bank, as long as it's, you know, reasonable."

Manager: "Okay."

Scott: "And I guess the last thing I'd like is that this particular statement umm, you know that charged me at that 13.99% rate, the $90 for the finance charges. I was hoping that you could refund the difference between that and the 9.99%."
Note: Since I got them to reduce the rate the next logical step is to ask them for a refund for the difference between the new rate and the old rate in the current month. In this case thats a $25 credit (90*(13.99-9.99)/13.99)!

Manager: "I see it's not retroactive, and since you are in the middle of your December cycle it's not going to be effective, like I said, until the 4th of January."

Scott: "Umm hmm."

Manager: "So, let me see..."

Scott: "Well, it's not much, but like a show of good faith kind of thing, for like you said, for having the account for eight years."
Note: I'm throwing in the fact that I deserve this credit because I've been a good customer.

Manager: "Right, it's not going to allow me to, I can't do anything as far as the effective date, but let me just see if it will give...Let me just see what that calculates out to be and see if it will allow a partial finance charge adjustment of some kind."

Scott: "It would be around something like $25."
Note: It's always good to do the math so you can tell them what it's supposed to be. Less work for the bank reps.

Manager: "Well, I mean, I need to see if the system will even allow it. To see if it would process any finance charge adjustment through."

Scott: "Right."

Manager: "Yep, it's coming out. Yep, you were close. I don't trust my judgement when it comes to, unless I hear you punching away on a calculator or a computer or something. It comes to $26.59, so it's going to give me just another minute to see if it allows it to go through. I'm going to document, 'Due to the long history on the account.'"
Note: She's going to document the reason for the adjustment ($26.59 credit) as being that the account has a positive and long history.

Scott: "Okay."

Manager: "And your promotion just expired. Yep, it allowed it to go through."

Scott: "Great."

Manager: "Courtesy waiving. Okay, so you'll see that credited on the following statement as well. Umm, oh you have already got your December, so it would be the next one."

Scott: "Okay great."

Manager: "Okay?"

Scott: "Well Angy, I'll tell you, that's treating the customer right."

Note: Throw them a nice thank-you when they treat you right. You always want to praise, and do business with, the banks that treat you with respect, and punish the ones that do not!

Manager: (Laughs.) "Well you've got a great account so I don't see why it wouldn't allow it to go through, but I'd never know until I put it through and see what it says."

Scott: "Okay, great."

Manager: "Okay?"

Scott: "Alright, thank you."

Manager: "You're welcome, thanks for banking...Oh, did you want to do any transfers also, before I let you go, with a 5.7% rate?"

Scott: "Oh, you know I have to think about it, because you know, I called first to see what was going to happen so. Now I can go back to the paperwork and see what we are going to do. But, no I am not prepared to do that right now."

Note: Be sure to always keep track of any offers that are given to you by phone. You may end up calling back and taking advantage of that offer.

Manager: "Okay, did you want our direct number here? Would that help?"

Note: So, do you think she's getting bonus points if I do the transfer? ☺

Scott: "Oh, to your office? Sure go ahead."

Manager: "Okay, it's..." (Gives me the number.)

Scott: "Alright, thanks a lot for your help Angy."

Manager: "You're welcome, bye-bye."

Scott: "Bye-bye."

CALL #5.12: THEY'D BETTER DEAL

Reason For Call:	Lower the interest rate
Result:	Wouldn't lower the rate on the existing balance but did lower purchase rate to 9.9% and gave offer for 2.9% transfer.
Difficulty Level:	Hard
Call Time:	8 minutes
Total Saved:	$354.92
$/hour to make call:	$2,661.90

Sometimes you're not going to be able to get the exact terms you want when you call. This call was made for my friends Mike and Donna Bailey (names have been changed). We're trying to reduce the interest rate on the current balance. The bank wouldn't budge from the current rate but the rep did give suggestions on how to get them to lower the rate by doing a few transfers. Mike did take those suggestions and got his rate down to 2.9%.

SUMMARY

I called to have the bank lower their rate on the existing balance. I threatened to transfer the balance to another bank if they didn't lower the rate, which is at 14.99%. I ended up speaking to the "rate negotiating department" and they said they don't have any way to lower the existing rate. Then Squashbug offered to extend the 5.99% offer until November 1st, but when I still complained she said I could transfer the balance out then back in at 3.9% until November 1st.

Finally, after I said that they should have something to keep good customers she offered 2.9% until November 1st and lowered the purchase rate to 9.9% on new purchases. I asked Squashbug to make sure this was noted in Mike's account.

The balance, after 6 months of paying 14.99% at $120 per month, on $6,000 would be $5,723.12. At 2.9% that balance would be $5,368.20. Total saved is $354.92

TRANSCRIPT

Scott: "I love this, it's like the car thing. Here we are again, years and years later, I'm still mad at someone that I'm calling."
Note: The "car thing" I'm referring to is when I got ripped off in the past on car purchases. I quickly learned my lesson and also began helping my friends save money by accompanying them to the dealership and making sure they didn't get ripped off.

Voice Menu: "Thank you for calling White Shepherd Bank. Your call may be monitored or recorded to ensure quality service."

Scott: "Yes, yours too."

Rep: "White Shepherd Bank my name is Shieldbug. Currently my system is updating and I am not able to access your account. Do you have a general question I might be able to help you with?"

Scott: "No, I need you to be able to access my account."

Rep: "Okay, I may be able to get somebody else on the line here. How long were you waiting to get in touch with me?"

Scott: "About one minute."

Rep: "About a minute. If you would like to wait for another minute I can get you a connect with somebody else who could probably assist you with that, so that you don't have to call back."

Scott: "Okay, let's do that."

Rep: "Okay, I'm sorry about that sir."

Scott: "That's okay."

Rep: "Just a moment."

On hold...

Rep: "Okay, I am able to pull up our account here, so I can go ahead and help you out. Can I get your name please?"

Scott: "Sure, Mike Bailey."

Rep: "Okay. Just one moment here Mr. Bailey. Alright, how can I help you today sir?"

Scott: "Alright, well I'm looking at my rate here, 14.99%."

Rep: "Okay."

Scott: "Now I know that's a fairly okay rate. Umm, however, I am about to do a balance transfer and transfer my entire balance off of this card, because I got an offer at 6.9%."

Rep: "Okay, yeah."

Scott: "But before I do that I wanted to see if White Shepherd Bank is going to give me something better than this 14.99%. Maybe like a 9.9%, something just more reasonable."

Rep: "Something a little bit lower?"

Scott: "Yeah, like 9.9% would be quite reasonable."

Rep: "Okay. Well it is possible that we might be able to work a lower interest rate for you. That department that does interest rate negotiation, however, they would need to speak with, is it Donna Bailey, is that correct?"

Scott: "Okay, yeah she's here."

Rep: "Is she there with you?"

Scott: "She is here."

Rep: "Okay, that's fine. You could just stay on the phone there and if they need to speak with her then you can just give her the phone so they can verify whatever they need to."

Scott: "Okay."

Rep: "Alright, can you hold for a moment and I'll give them a call?"

Scott: "Sure."

Rep: "Alright, I'll be right back sir."

On hold...

Rep: "Mr. Bailey?"

Scott: "Yes."

Rep: "Thanks for waiting. I've got Squashbug on the line to further assist you, okay?"

Scott: "Okay."

Manager: "Mr. Bailey."

Scott: "Yes."

Manager: "Hi, real quick can I just get your home telephone number, including area code?"

Scott: "Okay, home telephone number is..." (I give her the number.)

Manager: "Okay, and just to update our system, do you currently have an email address?"

Scott: "Yeah, but it's my wife's, I really don't know it off-hand."
Note: I actually do. But I don't want to clog-up Donna's email with SPAM!

Manager: "Okay, alright. And your available balance transfer offer is a 5.9% through August, which we can extend for you through November. But how can we help you today sir?"
Note: Right away she shows that she's willing to negotiate. This is always a good sign.

Scott: "Okay, well right now, I'm about to actually transfer my balance off of the White Shepherd Bankcard to a 6.9% I have from Gordon Setter Bank."

Manager: "Umm hmm."

Scott: "But, I am very happy with White Shepherd Bank and I wanted to call you to see if I could get a more reasonable rate, something like 9.9%. Something that's reasonable."

Manager: "Okay, actually, the company right now, we don't have a 9.9% rate. What we have that is that low is just promotional rates. Like you have a 9.9% for new purchases through October I can offer."
Note: That's what they all say at first.

Scott: "Okay."

Manager: "However, I wouldn't have anything that would affect the existing balance. We just don't have it as a company right now."

Scott: "Okay so nothing is going to affect this existing balance?"

Manager: "Correct. I mean if you did transfer out the balance for this, how long is the 6.9% good for?"

Scott: "Six months."

Manager: "Six months?"

Scott: "Umm hmm."

Manager: "Yeah, because if you did transfer it out to that, then when the 6 months is over, or even if you just want to transfer it right back on, I can give you a 3.9% through November."

Note: The rep is actually giving some strategy tips! She's suggesting that I take advantage of the other bank's offer then transfer the money back to this bank at a 3.9% which is 3% better than the rate she offered 2 seconds ago!

Scott: "Hmm."

Manager: "Which, I don't know if that would help you out at all. But I don't actually have anything right now for the existing balance. You are actually at one of the lowest we have for the company right now."

Scott: "Really, well let me get this straight. Originally, my 5.9% was a few months, then it was to November, but if I transfer it out and come back it's 3.9% to November."

Manager: "Uh huh."

Scott: "Okay, that's nice and all, that's going to save me money. But what I am surprised about is that, you know, that there is nothing in place to keep me as a customer from leaving. You know even something like a 9.9%, which would be much less expensive for White Shepherd Bank, because if I leave for 6 months, then White Shepherd Bank is not making anything. And I'm not even asking for 3.9%. I'm just asking for a more reasonable rate on my existing balance, like a 9.9% for six months from now, on that existing balance. And there is just nothing in place for that, nothing?"

Manager: "Correct, I mean like I said, for new purchases I can give you the 9.9%, or I can even drop the balance transfer rate to 2.9%, but there is not going to be anything which is going to help what is already on here right now."

Scott: "Hmm, so my, so I can actually get a 2.9% for a balance transfer rate?"
Note: Now the balance transfer rate is at 2.9%. Who knows how low they can go.

Manager: "Yeah, I did say that I could actually go ahead and actually lower it to that today."

Scott: "Okay, well, alright then you know what, maybe I will transfer it out and transfer it back at the 2.9%. Okay, that sounds pretty good, and how long on that 2.9%?"

Manager: "Right now it runs through your November statement. It's really going to depend on when you do the transfer."

Scott: "Okay, and what's your name again?"

Manager: "Squashbug."

Scott: "Squashbug, okay great. Can I contact you again? Is this all noted on my account Squashbug?"

Manager: "Yeah, I put it on the account and I can give you my extension, 5434."

Scott: "Alright, well I'll tall ya, this is great. Actually with all these options and transferring them all around, White Shepherd Bank is going to make less money than if they just lower my rate a couple of points today. But that may be a suggestion that you might want to send to them."
Note: Maybe the bank thinks that we'll be too lazy to transfer the money in and out of our accounts. That may be true for some people but not DebtSmart® people.

Manager: "Yeah, well, I know a lot of people have mentioned that before. I don't know if they would be coming up with anything."

Scott: "I mean I like this deal better Squashbug, 2.9% 'til November."

Manager: "Umm hmm."

Scott: "It's a little more work, but still."

Manager: "It's a lower rate, but, yeah, it is more work, so. Well, I'll go ahead and I'll notate that on your account. And that way you can get back to me if you decide you want to do that."

Scott: "Okay."

Manager: "And until then I'll just go ahead and put on for your new purchases the 9.9% through November just in case you needed to make any purchases that way you would have a lower rate."

Scott: "Okay, alright. Well, that is definitely accommodating. Thank you Squashbug."

Manager: "You have a great day sir."

Scott: "You too."

Manager: "Bye."

Scott: "Bye-bye."
Note: We did later move the money around and got the entire balance reduced to 2.9%!

CALL #5.13: DON'T TAKE "NO" FOR AN ANSWER!

Reason For Call:	Lower the interest rate
Result:	Rate reduced from 11.97% to 9.9%
Difficulty Level:	Medium
Call Time:	16 minutes
Total Saved:	$730.00
$/hour to make call:	$2,737.5

Whenever you take advantage of a balance transfer offer, you should get a better interest rate for a certain period of time. When that offer period ends, the bank will increase your APR back up to the normal rate. You should always call and attempt to keep the rate low at this time. However, the bank usually cannot reduce to the rate if you call prior to the end of the credit offer because the rate is already low. They'll tell you to call back once it ends, which of course means that they've already started charging you the high rate.

Be sure to track the date that your offer ends. Call the bank on the day the rate increases and ask them to keep the rate low. You're probably not going to persuade them to keep your promotional rate, but you may very well be able to get the normal rate reduced by advising them of your plans to use another transfer offer.

SUMMARY

I currently have a 1.7% deal that expires on April 17th. I called and spoke with Greenbottle Fly, who told me that the rate is going to 11.97%, when the deal ends tomorrow. She couldn't change my rate and transferred me to an account manager, Mr. Tumblebug. Mr. Tumblebug told me he could lower the rate to 10.99% because of my perfect history. I said that's still too high so he lowered it to 9.9% fixed effective April 19th. He also said that I could call back, once the promotion ends, to see if I have any other deals available.

My balance is $7,580 at 11.97% so it takes 69.36 months to repay at $152 per month. At 9.9% it takes 64.56. That's a savings of $730!

TRANSCRIPT

Scott: "Calling Basset Hound Bank to see if they are going to keep their rate low. Otherwise I am going to transfer it to Briard Bank."

Voice Menu: "Welcome to Basset Hound Bank..."

Scott: "This is their chance to keep it low, but I'm not going to keep it here anyway unless they give me 0%. And they won't do it. Come on give me a human! Yes, I'm pressing zero to get to a human."
Note: I can't stand these voice menus!

Voice Menu: "Please hold and the next available specialist will..."

Scott: "Finally. Get me with a specialist. What kind of specialist?"

On hold...

Rep: "Basset Hound Bank at your service. Greenbottle Fly. May I please have your full account number?"

Scott: "Sure Greenbottle." (I give her the number.)

Rep: "And your name sir?"

Scott: "Scott Bilker."

Rep: "And how may I help you with your Platinum-Plus Card today?"

Scott: "Let's look at my rates. 1.7%, is that correct?"

Rep: "Yes it is. And that's good through your closing date. Which would be the 17th. That's Wednesday."

Scott: "That's tomorrow."

Rep: "Everyday after tomorrow you're going to be computed at your low contract rate of 11.97% on the balance on this account."
Note: It wouldn't matter what the rate is because the rep would still say, "low contract rate." How about, "will be computed at your low contract rate of 35.67%." ☺

Scott: "Okay. So basically tomorrow it's 11.97%?"

Rep: "Exactly. After tomorrow."

Scott: "Got it."

Rep: "Tomorrow at midnight to be specific."
Note: My rate turns back into a pumpkin.

Scott: "Here's the thing, 11.97% is just too high."

Rep: "Um hmm. Let me get you over to an account manager to see if there is a different contract rate available to you then."

Scott: "That would be great."

Rep: "Okay hold one moment we'll get you right over there. Now is there any other question I can answer for you before I do transfer you?"

Scott: "No, that'll be fine."

Rep: "Alright Mr. Bilker please hold for that manager. You have a great day, and thank you for your business."

Scott: "You're welcome."

On hold...

Manager: "Basset Hound Bank at your service. Mr. Tumblebug speaking. Can I have your name please?"

Scott: "Scott Bilker."

Manager: "Sir, I'm looking at your Basset Hound Bank Platinum Card. How may I help you today sir?"

Scott: "I was just talking to the account specialist, Mrs. Fly, before we spoke. And I was asking her about my rate, and she was telling that it's 1.7% until tomorrow, basically, and then it's going to go to 11.97%, which is just too high. I'm hoping that you'll have something for me."

Manager: "Well, let me have a look at that here."

Scott: "Okay."

Manager: "What I'm seeing is that you have an 11.97%. You've got a promotional that's expiring on the account right now. You've got that 1.7% that covers all uses of the card." (Pause) "I can help you out a little bit Mr. Bilker. I can get you down to a 10.99% on this account here. That's a point, every little bit does help sir."
Note: Well, it is true that 1% is better than nothing.

Scott: "Every little bit does help, but this is the thing Mr. Tumblebug. You see, I have a lot of other rates from other cards. You know, and 10.99% is still high."
Note: Letting him know that I have options and hinting that I'll use them.

Manager: "What kind of rate offers do you have on your other cards Mr. Bilker?"
Note: Be prepared to name banks and offers from your daily junk mail.

Scott: "Well, you know, some as low as 2.99%."

Manager: "That's for balance transfers though."

Scott: "Yes, and that's what this would be. I would transfer my balance."

Manager: "The thing is with the promotional rates. I mean they do expire. In regards to carrying your current balance, I don't have anything. One is that your current promotion hasn't expired. You know it is still good for another day or so. So that's still on the account. Even if we did have something, it wouldn't be as low as that 2.9%. Whenever there is a promotional offer, sometimes there's something, maybe in-between. Between the contract rate and where you were at before. But again we never know until the promotional expires and we can look up on the screen and see what's available. So, what I'm saying is that we are not going to be able to beat the 2.9% that you have with someone else if that's what you're thinking."

Scott: "I know that you probably can't beat something like that. But I mean, can you do better than 10.99%? I mean, the swing there is awfully huge."
Note: I listened to his reasoning then I let him know that I'm still not satisfied. I know they can do better—almost always!

Manager: "Here's what I can do for you Mr. Bilker. I can put a fixed rate on your account here. You've got a great history with us. You've been with us for 8 years. We certainly appreciate that sir. I'm going to put a 9.9% on your account for you sir. That's the best rate we have in regards to fixed rates on Platinum Cards sir."
Note: So why didn't he offer this before? Because they must be trained to get every little percent out of the customer as is possible! Wouldn't it be nice if they just gave you the best rate that you deserve all the time? Yeah right, like that will ever happen.

Scott: "Okay."

Manager: "If you do need to move your current balance, I'm a consumer, I understand that sir. But you do have a nice credit line here with us. $27,400."

Scott: "Right."

Manager: "I'm going to put a 9.9% on the account and again, if you do need to move it there's usually a promotional offer, and hopefully we can get you back on our card here sir."
Note: Boy they really want to keep me. He's lowering the rate and letting me know that there will be more offers.

Scott: "Okay Mr. Tumblebug. Well you know what, maybe if I call back...You know, go ahead do that 9.9% fixed, that makes me feel good. And maybe I can call back tomorrow like you said and there will be some offers on the screen at that time."

Manager: "So we got that for you Mr. Bilker. We brought you down from an 11.99%. Now again, you know, sometimes offers do go on the account that maybe split the difference, maybe not even quite split the difference, that would cover that current balance, but we wouldn't know until that other one did expire sir."

Scott: "Alright, well that's fine."

Manager: "Okay?"

Scott: "Well that's good though. It makes me happy to know that I have the Basset Hound Bankcard, to know that you guys moved down a little at least."

Manager: "We are happy to have you for a customer sir."

Scott: "Alright, well thank you Mr. Tumblebug."

Manager: "You're welcome Mr. Bilker."

Scott: "Talk to you later."

Manager: "Have a great day sir."

Scott: "You too."

CALL #5.14: KNOCK OFF 4%!

Reason For Call:	Ask to reduce minimum payment
Result:	They don't reduce the minimum payment however, I got the rate reduced from 16.74% to 12.65% and got an offer of 3.9% with no transfer fees.
Difficulty Level:	Medium
Call Time:	5 minutes
Total Saved:	$1,141.00
$/hour to make call:	$13,692.00

Even if you're calling for one reason, like waiving a fee, it doesn't hurt to try to attempt negotiating other terms. While you have the bank on the phone try to get your rate reduced. You've already had to hold for a few minutes so you might as well make it more worthwhile.

The reason for this call is to get my friend's minimum payment reduced while he goes back to college. They don't lower the minimum payment so I go ahead and ask for the rate to be reduced.

SUMMARY

I called to ask the bank if they can reduce the minimum payment. My friend is going back to college for about 12 months. He wants to get the minimum payment reduced as much as possible while in school. I calculated the minimum payment to be around 1/48th of the current balance (and confirmed by the rep).

I called and spoke to Mrs. Bedbug. She said that the rate is 16.74%. I asked for that to be lowered. She lowered it to 12.65%. She offered me a transfer rate of 3.9%, no fees, I forgot to ask how long it's good for. Mrs. Bedbug also said that there was no way to reduce the minimum payment.

With a balance of $3,519.21 at 16.74% and payments of $73 (1/48th of balance) it takes 80.64 months to pay back. At 12.65% it takes 65.01 months. That's a savings of 15.63 payments or $1,141.00.

TRANSCRIPT

Voice Menu: "Welcome to Chihauhua Bank. For quality and training purposes your call may be monitored and recorded."

Scott: "Yours too. For the same purposes." ☺

Rep: "Welcome to customer service. My name is Ms. Bedbug. May I have your name?"

Scott: "Lewis Wilson."

Rep: "Good afternoon Mr. Wilson. May I have you mother's maiden name?"

Scott: (I give her the name.)

Rep: "How can I help you with the account?"

Scott: "What's my rate right now on my current balance?"

Rep: "It's 16.74%."

Scott: "That's definitely a little high. Can we lower that rate, Ms. Bedbug."

Rep: "I can take a look for you. Would you be able to hold for a minute?"

Scott: "I can hold."

On hold...

Rep: "I do show available on purchases the prime rate plus 7.9% which is currently 12.65%. Which would be a variable rate also."

Scott: "That's the best you can do?"
Note: I should have said, "I think you can do better than that. I mean, 12.65% is too high especially with all these low rate offers I get in the mail everyday." And by the way, why don't they send me letters saying, "You're qualified to have your rate reduced to 12.65%." Why is it that we have to call? It's that squeaky-wheel thing.

Rep: "Yes. That's the lowest rate for purchases. Now I do show that you already accepted a balance transfer special of 3.9%. Now that is still available if you had any other credit cards or loans you wanted to pay off. Or if you were planning a large expense, we could also send you a check to deposit into your checking account, and from that you could use it for whatever you would like."
Note: Now she's begging me to take money on this offer. Here's the catch that she is not telling me. If I take the 3.9% offer then I'll have balances at two different rates. The majority of the balance at 12.65% and the offer balance at 3.9%. When they receive payments, they no doubt have the right to credit the balances as they choose. And, they will choose to credit payments to the balances that are at the lower, 3.9%, which effectively locks the larger balance at 12.65% without any reduction in the principal from payments until the promotion ends.

Scott: "Hmm. But the best you can do on this current one it is umm..."

Rep: "To reduce it to 7.9% over the prime."

Scott: "Hmm. Let me ask you this, what's the minimum payment on the account? I know it's $73, but what's the minimum payment by percentage, or however it's calculated."

Rep: "Take your outstanding balance and divide it by 48 to obtain the minimum payment."

Scott: "Is there any possible way to get that to be reduced?"

Rep: "No there isn't."

Scott: "Alright, hmm. Are there any transfer fees on that 3.9% offer?"
Note: I certainly gave up on the minimum payment reduction too quickly. I became more focused on that low-rate offer.

Rep: "No there isn't."

Scott: "So there is no fee? If I do a transfer would it reduce my current balance to that rate?"

Rep: "No, not your current balance."

Scott: "Okay, alright. And uh...Alright Ms. Bedbug, I'll have to think about that."
Note: I didn't think so—no harm in asking. It would have been nice if the entire balance went to 3.9%.

Rep: "You did not want to complete the lowering the percentage rate for purchases?"

Scott: "Oh let's do that, yes. And that would lower my current rate right now?"

Rep: "That's correct."

Scott: "To what?"

Rep: "12.65%. You'll receive confirmation of that within the week."

Scott: "Okay. Alright Ms. Bedbug, thank you very much."

Rep: "Sure, any other questions?"

Scott: "No, that'll be all."

Rep: "We appreciate your calling. Have a good day now."

Scott: "You too. Bye-bye."

Call #5.15: Change Card Type to Reduce Rate

Reason For Call:	Lower the interest rate
Result:	Rate reduced from 13.72% to 8.76%.
Difficulty Level:	Medium
Call Time:	10 minutes
Total Saved:	$4,320.00
$/hour to make call:	$25,920.00

This call is for my friend Lewis Wilson. Lewis has very good credit and shouldn't be paying 13.72%.

SUMMARY

I called to see if I could reduce Lewis' rate. I spoke to Ms. Cicada and she said that she can't lower the rate but may be able to change the card product. I changed the card to a Shiba Inu Bank Prime-Plus-Four, which is currently 8.76%. It takes effect on June 9th.

With his balance of $11,832.60 at 13.72% and $200 monthly payments it would have taken him 8.28 years to pay back the entire amount. At the 8.76% rate it takes 6.48 years and saves $4,320 in payments!

When I told Lewis about the $4,320 savings, he jokingly said, "Can I have that in a check." ☺

TRANSCRIPT

Voice Menu: "Shiba Inu Bank. Please have your card available. This call may be recorded for quality purposes..."

Scott: "Yours too."

Rep: "Ms. Cicada speaking. How may I help you?"

Scott: "Hi, I just have some questions about my account."

Rep: "May I have your name?"

Scott: "Lewis Wilson."

Rep: "Okay, Mr. Wilson. And for security purposes can I please verify your date of birth?"

Scott: "Sure..." (I give her the date.)

Rep: "Thank you. And how can I help you today?"

Scott: "Okay. What's my balance right now?"

Rep: "$11,832.60."

Scott: "Okay. And what's the rate right now?"

Rep: "The interest rate for purchases is 13.72%, and for cash advances it's 17.74%.

Scott: "Okay, alright. What I'm calling about Ms. Cicada is that the rate is just getting a little too high for me. For this, even at 13.72%, I've just got other cards at lower rates. Some much lower, and I would like to continue to use my Shiba Inu Bankcard, but you know financially it's just not going to make any sense. I mean I'll be forced to transfer my balances. I've really had a fine experience with Shiba Inu Bank. I just can't continue to pay more of a rate than I think I should be paying. Is there anything you can do?"

Rep: "Okay look. We cannot change the rates on the accounts Mr. Wilson. But what we can do is transfer you to a different card product with a lower interest rate."

Scott: "Okay."
Note: In this case I have to change the type of card to reduce the rate. I personally believe it's just their way of saving face. They don't want to admit that they'll negotiate the rate so they just put you in a different card "product" that has a lower rate. It doesn't matter, just as long as you save money.

Rep: "Now let me just double-check and see what we have available. Do you mind holding for a minute."

Scott: "I can hold."

Rep: "Thank you."

On hold...

Rep: "Mr. Wilson?"

Scott: "Yes."

Rep: "Hi, I apologize for having you on hold, for the delay. Now in reviewing I have showing...We have a Shiba Inu Bank Prime-Plus-Four, which is currently 8.76%. That is the lowest card that we have."

Scott: "It's prime plus 4%?"

Rep: "Yes."

Scott: "So now how would this work? This balance will go to the new Shiba Inu Bankcard and you'll send me a new card?"

Rep: "Exactly."

Scott: "Okay. That sounds..."

Rep: "Everything will transfer over to that card, and the account remains the same. So just the interest rate is lowered."

Scott: "Okay. So can I continue to use my same card?"

Rep: "You can still continue to use the same card in the meantime while you receive the new one. Everything remains the same."

Scott: "Okay."

Rep: "Now, in order to transfer you there are small numbers on the back of the card that I need. Can I have those please?"

Scott: "I don't have the card on me right now! Could you hold on one second while I look for it?"

On hold...

Scott: "Yeah okay I got it. Ms. Cicada?"

Rep: "Okay. Can I have the numbers please?"

Scott: (I give her the numbers.)

Rep: "Okay, your account is scheduled to transfer on June 9th."

Scott: "Okay great. How long before that new card will be sent to me?"

Rep: "June 9th. Around that time the account is scheduled to transfer and around that time you'll be receiving the new card. The balance will transfer over to that account."

Scott: "Okay."

Rep: "Okay. Also there is a new benefit that Shiba Inu Bank is adding to the card called the Membership Reward Options Program. And what it does is it enables you to earn one point for every dollar you charge on your account. Now this is a free benefit for the free card that you hold. Umm, there is no additional cost for having it. It is to encourage you to use your Shiba Inu Bankcard. Would you like to start earning your points as of today on your account?"

Note: They're always trying to sell you something.

Scott: "Okay. So it's one point for every, how much?"

Rep: "For every dollar you spend."

Scott: "And the points go towards stuff?"

Rep: "You can use with airline partners, hotel partners, car rental..."

Scott: "And there is no charge?"

Rep: "No charges. Free benefits for the free card that you hold."

Scott: "Oh, that sounds like a good benefit."

Rep: "Yes. And there is no maximum number of points that you can earn with the program. If you cancel this account but maintain at least one card issued by Shiba Inu Bank. You have 6 months from the date of cancellation to redeem the points you accrued. If you cancel all your cards then all your points are immediately forfeited. And if you would like to redeem points, add or delete cards, feel free to call us back at...Or access our web site at ShibaInuBank.com."

Scott: "Great. Ms. Cicada, just so I'm clear, it's going to be 8.76%, that's prime plus 4%. The whole balance transfer is in there. And then I'll be able to use...the account number stays the same. And I'll get a new card that will look different?"

Rep: "Correct."

Scott: "Okay, that sounds great."

Note: So basically, it's the same account with a lower rate.

Rep: "Alright?"

Scott: "Alright. Thank you very much."

Rep: "You're welcome, goodbye, have a great day."

Scott: "You too. Have a good day."

CALL #5.16: SURE IT'S THE LAW

Reason For Call:	Ask to reduce minimum payment
Result:	Rate reduced from 13.72% to 8.75%.
Difficulty Level:	Easy
Call Time:	10 minutes
Total Saved:	$2,811.34
$/hour to make call:	$16,868.04

Another call for my friend Lewis Wilson to ask to have his minimum payment reduced. Again, most banks will not allow you to pay less than the current minimum. Well, the only exception to that is when you're totally behind or in default. In that case, they'll probably take whatever they can get. My friend Lewis is very good with his finances and therefore will probably not be in a position to pay less per month. You would think that the bank would want him to pay less since they would be able to collect more interest charges.

As it turns out, I wasn't able to get the minimum payment reduced, but I was able to get the interest rate lowered. A lower interest rate is much more important in the long run anyway.

SUMMARY

My strategy is to tell them something like, "I'm going back to college for about 12 months and I want to get my minimum payment reduced as much as possible." Then ask if it can go any lower than the current minimum.

I called and spoke to Locust. The minimum payment is 1/50th and Locust said it's a "federal law," that's as low as it can go. When I asked him "what federal law?" he was stumped.

The interest rate is 13.72%, so I had it lowered to 8.75%. With a balance of $11,592.93 at 13.72% and payments of $232 (2% of balance) it takes 74.52 months to pay back. At 8.75% it takes 62.4 months. That's a savings of 12.12 payments or $2,811.34.

TRANSCRIPT

Voice Menu: "Thank you. Just a moment please while we obtain the records. To verify identity please enter the last four digits of your social security number…"

Scott: (I enter the numbers.)

Voice Menu: "This call may be recorded for quality purposes."

Scott: "Yep. Yours too."

Rep: "Hi. This is Locust. How may I assist you?"

Scott: "I have some questions about my account. What's your name again?"

Rep: "My name is Locust sir. And who am I speaking with?"

Scott: "Lewis Wilson."

Rep: "How are you doing today Mr. Wilson?"

Scott: "Very good."

Rep: "Alright Mr. Wilson, just give me a moment while I pull up your account information."

Scott: "Okay."

Pause...

Scott: "Got that Locust?"

Rep: "Yes. Just give me a moment Mr. Wilson. Thank you very much. Yes sir. Could you provide me with your last four digits of your social security number?"

Scott: "Excuse me."
Note: I already did this with the voice menu system. That information apparently didn't come through to the rep, as is the case most of the time.

Rep: "Umm hmm. Could you just provide me with the last four digits..."

Scott: (I give him the numbers.)

Rep: "Thank you very much. And how can I help you Mr. Wilson?"

Scott: "Alright. Let's start with my balance."

Rep: "Okay. The total balance is $11,592.93."

Scott: "And the rate?"

Rep: "And the rate on your card, or percentage is prime plus 8.99%. That would be 13.72%. For cash it's prime plus 12.99%. That would be 17.72%."

Scott: "How about for my balance right now. What's the rate on my balance?"

Rep: "The rate on your balance is 13.72%."

Scott: "13.72%. And what's the minimum payment? As a percentage of the balance."

Rep: "Percentage of the balance. Just give me moment. The minimum payment as of now...There is no current due on your account sir."

Scott: "No current what?"

Rep: "Current due on your account because we have received your payment. So right now you do not need to pay anything. You do not have any minimum due."

Scott: "Okay. So what is the minimum payment?"

Rep: "If you want we can go ahead and calculate it for you. Just give me a moment."

Scott: "Okay let's calculate."

Rep: "It would be 1/50th or 2% of your total outstanding balance."

Scott: "Is it possible to get it lowered to less than that?"
Note: This is the goal of the call. It's what Lewis asked me to do.

Rep: "Sir no. The minimum due is calculated in a standard way."

Scott: "I know, but is it possible to reduce that minimum due?"

Rep: "That's not possible sir."

Scott: "Anything is possible Locust. I mean, you're telling me that's impossible?"

Rep: "No. Mr. Wilson this thing is not possible because I tell you we need to go ahead with the Federal law."

Scott: "Oh, there's a Federal law."

Rep: "That's right. The government, they tell us that it's just a policy of Steinbracke Bank and as well as any other credit card companies. They have a maximum 2% or 1/50th of the total outstanding balance."

Scott: "So there's a Federal law that says that 1/50th is it?"
Note: What Federal Law is that? I have a $10,730 balance on one of my other credit cards and the minimum payment is $15!

Rep: "That's right sir. The policy of Steinbracke Bank says that."

Scott: "Okay. But what's the…"

Rep: "We have to go according to the norms of Federal law."

Scott: "Okay. I didn't know that. What Federal law is it?"

Rep: "Not sure about that Federal law sir. But uh, this is…You have a cardmember agreement with you?"
Note: Seems like the details of this supposed law are slipping from the rep's mind. "Your honor, it's the law." The judge replies, "What law?" Confused rep says, "Not sure."

Scott: "I know that that's what it is. I'll tell you why I am asking. Because I am going to college for 12 months, and I want to see if I can reduce my payment to as little as possible while I am in school since I have other expenses. So if it can go to just the interest that's due that would be fine. Is it okay to do that Locust?"

Rep: "No Mr. Wilson. Unfortunately, I would like to help you in each and every way. But unfortunately it would be very difficult."

Scott: "Okay. Well maybe you can help me in another way. I've got to tell you that 13.72% is insanely high. So I'm hoping that you can reduce that for me. I know that that's possible."
Note: So I couldn't reduce the minimum payment. That's okay. I knew that might be tough. However, while I'm already talking to this bank, I may as well ask about lowering the rate.

Rep: "Just give me a moment."

Pause…

Rep: "In fact we have to fit you to a product called Steinbracke Bank Platinum Prime Plus 4%. Right now your total interest would be around 8%…8.75%."

Scott: "Okay. So…"

Rep: "Alright. Now I just told you 13.72% on your purchases. But you do not need to worry about that. Your total purchase is raised to be 8.75%."

Scott: "And what about the rate on my outstanding balance? Would that go to 8.75%?"

Rep: "That would be also going to 8.75%."

Scott: "Okay. Well that sounds like a good plan. I definitely feel good about that, Locust."

Rep: "Not a problem at all sir."

Scott: "And would that be effective immediately?"

Rep: "It would be effective immediately..."

Scott: "Oh, I love immediately."

Both laugh...

Rep: "And you would see it in your next month's statement Mr. Wilson."

Scott: "Okay great Locust. Well that definitely is helpful."

Rep: "Okay Mr. Wilson. One more thing that I would like to tell you, since you are an old cardmember with Steinbracke Bank..."

Scott: "Okay."
Note: I hear the sales pitch coming.

Rep: "And we do appreciate your business. Thank you for having a high balance and a good spending pattern."
Note: You gotta love that statement. Might as well say, "Thank you for allowing us to encourage your spending and gouge you for eternity."

Scott: "That's a great deal. You've got to love that high balance and good spending pattern."

Both laugh...

Rep: "So okay. So what I am trying to say is that right now you have two solicited offers from Steinbracke Bank."

Scott: "Uh huh."

Rep: "You can go and get yourself enrolled in our automatic flight insurance program for $500,000 coverage absolutely free."

Scott: "Hmm."

Rep: "There is no charge for that. No monthly charge, no yearly charge, and there is no minimal fee. It is free for lifetime."

Scott: "Umm, what is it? Life Insurance?"

Rep: "That's automatic flight insurance."

Scott: "And it's totally free?"

Rep: "That's right."

Scott: "Forever?"

Rep: "That's right."

Scott: "And I never pay a dime at any time for anything?"

Rep: "Alright. I would go ahead and tell you sir. I will be very blunt to you. If you would go ahead and buy a ticket with a Steinbracke Bankcard, only when you are going ahead and flying. At that point in time normally a premium of $7.50 would be charged."

Scott: "Ah, I see."

Rep: "But apart from that there is no enrollment fee at all..."

Scott: "You know what at this point in time I wouldn't want to do that Locust, but I do appreciate your candor."

Rep: "Not a problem at all sir."

Scott: "And I thank you for..."

Rep: "Not a problem at all sir."

Scott: "And all the rate stuff is taken care of?"

Rep: "That's right."

Scott: "Great, I like to hear that. Thank you very much for your help."

Rep: "Thank you for calling and have a wonderful day."

Scott: "You too. Bye-bye."

Rep: "Bye-bye."

CHAPTER 6

SHOPPING 'TIL YOU DROP—THE RATE!

CREDIT OPTIONS

There's a lot of bad "expert" advice out there that says to consolidate your credit cards, close zero-balance accounts, and cut up the cards. Be wary of this advice because you need credit options! If you cut up your credit cards, you cut out your credit options!

Closing zero-balance accounts in haste may be a big mistake! Especially when all your debt is on a single credit card. If something happens, and the bank raises your rate, you'll be stuck at a high rate with no place to go shopping for money. You need places to go shopping for money so you're not at the mercy of any single bank!

Having one credit card is like shopping in only one store. Imagine only shopping in one place no matter what the prices are in another store. Let's say someone that shops in only one department store is looking for a television. They find that television selling for $350. Imagine that the same exact television is selling for $175 at another store in the same town. Wouldn't it be insane to shop solely in one store without looking around for better deals?

It's just as insane to use only one credit card. Money is the same physical product no matter where you get it; green paper you buy stuff with—that's it. The only difference is the price you pay to use it. You must be sure to make the banks compete for their very plain, but useful product.

If you have debt at high rates and your current banks won't budge, then you'll need to find other credit sources with lower interest rate deals in order to save money. That's one of the reasons I have so many credit cards, so I have many places to go shopping for money.

LOOKING TO USE THE BEST CARD

I'm always asked, "What's the best credit card? Where do you get low rate offers? How do you keep your rates so low?"

The answer is that almost all banks have "good" and "bad" offers. It depends on your personal relationship with that particular bank. The best offers, and lowest rates, are most likely to originate from your existing credit card accounts. One of the easiest ways to find low rate credit options is to call your credit card bank and ask. There may be a great rate offer available to you right now and you don't even know it!

When you call the bank, make sure you are prepared to take immediate advantage of any good offers. That means having the statement(s) of the high rate loan(s)/credit-card(s) handy so you can do all the balance transfers on the phone if a better deal is available.

A good offer, one that's better than a your current credit cards, may include one or more of the following: (1) a lower APR, (2) low or better yet, NO transfer fees, and (3) the deal lasts for at least six months

Remember to take good notes about the details of the offer. If you're getting the offer during a phone call you'll need to get some type of proof that you did get that offer. Get the rep's name. Record the date and time in your notes. You should also ask them to make a note of that offer on their computer.

By the way, if you're planning to go on a vacation, holiday shopping, or make a major purchase (furniture, appliances), be sure to call your banks and let them know that you'll use their card ONLY if they give you a good deal. I've done this many times, but that was before I started recording calls.

Play all your credit card banks against each other. Make them fight for your business!

WHEN THE BANKS CALL YOU

You know the pesky telemarketing calls you get from your banks offering you a low rate? Well, you may want to consider them because some can actually save you a bundle of money. However, always, I repeat, always negotiate a better rate than the first one offered.

Almost every time I'm called by one of my banks to receive a low rate offer they start with something like, "Mr. Blicker (they never get your name right) this is Mr. Drone. I'm calling from Saint Bernard Bank to offer you 6.9% fixed on balance transfers." And I say, "Gee, that's awfully high. Do you have anything better?" The response is "Well, the BEST I can do is 4.99% for 6 months." My retort is "That's still a little too high." To which I get, "Well, the BEST I can do is 2.99% for 6 months."

It's always the BEST they can do. Keep in mind that 90% of the time they can usually do better.

One word of caution: if you're getting an offer from a bank that's calling you, then you don't know if it's really the bank or some scam artist on the other end of that phone. Do not give your social security number or other personal identification information. If the phone rep says they need your personal information to complete the transaction, ask them to call back. Then you need to call your bank directly to verify that the offer and caller are real. This way you add a layer of protection against possible identity theft.

BALANCE TRANSFERS DONE RIGHT

If you're considering a low rate promotional offer for a transfer onto one of your existing credit cards, be careful to make sure that your balance is zero before taking advantage of that offer. That's because banks typically have the right to apply payments to your account as they choose. You can be sure they will choose to apply payments to the balance with the lower rate. This technique effectively locks your other balance at the higher rate.

For example, say you have a $5,000 balance at 13% on your card. Let's say you also have a $2,000 balance on that same card, at 2.9% for 6 months. Every time you make a payment, your balance at 2.9% is being reduced, but you'll still owe $5,000 at 13% until you pay off the 2.9% or the 6-month period ends. The way around this is to use another card and transfer the balance of $5,000 prior to using the 2.9% offer. Now you have a zero balance on the first card and $7,000 available at 2.9%. Then transfer all the money back to the first card at the lower 2.9% rate.

KNOWING WHEN THE DEAL "REALLY" ENDS

Most of the time, balances that are transferred to lower rates expire at some future date. At least the lowest rate deals. For example, you may get a 0% APR but it lasts for only 6 months. That's fine. But you must be careful to pay that balance off before they start charging you the higher interest rate.

But when does the transfer deal really end? When do the banks start charging you interest?

Let's say you transfer your balance to a credit card that gives you a 0% APR "through" your June closing date. After the deal ends the rate jumps to 15%. The closing date is the day that interest charges are calculated and the monthly statement is finalized.

When the offer is valid "through" the June statement, it means that the closing date is in June and that statement is the last one that's going to have a 0% APR. Once you've received the June statement, your account is already being charged the new interest rate on all balances after the closing date. So, essentially, it's already too late to pay the balance off in full and avoid interest charges for the next statement. Let's put some specific numbers and dates to that example.

Let's say that you transfer $10,000 to the 0% APR offer that's good through the closing date on your June statement (June 24th). Let's also say your June statement arrives on July 1st and has a payment due date of July 19th. The balance is $10,000. The interest rate shown at the bottom of your statement is 0%. You know that the deal ends in this statement so you decide to pay off the balance in full right away.

You send the check out that very day in the amount of $10,000. That is the full balance shown on the June billing statement. It arrives at the bank 2 days later and is credited to your account at that time. You believe that since you paid the balance in full from your June statement that you avoided paying any interest charges because you know that the rate is going to jump to 15% the very next month.

Well, the next month's statement arrives and you notice that there's still a balance of $36.99 remaining. "How could that be?" you ask yourself since you haven't made any new purchases. "I paid off the entire balance last month!"

Then you look at the bottom of the statement and notice that the $36.99 is an interest charge! "I'm not supposed to be charged any interest. It was 0% until June and I paid off the entire balance!"

What happened is that the 0% APR deal was valid through the June closing date. That day was June 24th and the June statement does show 0%. However, all balances on the card after June 24th will be charged the new 15% APR. Since you received your statement on July 1st it's already 7 days after the closing date of June 24th. Even though you promptly mailed out the payment for the full amount it takes 2 days to get there so now it's day 9.

That means the $10,000 balance was on your account for 9 days after the 0% APR ended, so you're going to be charged 9 days of interest at 15% on the $10,000. That's 15% divided by 365 days to get the daily interest rate or 0.04109589% multiplied by $10,000 which is about $4.11 per day. And $4.11 for 9 days is a total of $36.99. Gotcha!

To avoid any interest charges, it's important to pay your balance off, in full, prior to the closing date of the last statement with the low rate. In this example case, that would be the May statement (one month prior to June 24th).

ASK FOR A CREDIT LINE INCREASE

If you're about to take advantage of a low-rate credit transfer offer, then be sure to ask for a credit line increase. This way you can transfer as much as possible thus saving the most money!

You're already on the phone so make the call even more valuable by saying, "Okay, I'll transfer $2,000 under those terms. However, I could transfer $4,000 if my credit line were increased."

You're really in a good position to get that credit line increase because it's a win-win situation. The bank gets to make more money in interest charges and you get to save more money in interest charges. Of course, the bank is hoping that you'll forget about any time limits on these offers so the entire balance will move to that higher rate when the offer expires. We're not going to let that happen because we're all DebtSmart®.

BALANCE TRANSFER CHECKLIST

The key to shopping for the best transfer deals is to be ready to take advantage of them immediately when you find a good one. Be prepared with the following items when calling for balance transfer deals:

- Details of any existing mail offers.
- The physical credit cards of all banks involved.
- The last statement for each credit card involved so you can check the balances of both accounts and have the mailing addresses of the accounts to which you're transferring money.

CALL #6.01: LOAN SHOPPING FROM HOME

Reason For Call:	Loan shopping
Result:	Received offer of 6.9% on existing account and transferred balance.
Difficulty Level:	Easy
Call Time:	16 minutes
Total Saved:	$129.01
$/hour to make call:	$483.79

I had a credit offer on one card (Deerhound Bank) that was nearing its end. When it ends my rate is going to shoot to 19.8%! I called the bank to see if they would keep the rate low and they said "no." Now I have to go shopping with my other cards to see if I have any deals.

The idea is to use your existing credit cards to "go shopping" for lower rates. It's like comparison shopping in any store where the product is exactly the same. The only difference is the price. In this case the product is money (the loan) and the price is the interest charges and any other fees.

SUMMARY

Since Deerhound Bank wouldn't lower my rate, I want to see who will give me a deal. I called Rottweiler Bank and spoke to the rep. I asked her to check both Rottweiler accounts (Gold and Platinum) for any offers. They quickly came up with a 6.9% for 6 months offer on my Gold Card account. I did take advantage of that offer and paid off the $2,000 balance at Deerhound Bank.

There were no other offers available on my Rottweiler Bank Platinum account so they gave me these options: (1) putting in for an offer (14 days), or (2) combining my accounts, which raises my limit. To do option (2) I have to call back in 2 business days.

After 6 months of paying $40 per month (the minimum payment) the balance would be $1,956.67. At the lower rate of 6.9%, the balance, after 6 months, is $1,827.66. The total savings for that six-month period are $129.01.

TRANSCRIPT

Right now I have no offers, or balance, with Rottweiler Bank. I am going to call and see if they want to make some money.

Rep: "Rottweiler Bank customer service, this is Armyworm. Can I have your name please?"

Scott: "Hi Armyworm. Scott Bilker."

Rep: "Thank you. And your mother's maiden name?"

Scott: (I give her the name.)

Rep: "And how can I help you today?"

Scott: "Okay, I wanted to call and ask Rottweiler Bank Platinum Card if they had any kind of special balance transfer offers available for my account. Not just this one, I also have a Rottweiler Bank Gold Card account."
Note: If you have multiple credit cards from one bank, then you can get all the deals with a single call.

Rep: "Okay, because they are specific for each account."

Scott: "Okay, well we'll start with this one."

Rep: "Okay, let's see. In order to go ahead and get a balance transfer offer on this account I would need to process a referral um, to our new business department. Let's see if we have another, um, offer on your other account."
Note: What is she talking about? I've never heard of the "referral" thing.

Scott: "Okay, you want the number?"

Rep: "Yeah, what's the other account number?"

Scott: (I give her the number.) "So are you saying there are no offers on my Platinum Card account?"
Note: Always be prepared with all the account numbers.

Rep: "Right, there's not a current balance-transfer offer on that account. Umm..."

Pause...

Rep: "Okay, there is an offer on this account on your Platinum Card."

Scott: "Oh, my Platinum Card or my Gold Card?"

Rep: "Oh, I'm sorry, it's on this one you just gave me. The Gold Card."

Scott: "Okay."

Rep: "There is an offer on this account for a 6.9% for 6 months."

Scott: "Uh, huh."
Note: Great! Now I can keep Deerhound Bank on their toes by transferring my balance! Once my balance is $0 I'm sure they'll send me another great offer.

Rep: "And that would be balance transfers and then any new purchases and cash advances once the transfer went through."

Scott: "Oh really."

Rep: "Emm, hmm."

Scott: "6.9% for 6 months."

Rep: "Right."

Scott: "Okay, um, okay that's reasonable. I tell you what, if you can do that on the other account I'll transfer a total of $5,560."

Note: There's the negotiating technique. Since she offered me the deal on one card, I told her I'd spend more money if she gives me that deal on both cards.

Rep: "Okay, umm..."

Scott: "I know there's only $2,100 available on the Gold Card account."

Rep: "Yeah, because I can't...again, balance transfers are specific for each account. The only other thing I can do for you on the other account is send it for review to our new business department. And then they would notify you in writing within 7 to 14 days."

Scott: "Oh, it would take 7 to 14 days?"

Rep: "Right. For them to get to that, an offer on that account for you."

Scott: "Let's do the Rottweiler Bank Gold Card transfer."

Rep: "Okay, in order to do it over the phone we do need the address that you mail your payment to on the other account. Do you have your Rottweiler Bankcard there with you?"

Scott: "The physical card?"

Rep: "Right."

Scott: "I've got a statement in front of me."

Rep: "Okay, do you have the physical card there with you?"

Note: Make sure that you not only have the statement of both accounts handy for addressing information but you also have the physical credit cards for both accounts.

Scott: "Yeah, I sure have the physical card somewhere. Let me, give me a moment...okay, I have the card."

Rep: "Okay, on the back of that card, I just need to verify the last 3 digits located on the signature strip."

Scott: "Cool, I like this, it makes it safe." (I give her the numbers.)

Rep: "Okay, alright. And the amount you wanted to transfer?"

Scott: "Can I do the whole balance, $2,100?"

Rep: "You can but interest starts accruing the moment that we send it out."
Note: Just like any cash loan, like a mortgage, interest is charged from the moment you are given the money. If this were a purchase then you'd get a grace period.

Scott: "Well, I..."

Rep: "In other words, on your first statement you're going to have interest charges."

Scott: "Okay, but will that be a problem as far as..."

Rep: "Well, it may put you over the credit line if it, you know..."

Scott: "Okay, let's make it..."

Rep: "I would, if I were you, I'd do like $2,000."

Scott: "$2,000 it is."
Note: I should have calculated the max I could transfer. That would be my credit line divided by one plus one-twelfth the APR. In this case $2,100/(1+.069/12)=$2,087.99. Or to be safe, $2,085. That would give me approximately one month at the new low rate, in interest charges, so I wouldn't go over the limit.

Rep: "Okay. Alright, and the name of the card issuer?"

Scott: "Umm, Deerhound Bankcard Services."

Rep: "Okay, and your account number with them?"

Scott: (I give her the number.)

Rep: "Alright. And the address that you mail your payments to on that account?"

Scott: (I give her the address.)

Rep: "Okay, alright. A check will be submitted in 7 to 10 days. Once the balance transfer has been processed, no changes, corrections, or cancellations can be made."

Scott: "Emm, hmm."

Rep: "And, just one second...and you wanted to look at the other account to see if something can be done...just one second..."

Scott: "Right, if they can do this on the other account I'll do a few thousand there right now."
Note: Remember that I am trying to get that low rate on all my accounts at Rottweiler Bank.

Rep: "I don't know...hold on just one second?"

Scott: "Sure."

On hold...

Rep: "Okay, cause the only thing that I can do at my level..."

Scott: "Emm, hmm."

Rep: "Is if there's not a balance transfer offer on the account, the only thing I can do is, is put it on referral to our new business department."

Scott: "Is there a manager there that might be able to help you out?"
Note: Okay, it's clear that this rep cannot help me any further. To continue shopping at this bank I'll need to speak to someone with the power to help me. Don't give up. Just ask for a manager.

Rep: "Yeah, sure. Hold on just one second."

Scott: "Sure."

On hold...

Rep: "Mr. Bilker?"

Scott: "Yes."

Rep: "I do have a supervisor on the line to further assist you."

Scott: "Okay great."

Supervisor: "Yes Mr. Bilker. My name is Mrs. Antlion. I understand that you were in a promotion at one point on the classic card ending in (account number) and that was good for almost 6 months, well actually 6 months."

Scott: "Right. Correct."

Note: Seems that I was just coming off an offer on that card not too long ago. This may be why they're being hesitant in giving me another low, 6-month offer.

Supervisor: "Um, the only suggestion that I would have for you on the other account..."

Scott: "Uh huh."

Supervisor: "She did explain to you what other options you did have?"

Scott: "Right, she said she could submit something, I was just hoping someone else, you know, could do this like right now, because I could..."

Supervisor: "It won't happen today, but what I will do for you is we can do the referral. Which normally takes two weeks or what you could do is you could wait until you do the balance transfer with the Gold Card."

Scott: "Emm, hmm."

Supervisor: "After you're into that rate, you can ask us to go ahead and combine both accounts into one. And then that way you have just the one card and then you would have it at the 5 point...you don't pay finance charges, by the way, in the first place. You pay it off in full, correct?"

Scott: "Which one?"

Supervisor: "You pay your account off in full each month anyway?"

Scott: "No, not always."

Supervisor: "You really don't?"

Scott: "No, not, well the 6.9% offer for 6 months, I'm not going to pay that off in full."

Note: That's what they want to hear! That I'll be in debt forever! That I don't pay off my balance in full but I do pay on time.

Supervisor: "Oh, what I, what we can do, is after you do the balance transfer on the Gold Card."

Scott: "Uh, huh."

Supervisor: "If you wanted. You could ask us to combine both to one..."

Scott: "To one account?"

Supervisor: "Correct. That would be an option."

Scott: "Oh, you mean I could combine them to one account and that gives me the 6.9%?"

Note: That's an interesting option. The more you talk to them, the more you can learn how they can get you a better deal. Here though, they want me to cancel one account and combine it with the other. This way, I get the low rate with a greater credit line. But the drawback to this is that now I only have one account to bargain with in the future. Remember how, in the beginning of this conversation, I did a check first on my Rottweiler Bank Platinum Card account, and there was no offer. Then I found an offer on the Rottweiler Bank Gold Card. If I didn't have two accounts to work with I may not have been able to get the 6.9% offer. However, if I really need to get more money at a lower rate, and don't have many other choices, I may have to consider the combining-accounts option.

Supervisor: "Well, what's going to happen after the balance transfer is done, is what she explained, meaning...oh, actually, I could do it for you now, hold on."

Scott: "Okay."

Note: Instead of my having to wait until the transfer check is cut, to have my account locked-in at the new 6.9% offer, the supervisor is going to make that happen right now.

Supervisor: "I can just lock you in. What I would advise you to do is wait until you're actually on the system, on the statement itself states 6.9%. When it states 6.9% at that point, call back and ask us to consolidate both accounts into one. You understand?"

Scott: "Oh yeah, but I have to wait like, well at least one month, so I could call back and consolidate them at that time."

Supervisor: "No you don't have to wait a month. Actually if you want to go ahead and check back with us...your statement is going to print, it's not a month, your statement will be printing around the 23rd. So when your statement prints, when you get your next statement..."

Scott: "Okay."

Supervisor: "Call us and say 'I want to combine both into one.' And then everything would be at the low rate."

Scott: "Okay. Well then..."

Supervisor: "Do you understand?"

Scott: "That's sounds like an interesting option. As long as I have that transfer available at that time, I'd take advantage of it."

Supervisor: "Sure."

Scott: "Would I have to close my Platinum Card account?"

Supervisor: "It's a consolidation meaning we're going shut down that one, yes. We're going to move over to the Gold Card."

Scott: "I'd only have my one Gold Card account?"

Supervisor: "Correct. You're going to have one card only."

Scott: "I don't know. I just like to have both."

Supervisor: "You want to have both?"

Scott: "I don't know."

Supervisor: "Honestly I, me personally, I'm looking at this account..."

Scott: "Uh, huh."

Supervisor: "And just to be honest with you, this account looks really good. The other account, you haven't been active at all. The scoring on the other account doesn't look as good as this one here. Doesn't look very good."

Scott: "Really, why wouldn't it look good. I never was late on my other account?"
Note: So it seems scoring has been expanded to include activity as well as credit history. That's why I now always use every credit card account for at least 2 weeks each year so they show some type of activity.

Supervisor: "I know, but you haven't been using the credit card either."

Scott: "Well, since..."

Supervisor: "It's like, inactive."

Scott: "Well, since the beginning of this year. I'm about to activate it now. That's why I was hoping there was some offer, I'd be using it right now."

Supervisor: "Well, you have a couple options that I did give to you if you want to think them over and think about what you want to do and how you want to handle it."

Scott: "We can combine them right now and I can get the 6.9% right now?"

Supervisor: "I just locked you in. Actually, let me see, I locked you out but now, I would give it, give it at least two business days."

Scott: "Okay."
Note: Oh, now the story is changing. You've got to be careful and double-check all the terms while the rep is on the phone. If you move too fast you could make a mistake that could lock you in a high rate. Then you'll have to fight to get the deal you bargained for initially.

Supervisor: "If you do it now. You're going to go to 17.9%."
Note: See that. Be careful.

Scott: "Okay so, oh, so I could call back in two business days and do this."

Supervisor: "Or in a week. Yeah, wait until you call in and you check to see what the rate is. This system generates everything depending on how long that takes. Normally it should take about two days. Me personally, I'd give it at least a week. Just write down on your calendar 'call back, consolidate after a week.'"
Note: So it was, "you can do it right now" then "wait two business days" now it's "or in a week." What's the bottom line?

Scott: "Well you know what? That sounds like my best option."

Supervisor: "Mmm, I would do that. That's why I offered it to you."

Scott: "Alright, I originally misunderstood. I thought you meant that I would have to wait until I physically had the printed one in my hand."
Note: I'm just letting her save face since she did give me a good offer.

Supervisor: "Well you want to see the system stating that you are in that rate."

Scott: "Right, but if I call back, like you suggest, and ask if the system is saying that rate, then I'd be good to do it then."

Supervisor: "Correct."

Scott: "Okay, well, thank you for all your help."

Supervisor: "Have a good day. Bye now."

Scott: "Bye-bye."

CALL #6.02: KEEP ASKING

Reason For Call:	Loan shopping
Result:	Fight to get offer of 9.9% but that is still too high for my purposes.
Difficulty Level:	Easy
Call Time:	6 minutes
Total Saved:	$0.00
$/hour to make call:	$0.00

I called this card to see if I can get a new offer. I first met with the usual "no" from the rep. Again, you must always ask to speak to a supervisor! After that I was able to get the deal.

SUMMARY

The first bank representative said he can't do anything about the rate (14.47%) but he could let me know by mail when there's a low rate available. I also asked the rep if the supervisor could lower the rate. He said "No they can't." I said that I want to speak to one anyway. What happened? The supervisor immediately offered me 9.9%. It wasn't good enough for me so I passed on the offer. I ended up just entering this as a new credit offer in my notes for this bank.

TRANSCRIPT

Rep: "Thank you for calling Cattle Dog Bank. This is Mr. Slug, may I have your name and social security number?"

Scott: "Hi Mr. Slug. My name is Scott Bilker." (I give him the number.)

Rep: "And how can I help you today?"

Scott: "Umm, seems I have an opportunity here to transfer some money and I was wondering if there was any kind of low-rate offer available to entice me into doing so."

Rep: "Okay, and let me take a look and see what our rates currently are set at. It'll be just one second sir."

Scott: "Sure."

Rep: "Thank you."

Pause...

Rep: "Hello sir."

Scott: "Yes."

Rep: "Thank you for holding. Looks like the rate that is currently on your account is the only one we have available. Umm, whether it be for cash advances or promotionals or any, anything else. Umm, but that rate right now is at 14.47%."

Scott: "Oohh, yikes. Oh well, I guess I'm not going to be able to do anything. I mean, I've got $3,500 to transfer. I already talked to Golden Retriever Bank, that said that they couldn't do the promotional rate today. I'd just have to call back on Monday."

Rep: "Okay."

Scott: "I said, 'Okay.' But then I got my Cattle Dog Bankcard and I thought, you know, I'll give them a shot, why not give them $3,500 worth of business. Is there anyone there who might be able to help me?"
Note: Offering them business if they give me a good deal.

Rep: "Ah, no sir. Our marketing department set these rates. And ah right now they do not have anything else available."

Scott: "Hmmm."
Note: I wonder...are the reps lying or do they really believe this themselves?

Rep: "What, what we can do is as soon as I have something available I can have you notified by mail but I can't say, you know, it won't be as quick as Monday."

Scott: "Hmmm, is there any supervisor that might be able to help me?"

Rep: "Uh, no sir. Supervisors do not have any control over the rates on the account."
Note: This must be some kind of standard response in their scripts. Be persistent and do not be deterred by that response. Always ask to speak to a supervisor.

Scott: "Hmmm, well could I talk to one anyway?"

Rep: "Sure. Let me see if I can get one for you."

Scott: "Okay."

Rep: "Just one second sir."

On hold...

Rep: "Thank you for holding. I have Ms. Grub on the line, she'll be able to help you."

Scott: "Okay."

Rep: "Thank you."

Supervisor: "Good afternoon Mr. Bilker, Ms. Grub here. What can I do for you?"

Scott: "Hi Ms. Grub. I was calling to see if Cattle Dog Bank might have some kind of low-rate introductory offer to welcome me into their establishment now that I've finished with Mudi Bank. I have $3,500 to transfer and I will do it with Cattle Dog Bank if they have something for me now."
Note: Cattle Dog Bank recently purchased Mudi Bank and I just received the Cattle Dog Bankcard in the mail.

Supervisor: "Let me take a quick look for you. Can you hold?"

Scott: "Sure."

On hold...

Supervisor: "I can do 9.9% for 6 months."
Note: Well that was easy. Sure seemed like the supervisor did have some control over the rates. Either the first rep was: (1) lying, (2) trained to lie, or (3) uninformed.

Scott: "9.9%? Well, that's ah kinda alright. I tell you what. See Golden Retriever Bank is offering me 6.9%. And the only reason I didn't do it with them today is because I have to call back Monday, and I just got the Cattle Dog Bankcard and I thought, you know what, I might as well give them my business since I just got this new card."

Supervisor: "Gotcha. If they're offering you something...well how long are they offering it for, a year, or six months?"

Scott: "Six months."

Supervisor: "Six months. I'd make the call back on Monday to be honest. You're going to save 3 points."
Note: Talk about calling my bluff! I really believe she meant this but I want to press on to see what else they have for me.

Scott: "I know but I was hoping that I could get ah, something you know, similar with ah Cattle Dog Bank."

Supervisor: "Ah, I see."

Scott: "If I could get that then I'll go with Cattle Dog Bank because I might as well start something with you guys."
Note: This statement was a little weak. Something better like, "I'd rather do the transfer right now with you if you can match the rate. That would save me from having to call back on Monday."

Supervisor: "Sure."

Scott: "I haven't used this account..."

Supervisor: "You never know. We may be the same one someday too. Now with the way banks are merging together." (Giggle)

Scott: (Giggle) "That's true."

Supervisor: "Sure. Sorry I couldn't wow you with a 6.9% but I'd take them up on that for now."

Scott: "You can't match that?"

Supervisor: "No sir, unfortunately I can't. Wish I could."
Note: She sounded really genuine. I do believe that the 9.9%, is the best she could offer.

Scott: "Okay, but the best you could do is 9%?"

Supervisor: "9.9% right now."

Scott: "9.9%. Okay, well um, but thank you very much for trying Ms. Grub."

Supervisor: "Sure. Have a good weekend."

Scott: "You too."

Supervisor: "Bye-bye."

Scott: "Bye-bye."
Note: Looks like I have more loan-shopping to do today. ☺

CALL #6.03: NOT LOW ENOUGH

Reason For Call:	Reduce the rate
Result:	Didn't reduce the rate but did offer a 5.99% transfer deal. I punish them in the next call (#6.04).
Difficulty Level:	Hard
Call Time:	7 minutes
Total Saved:	$0.00
$/hour to make call:	$0.00

Reducing the rate was the goal of this call, but they wouldn't budge. They did offer a balance transfer, which can save money, but first I would have to clear off the balance then transfer the money back at the lower rate. Maybe they just think people are lazy and won't do it. In the next call I will punish them by transferring the balance to another bank. This call is for my friend Lewis Wilson (name changed).

SUMMARY

I called to attempt to get the rate reduced. The computer said the balance is $8,945.46 and available credit is $11,255 ($4,728 for cash advances). I spoke to Mr. Mosquito. He said that the purchase rate is 16.74% and cash advance rate is 19.99%. He wouldn't move on the rate, but he did offer 5.99% for a balance transfer, so I spoke to supervisor Ms. Glowworm. She also wouldn't move on the rate. I explained that I'm going to transfer my balance to Wetterhoun Bank, and she still didn't do anything. I said that when I do that they'll be making nothing, and then they'll offer me the 5.99%. They could have simply lowered my rate to 9.9% right then to satisfy me.

TRANSCRIPT

Voice Menu: "Please enter your 16-digit card number..."

Scott: (I enter the numbers.)

Voice Menu: "Please speak the last four digits of the social security number..."

Scott: (I speak the numbers.)

Voice Menu: "Please hold. For quality and training purposes your call may be monitored and recorded."

Scott: "Yours too."

Rep: "Welcome to customer service. My name is Mr. Mosquito, can I get your name please?"

Scott: "Lewis Wilson."

Rep: "Thank you, and if you could, Mr. Wilson, please verify your mother's maiden name."

Scott: (I give him the name.)

Rep: "Thank you. What can I do for you Mr. Wilson?"

Scott: "Okay Mr. Mosquito, what's my rate right now?"

Rep: "For purchases?"

Scott: "Yeah, let's go with that."

Rep: "Okay, let's take a look here. Your current interest rate on purchases is a variable prime plus 11.99%. Which settles 16.74%. Plus, you carry a cash balance which is at 19.99%."

Scott: "Okay, my balance right now, that $8,945.46. What's the rate on that?"

Rep: "That's split into 2. It's $6,400 is at your purchases, which is 16.74%. And $2,400 of it on cash advance, which is 19.99%."

Scott: "Okay. And I've got like $11,000 available?"

Rep: "That's right. We do have a lesser rate here, it's 5.9%, it's considered a balance transfer. But if you have a large purchase that you want to do we can send out a check on in. And it would be at 5.9% until the first day of September."

Scott: "Yeah, you know what I would be interested in doing something like that. However, these things would stay at these high rates?"

Note: You must verify the rates for all existing balances before doing any transfers. If the other balance will still be at a high rate, then you'd only be saving money on the new transfer. The goal would be to make sure that all outstanding debt, at least for each bank, is at the lowest possible rate.

Rep: "That's correct."

Scott: "So, now, how long have I had this card?"

Rep: "You have been with us almost 8 years."

Scott: "How does my payment record look?"

Rep: "Above average. It looks like there were a couple of issues somewhere in the past of some sort. I'm not sure. Not really true payment issues, it's more the size of the payment rather than the timeliness."

Scott: "Alright, well above average payment options, but I think this rate is just too high. You know, 16.4% on purchases, 19.9%, and you know that combination of those rates right now is like over 17% on that whole balance."

Rep: "Well, I can see if there is anything that I can do on the purchase rate, but the cash advance rate will be remaining at 19.9%."

Scott: "I mean the entire rate at whatever my balance is right now."

Rep: "It's not. That's not really the way to look at it right now. Because most of your balance is not in cash advance, it's not split evenly."

Scott: "I understand. But I'm just going to ask you if you can reduce the rate on all the balance. The entire balance."

Rep: "Okay. First of all, the cash advance balance. That will be at 19.99%. We don't change that interest rate. That's clearly set forth in our cardholder agreement. As far as the purchases, let me take a look here. It's actually not giving me any options for a decreased interest rate. That's the lowest rate it's showing available."

Scott: "Okay. Well, I guess I'm going to have to transfer my balance to another card because, I'll tell you what, these rates are totally insane. 17% on purchases, 20% on cash advances. I've got a Wetterhoun Bankcard and they're offering me a nice low rate, like 5.9%. And I know you guys are offering me a 5.9%, however these rates won't change. I mean I could transfer my entire balance to them, I've got plenty of available credit to do that. And I won't be able to use this card really, with a rate this high. I mean it just; it's leaving me no option. I'd think that being a valued customer for this much time is worth something here, and not budging on these rates is not showing me anything."

Rep: "I'm afraid there is nothing that I can do on the interest rate."

Scott: "Well, can you transfer me to someone who might be able to do something? Like maybe your supervisor."

Rep: "My supervisor can't, we actually have departments that handle interest rate decreases of, you know, if you say that you are going to transfer your balance, you're not eligible to actually go there. Or if you were going to say close your account, and actually, we don't have any access to go there either. If you request to close, we would just close."

Scott: "Right."
Note: I guess there's no way to get to that department. Why do they have that department?

Rep: "So, I can transfer you to a supervisor if that's your wish. They have the same options I do as far as interest rates go."
Note: I hear that all the time, "the supervisor can't do it either." As you have learned from many, many other calls, the supervisors can do it.

Scott: "That's my wish."

Rep: "Okay one moment."

On hold...

Rep: "Thank you for holding. I have a supervisor on the line as you requested."

Scott: "Okay great."

Supervisor: "Hi, my name is Ms. Glowworm. How can I help you today?"

Scott: "Hi, Ms. Glowworm. I was calling to see if you guys would lower my rate, because I've got to tell you, 17% for purchases, 20% for cash advances, whatever that amounts to on my balance right now, is totally unacceptable. After being with Shih Tzu Bank for 8 years with a great payment history, I just don't feel that these are fair. And the bottom line really Ms. Glowworm, and I know you don't make policies, you personally, so don't feel like I'm attacking you cause I'm not..."
Note: You don't want to attack the reps, unless they insult you, so I'm letting Ms. Glowworm know that it's the "big bad bank's" policy, not hers personally. On the other hand, it may not be wise to give them an excuse to stop working to get you a better deal.

Supervisor: "That's okay."

Scott: "It's that, Shih Tzu Bankcard is a business. And I deal with other businesses. I have a Wetterhoun Bankcard, their offering me a...My next call will have to be to them to transfer my balance, if I can't do something here. I know you can't give me 0%, but I just don't feel I'm being treated well, after being a good customer for so long. Is there anything that you can do for me Ms. Glowworm?"

Supervisor: "I do not have a lower rate for you at this time. It can be called back on periodically, but no, right now we don't have anything lower to offer you."

Scott: "Okay. There's nothing that can be done."

Supervisor: "Right."

Scott: "Because right now Shih Tzu Bank is making some money. But in 10 minutes they'll be making nothing. I mean I'll have nothing to offer them. You know how they don't have something to offer me, I'm not going to have anything to offer them."

Supervisor: "I understand your position there, but I don't have anything that I can change it to. Nothing lower."

Scott: "Okay, you know what Ms. Glowworm, what's the payment address?"

Supervisor: (Gives me the address.)

Scott: "I've got to tell you that I can't believe that after being a good customer for this long, that Shih Tzu Bank is gonna try to continue to gouge me like this when I have so many credit options. It doesn't make sense to me Ms. Glowworm. Do you think that policy even makes sense?"

Supervisor: "Well, I mean you have to be one to retain your business, but I don't have a way to do that by offering you a lower interest rate, it's just not available."

Scott: "Alright, well, that'll be all."

Supervisor: "Alright, have a good day."

Scott: "You too, bye-bye."

CALL #6.04: PUNISHING BY TRANSFER

Reason For Call:	Shop for rate, transfer, and punish
Result:	9.99% fixed transfer offer
Difficulty Level:	Medium
Call Time:	13 minutes
Total Saved:	$3,727.44
$/hour to make call:	$17,203.57

The bank from call #6.03 (Shih Tzu Bank), didn't reduce the rate. I went shopping with another card that I had called the previous month (Wetterhoun Bank) to cash in on the deal they offered. This transfer was the punishment for call #6.03 because they did not accommodate my needs! I must spank their bottom lines. ☺

SUMMARY

I called to make a transfer from Shih Tzu Bank (call #6.03). The current balance is $16,989.30 and available credit is $32,710.70. I spoke to Mrs. Gnat in the transfer department. She wouldn't give me the 6.9% that I was promised by Mr. Monarch Butterfly when I called last (call #5.09). I had her ask someone about it and was told that it's only available if I stayed at 16.99%. I did a transfer of $9,000 at 8.9% until April then it goes to 9.99% fixed. After reviewing the recording from 1/31 it certainly seems that Mr. Monarch Butterfly offered me the 6.9% without any other conditions—oh, well they got me. As soon as this transfer is complete I'm going to transfer the money back to the Shih Tzu Bank (call #6.03) since they offered 5.9%.

Savings: $9,000 at 17% with $186 monthly payments is 82.32 payments. At 9.99% it's 62.28 payments or a savings of 20.04 payments which is $3,727.44. Actually, the savings are going to be much more since there are a few months at 8.9% plus I'm going to transfer it back at 5.9%.

TRANSCRIPT

Voice Menu: "Welcome to Wetterhoun Bank."

Scott: "Okay." (I enter the account number using the phone.)

Voice Menu: "Please hold and the next available specialist will be with you."

Scott: "Right."

Voice Menu: "Thank you for your patience...Please have the following information available..."

On hold...

Rep: "Wetterhoun Bank at your service. This is Mrs. Gnat in the balance transfer department. May I complete a balance transfer for you today?"

Scott: "Very likely so, Mrs. Gnat."

Rep: "Okay."

Scott: "First I just want to look at my account real quick to make sure everything is what I believe it is."

Rep: "Okay, let me bring it up for you. What is your name please?"

Scott: "Lewis Wilson."

Rep: "And the last four numbers of your account Mr. Wilson."

Scott: (I give her the numbers.)

Rep: "This is your Wetterhoun Bankcard."

Scott: "Right. Okay, now the rate on there should be like 9.9%?"

Rep: "The fixed rate is 9.99%."

Scott: "Okay, and then my balance transfer rate was something like 6.9%?"
Note: That was an offer from call #5.09.

Rep: "What I have is 8.9%, which is good through your April statement closing date."

Scott: "Last time I spoke with, on the 31st of January, umm, Mr. Monarch Butterfly. He said that when he lowered that rate, he also said that he can drop the transfer rate to 6.9% until July."

Rep: "Umm hmm, and that is what he had available. I don't have that available today. That was an offer for that call."

Scott: "Okay, so the best you can do is 8.9%?"
Note: Another important point is that if you're calling to do a transfer, and you do get a good offer that day, be totally prepared to take advantage of it on the spot because it may be limited to that moment.

Rep: "The only thing I have to offer today is the 8.9% until April."

Scott: "Until April. April is like in a month."

Rep: "Two months yeah."

Scott: "Uh, that's just…"

Rep: "It's been on there for awhile, we put it back on in November."

Scott: "Yeah, I've got like $9,000 I wanted to transfer but that's just not gonna work. I'll have to call other places first. I mean, if you can do that until July, even at the 8.9% I'll do it now."
Note: That's a complete bluff. I'm going to make a transfer on this call to punish Shih Tzu Bank.

Rep: "I wish I could do that, but I don't have anything available. No way to extend that out."

Scott: "That was only 15 days ago that they offered that to me."

Rep: "I know it, I know it. They do change every day."

Scott: "Is there anyone you can ask about this right now, and I can hold."

Rep: "Yeah, if you would like to hold, Mr. Wilson, I can ask about that. Can you hold on for a moment?"

Scott: "Okay, you can let them know that it's going to be about $9,000."

Rep: "I will. Hold right on."

On hold…

Rep: "Hi Mr. Wilson. Thank you very much for holding, I'm sorry to keep you."

Scott: "Okay."

Rep: "I did speak with a manager regarding that, and what happened was a couple of weeks ago we changed the contract rate on your card. We lowered it to the 9.99%."

Scott: "Right."
Note: We took care of that in call #5.09.

Rep: "And I don't have that to offer, but the department that actually lowered your contract rate may have that. Let me get you in touch with them."

Scott: "Okay."

Rep: "I'll explain the situation and see if that's available for you this morning. Okay?"

Scott: "That would be great Mrs. Gnat."

Rep: "Alright, hold on just a moment I'll get someone on the line."

Scott: "Okay."

On hold...

Scott: "Suddenly things are popping up." (Talking to myself.)

Rep: "Thanks again for holding. I did speak with someone in that department apparently the 6.99% is available, if you keep the 16.99% contract rate. With the 9.99% fixed that's a rate that goes across the board so we really don't have a promotion to offer at all, with the 9.99%, except that 8.9% until April. So they are not able to do that either."

Scott: (Sighs.) "Alright, let me see."

Rep: "I'm trying every avenue, but I can't get anywhere."

Scott: (Whispering) "Let's see, Pug Bank 7.9%..." (Out loud) "Oh wait, it would be 8.9% until April, then 9.9% fixed."

Rep: "And then 9.9% fixed."

Scott: "Okay. Well you know what, let's go ahead anyway."

Rep: "Okay. Now what I do need is the account number of what you would like to transfer..."

Rep continues to ask me questions about the bank that we're doing the transfer to, name, account number, address, etc. Be sure to be prepared with that information.

Rep: "Now, keep in mind I am charging a transaction fee of 3%, I count that as $40 total for you. So any further fees are waived today."

Scott: "Further fees? What further fees would there be?"

Rep: "Well, further fees if you call back you would have another transaction fee."

Scott: "Oh, if I call back today?"

Rep: "Even if you call back today. Now another thing that I can do is direct deposit any portion of your available credit into your checking account..."

Scott: "No, that wouldn't be needed right now."

Rep: "Okay."

Scott: "So it's 3% capped at what?"

Rep: "$40."

Scott: "Okay, well that's good. Alright capped at $40 fine."

Rep: "So if you have any other transfers..."

Scott: "I don't right now. I'm not prepared to do that now."

Rep: "Alright, well let me finish this one up for you. I will send you out a confirmation number by mail as well. May I have your approval to complete this transaction?"

Scott: "Yes."

Rep: "Anything else I can help you with today Mr. Wilson?"

Scott: "No, that will be all Mrs. Gnat."

Rep: "Alright, well thank you very much for doing business with us once again."

Scott: "Alright you have a good day."

Rep: "You too. Thanks."

Scott: "Bye."

Rep: "Bye."

CALL #6.05: CALL ABOUT TRANSFER FEES

Reason For Call:	Transfer revenge for another bank
Result:	Transferred money at 6.9% and got transfer fee waived.
Difficulty Level:	Easy
Call Time:	7 minutes
Total Saved:	$138.00
$/hour to make call:	$1,182.86

This call demonstrates that you can sometimes eliminate transaction fees by calling even if the offer in the letter you receive says that fees will be charged.

SUMMARY

Spoke with Ms. Yellowjacket about 6.9% transfer offer on Larissa's account. The letter mentioned that there was a cash advance fee, but upon calling I found that there was no fee if I did the transfer by phone. That's because this bank considers it a balance transfer if you call, as opposed to a cash advance, using checks.

The money was transferred to Sheepdog Bank as a first step in my revenge because they wouldn't waive the $25 late fee when I called on 10/2 (story in chapter 4). I transferred $1,500 tonight. I'll still owe about $500. Once that's paid I'll threaten to close my Sheepdog Bank account and see what happens. Saved about $98 in interest for 6 months plus the $40 transfer fee.

TRANSCRIPT

Voice Menu: "Thank you for calling. For Elkhound Bankcard press 1. For faster service please enter your account number."

Scott: "I'll take the slow service. Give me the slow service. Just give me a human!"

Rep: "Hello, my name is Ms. Yellowjacket. How may I help you?

Scott: "Hi Ms. Yellowjacket, my account number is..." (I give her the number.)

Rep: "Okay, and is this Larissa?"
Note: Do I sound like a Larissa? ☺

Scott: "No that's my wife."

Rep: "Okay, and is Mrs. Bilker available?"

Scott: "She's available."

Rep: "Okay, could I speak with her please?"

Larissa: "Hello."

Rep: "Hi, Mrs. Bilker."

Larissa: "Yes."

Rep: "Hi, this is Ms. Yellowjacket with Elkhound Bankcard, could you please verify your mother's maiden name."

Larissa: (Gives her the name.)

Rep: "Okay, and what information are you looking for on the account."

Larissa: "What information am I looking for on the account?"

Rep: "Um hmm."

Scott: "Uh, I'll talk about it."

Larissa: "Oh, can I have my husband talk about my account for me?"

Rep: "You can go ahead and put him on the line ma'am."

Larissa: "Okay, thanks."

Scott: "Hi Ms. Yellowjacket."

Rep: "Hi."

Scott: "Okay, where were we? Okay, is everything cool."

Rep: "Yeah, everything's fine."

Scott: "Okay, good. Okay, I got a nice 6.9% balance transfer offer. I'm looking at it right now."

Rep: "Um hmm."

Scott: "And could you just tell me the terms on that real quick."

Rep: "What types of terms are you looking for sir?"

Scott: "Well, umm, is there a transfer fee involved?"

Rep: "No, there is no fee. You will receive the interest rate of 6.9% until June. Once that rate is done it will go to whatever the purchase rate is at that point in time. They will receive their funds within two weeks from the time that it's authorized. And no, there is no fee."

Scott: "Great, so no cash advance fee, nothing?"
Note: That's not what the letter says but it's fine with me.

Rep: "Nothing, no fee."

Scott: "That sounds great. Let's go, I'm ready."

Rep: "Alright, one moment."

Rep: "And what is your home phone number with area code?"

Scott: (I give her the number.)

Rep: "Okay, and what is the name of the company that you are paying off?"

Scott: "Sheepdog Bank."

Rep: "And what's the account number?"

Scott: (I give her the number.)

Rep: "And what's the amount?"

Scott: "Her (Larissa's) max is $1,500, can we do the entire amount?"

Rep: "That would be fine."

Rep: "Okay. And the PO box for payment?"

Scott: (I give her the address.)

Rep: "And what is the 1-800 number for customer service."

Scott: (I give her the number.)

Rep: "Okay, we'll go ahead and take care of the balance transfer for you. Let me just verify the information."

Scott: "Okay."

Rep: "Upon approval we will issue payments to your creditors and transfer your balance. The amount of the transfer will be posted upon date of payment of the balance transfer, not as a cash advance so there is no transaction fee."

Scott: "Okay."

Rep: "Please continue to make any necessary payments to the other account in order to avoid late charges, as it will take up to two weeks for the transfer to take place. You may request additional balance transfers if you have the available credit up until the 30th of November."

Scott: "Okay."

Rep: "After this date, additional balance transfers are not available until one month after this offer expires. The balance transfer rate of 6.9% is effective until your billing cycle that ends in June. If you miss a payment, and do not make this payment by your next payment due date, or since your last anniversary date you missed the payment, and do not make this payment by your next payment due date, that means if you missed two months consecutively, the rate will increase to 22.49%."

Scott: "Ouch!"
Note: That's is an obscene penalty for being late. Oh, and they'll also be charging a flat late fee on top of the interest rate hike. That's why it's so important to pay on time. Even if you have to borrow from one card to pay another!

Rep: "Okay, balance transfers are not considered qualified purchases for purposes of establishing your annual percentage rate, and you do not receive a cash back bonus award on the balance transfer. You have any questions sir?"

Scott: "Nope."

Rep: "Alright is there anything else I can help you with today?"

Scott: "That will be all for tonight Ms. Yellowjacket."

Rep: "Alright, well thanks for calling Elkhound Bankcard. Goodbye."

Scott: "Bye-bye."

CALL #6.06: RAISE MY LIMIT

Reason For Call:	Credit Limit Increase
Result:	Increased limit on the spot by $500 and put in application to raise to $5,000.
Difficulty Level:	Easy
Call Time:	3 minutes
Total Saved:	$0.00 (however I will save when I use the offer in the future.)
$/hour to make call:	$0.00

It's always great to get low rate offers. However, if you don't have a high enough credit limit to use the offer effectively then it doesn't matter. Of course, you want to save as much money as possible so you should take the best deal. Just be sure to always ask for a credit line increase in conjunction with a low-rate offer to further maximize savings.

In this call I'm just seeing how high they'll go. I'm going to take advantage of this offer shortly, but first I want to get the limit as high as possible.

SUMMARY

I apply for a higher limit on my Iceland Dog Bankcard to take advantage of the 5.9% offer. My limit is a measly $1,600 and they approved $2,100 on the spot (because of my good credit), but I needed to give them more information to get the limit raised to what I requested, $5,000.

TRANSCRIPT

Scott: "Hello?"

Rep: "This is Iceland Dog Bank. I'm Ms. Firefly and your name please?"

Scott: "My name is Scott Bilker."

Rep: "And the card number please."

Scott: (I give her the number.)

Rep: "And what is your mother's maiden name sir?"

Scott: (I give her the name.)

Rep: "And how can I help you?"

Scott: "Okay, last I checked my credit max was $1,400. Is that still true?"

Rep: "No it's sixteen hundred now."

Scott: "Oh, $1,600. Alright..."

Rep: "You want it increased to $2,100?"
Note: That was easy. I didn't even have to ask.

Scott: "Um, well I tell ya, I've got this 5.9% fixed APR that I'd like to take advantage of and $1,600, even $2,100, is still pretty small."
Note: I know I've got that up $500 so I'm pushing for more.

Rep: "How much did you have in mind?"

Scott: "Um, well how much can I...how high can I go?"

Rep: "$2,100 is all that's automatic, anything else would be reviewed with a credit bureau and you'll also have to put in an application."
Note: You may also have an "automatic" credit increase available. Call about it today!

Scott: "Okay, that's fine. Why don't we, why don't we go for $5,000?"

Rep: "Okay, your total income?"

Scott: (I tell her the income.)

Rep: "Your occupation?"

Scott: "Electrical Engineer."

Rep: "Where at?"

Scott: "Naval Air Engineering Center in Lakehurst, NJ"

Rep: "Okay, ah you'll receive a letter on that within two weeks. If you need to know sooner call back in about five days."

Scott: "Okay, great."

Rep: "Thank you for your call."

Scott: "Okay, bye-bye."

Rep: "Good bye."

CALL #6.07: 23.9% CARD WITH 6.9% DEAL!

Reason For Call:	Lower the interest rate
Result:	Took advantage of low rate offer to transfer balance from 13% to 6.9%.
Difficulty Level:	Easy
Call Time:	7 minutes
Total Saved:	$323.43
$/hour to make call:	$2,772.26

This call is for my friend Mike Bailey. He's shopping around on his cards with a zero balance to see if any want to give him a deal. This particular card has an incredibly high interest rate of 23.9% but that doesn't mean they don't have any lower-rate deals. As usual, you must call to find out if anything is available.

SUMMARY

The rate on this card is an unbelievable 23.9%. I called to see if they had any transfer deals. The first bank representative said "no" so I asked to speak to a supervisor. I spoke to Ms. Diving Beetle and she offered 6.9% for 6 months so we transferred $10,700 from Otterhound Bank that has a rate of 13%. The savings of going from 13% to 6.9% for six months, are $323.43.

TRANSCRIPT

Voice Menu: "Welcome to Stabyhoun Bankcard. For Quality and training purposes your call may be monitored and recorded."

Scott: "Yeah, yours too..."

Rep: "Customer service. My name is Mr. Water Bug. Can I have your name please?"

Scott: "Hi Mr. Water Bug, my name is Mike Bailey."

Rep: "Thank you. And your mother's maiden name?"

Scott: (I give him the name.)

Rep: "And how may I help you?"

Scott: "Okay. Right now what's my balance?"

Rep: "Okay, let me see. I'm showing, you have a zero balance."

Scott: "No balance. Okay very good. Alright, now I'll tell you what. What's my credit max? About $8,100?"

Rep: "The credit line is $11,350."

Scott: "Okay $11,350. Okay that's great. Now, I'll tell you what, I'm going to be doing a balance transfer, and I'm looking through all my cards to see which one is going to give me a good deal. What is the best deal I can get from Stabyhoun Bank right now?"

Rep: "We don't have any offers at this time unfortunately."
Note: Here we go again. The first rep usually doesn't know what's going on or may be trained to deter you from pursuing a better deal.

Scott: "No offers. How about if I transfer $10,700?"

Rep: "Right."

Scott: "You guys don't want the business?"

Rep: "Unfortunately, we don't have any offers."

Scott: "Okay. You know what, can I talk to your supervisor?"

Rep: "Okay. Hold on one second. Stay on hold for a supervisor Mr. Bailey."

Scott: "Okay."

Rep: "It will be one moment, hopefully."

Scott: "Alright."

On hold...

Rep: "We are still on hold, it is taking too long. Would you like to continue to hold?"

Scott: "What seems to be the problem?"

Rep: "There is no problem at all. It's just a busy time."

Scott: "Do you have a special balance transfer department by any chance?"

Rep: "That's the one I am getting to."

Scott: "Yeah, okay, I'll wait for them."

Note: Be patient, it's worth the wait.

Rep: "Alright, no problem."

On hold...

Rep: "Mr. Bailey."

Scott: "Yes."

Rep: "I have a supervisor on the line for you sir."

Scott: "Okay great."

Rep: "Thank you."

Supervisor: "Hi Mr. Bailey. My name is Ms. Diving Beetle and I'm a manager here at customer service. How can I help you today?"

Scott: "Hi Ms. Diving Beetle. Well, I'm calling because I'm about to make a balance transfer of about $10,500 and I'll do it if I can get a good offer from Stabyhoun Bank. But my current rate, what is it 23.9%."

Supervisor: "Yeah, it does look like the account went into default a couple of months ago due to some late payments. Let me take a look to see what we can do here."
Note: Defaults and late payments are obviously a problem. However, you must always call no matter what your current situation is. Start today and it won't be long before you're in a better position and getting better deals.

Scott: "Okay, we were having some difficulty at that time and I have since taken control of making sure everything is being paid on time. That's why it's clear right now."

Supervisor: "It looks like the lowest rate I have to offer to you at this time for balance transfers would be a 6.9% for a length of 6 months."
Note: Pretty good deal for a defaulted account with late payments—see what I mean. ☺

Scott: "Okay, that'll work."

Supervisor: "Would you like to go ahead and do that."

Scott: "Sure, 6.9% for 6 months?"

Supervisor: "That's correct."

Scott: "Okay, great. I'm ready to do it Ms. Diving Beetle."

Supervisor: "Just one second here. Let me pull all the information up. And can you verify for me again your mother's maiden name?"

Scott: (I give her the name.)

Supervisor: "And do you have your Stabyhoun Bankcard available there?"

Scott: "It is in my hand as we speak."
Note: Always have the physical card available. They want to make sure that the cardholder is actually authorizing the transaction. And the cardholder should be holding the card. ☺

Supervisor: "Okay, can you turn that card over and read me the last 3 digits located on the back of the card on the signature strip."

Scott: (I give her the numbers.)

Supervisor: "Okay, one moment. Okay, whenever you are ready. What I will need will be the account number of the creditor you'd transfer."

Scott: (I give her the number.)

Supervisor: "And the amount."

Scott: "The amount is $10,700."

Supervisor: "$10,700 even?"

Scott: "That's correct."

Supervisor: "Is that with Otterhound Bank credit services?"

Scott: "Yes, I have the payment address but it sounds like you already have it."

Supervisor: "Yeah we do. We keep some of the more common ones in our system."

Scott: "Yeah, I guess the first 6 digits are the bank, right?"

Supervisor: "Right. That does verify the bank. Give me just a moment."

Scott: "Okay."

Supervisor: "Alright let me put you on hold just a moment while I go ahead and process this for you."

Scott: "Great."

On hold...

Supervisor: "Thank you so much for your patience in holding Mr. Bailey. Let me just verify the account number..." (She reads me the numbers.)

Scott: "That is correct."

Supervisor: "You know that there is no grace period on the finance charges for a balance transfer. So they will begin to accrue immediately once it has been posted to the account."

Scott: "Okay."

Supervisor: "And any payments or credits sent in will go to the lower rate first."
Note: In other words, when Mike sends in his payments, they'll apply that payment to the balance with the lower rate. This effectively locks-in any other balances at higher rates for the term of the offer, thus making more money for the bank. The way to avoid that is to be sure that the account balance is zero before using the transfer offer, as is the case here. You can get your account balance to be zero by using another credit card to clear the balance then transferring the balance back.

Scott: "Right."

Supervisor: "Okay, I will go ahead and get it done for you in 7 to 10 days."

Scott: "Okay, thank you."

Supervisor: "Okay. Anything else?"

Scott: "That will be all."

Supervisor: "Okay, you have a great day."

Scott: "You too, Ms. Diving Beetle."

Supervisor: "Goodbye."

Scott: "Bye."

CHAPTER 7

NEGOTIATING SETTLEMENTS

WHAT ARE SETTLEMENTS?

A settlement is when you negotiate with your credit card bank to reduce the total amount you owe. You may, for example, have a balance of $5,000 and have lost the ability to make payments for any number of reasons, like job loss, divorce, or other hardships. You can call the bank and ask to speak to their settlement department, explain your situation, and make a deal to reduce the balance to say $2,500.

On the surface, this seems even better than reducing the interest rate! Not only does the rate go to zero but you also got to spend $5,000 on stuff and only repay $2,500. Sound too good to be true? That's because it is!

First of all, if you're already paying on time, the bank will most likely not make any settlements on the account because there's no need for them to deal with you. You're already paying on time so why settle for less?

Even if you tell them that you're headed for trouble they won't know that for sure until you actually stop paying. That's why debt negotiation companies need you to stop paying your bills. You'll have to be in a seriously bad position before they can make any settlements. Of course, this will have a negative effect on your credit record.

I do not suggest that you stop paying your bills. What I am saying is that you're not likely to be able to negotiate a good settlement unless you have several past-due payments. That's how the banks seem to operate.

If you are seriously considering doing a settlement, and you have already missed several payments, then you'll want to start saving money in an account. This way you will be able to pay off any settlement you do negotiate.

I know you're thinking, "Scott, I already cannot pay my bills so how can I put money aside for a settlement? If I had the money I would just pay my bills?" That's a fair comment. However, the reality is that to get a good settlement, that will eliminate most of your debt, you will have to come up with cash.

Let's say you haven't paid on the account for 6 months and then your financial situation changes and you come into more money somehow; a better paying job, inheritance, lottery winnings, etc. You may want to consider saving that money and negotiating a settlement.

Another source of money is a second mortgage on your home. However, I must caution you that this can be risky. That's because you're going to be using your home as collateral for debt that is probably unsecured. On the other hand, this will enable you to pay off your unsecured debt at a very reduced amount. The trade-off may be worthwhile as long as you are not in danger of going bankrupt after the settlements are paid with the second mortgage.

Credit counselors and debt negotiators may tell you that you won't be able to negotiate a good settlement with your creditors without their help. That is simply not true! You should call your bank to see what you can do yourself and compare that to what any other company is promising.

Debt negotiation companies typically charge 25% of what they save you. So if they settle a debt for 50%, when you add in their fee, it's like it was settled for 62.5%. That is why I always opt to make the initial calls myself. I can then use my results to determine whether it's better to settle the account myself or use the services of a professional debt negotiator.

Keep in mind that settled accounts may be reported as such to credit bureaus. This can negatively affect your credit history. When you're negotiating a settlement with the bank, try to make it a part of the settlement agreement that they report the account "paid in full." This would look the best on your credit report. However, that condition may not be possible to attain in most cases.

You may also have to pay taxes on the difference between the settled amount and the true balance! You could be sent a Form 1099, which will show the amount forgiven in the settlement as income.

When you contact the bank to negotiate a settlement, be sure that they are clear that your only other option is consulting a bankruptcy attorney. They must be convinced that they can either: (1) deal with you now and get something or (2) you'll go bankrupt and they'll get nothing! However, this does not guarantee that they will offer you a good settlement.

How much is a "good" settlement?

I consider "good" to be 50%, or less, of the outstanding balance, as the amount needed to pay off the account. If you do work out a good settlement, then be sure the bank puts it in writing before you send them the check! You want to be absolutely certain that once you pay the agreed amount, the debt is concluded. Of course, if you have exhausted all your options for settlements, then you may want to consult a bankruptcy attorney in your state.

Lastly, you need to be prepared with all your information when you call the bank. They might not be able to give you a settlement option on the spot. They may ask you for key information, and/or make you submit an application before deciding what kind of deal they are willing to offer you. When you call, be prepared to disclose financial details like mortgage amount, income, explanation of why, etc.

This chapter contains three calls that end with two settlements for a friend. I have, of course, changed her name.

CALL #7.01: NOT SETTLING FOR 90%

Reason For Call:	Negotiate settlement
Result:	Offer of 90% settlement
Difficulty Level:	Medium
Call Time:	10 minutes
Total Saved:	$476.00
$/hour to make call:	$2,856.00

In this call I'm negotiating a settlement for a friend, Cindy Rogers. I cannot initially get the deal I want. However, they said they'd consider it and get back to me. Well, they did get back to me but didn't offer anything more than what was offered in this call. Personally, $476 is not enough of a savings here to do the settlement—in my opinion.

SUMMARY

As Cindy's friend, I called and spoke to Mr. Mite. I explained the situation, and he transferred me to the proper department. Mrs. Scorpion made a memo that I can talk about the account and discuss doing a settlement for Cindy.

Mrs. Scorpion said that Cindy is eligible for a 90% settlement on her balance of $4,766. They'd reduce that amount by 10%.

How does a "settlement" work? It will negatively impact her credit for 7 years and Cindy may have to pay taxes on difference between the settled amount and the original balance.

Mrs. Scorpion is going to submit this to a supervisor. If they do accept this Cindy will have 14 days to pay.

I asked for a 50% settlement and said that Cindy has a friend that will lend her the money, but she'll only borrow the money if she can pay off the account in full. Mrs. Scorpion filled out a form to turn in to her superiors. She said that she'd be in contact with me by Thursday or Friday morning.

Possible savings of $476, not really too much.

TRANSCRIPT

Rep: "Thank you for calling customer service. Mr. Mite, may I have your account number please."

Cindy: (Gives him the number.)

Rep: "And your name."

Cindy: "Cindy Rogers."

Rep: "And your mother's maiden name Ms. Rogers."

Cindy: (Gives him the name.)

Rep: "Thank you. And what can I help you with?"

Cindy: "Um, actually, I'd like to know if a friend of mine that does my bills for me can speak about my account with you?"

Rep: "Sure."

Cindy: "Okay, thanks."

Scott: "Hello."

Rep: "Hello sir. What can I help you with?"

Scott: "My name is Scott. What's your name?"

Rep: "Mr. Mite."

Scott: "Alright, I'm helping Cindy with her bills and she's come to a fairly dire financial position. If you look back on her history, I'm sure you can see that she's been late and having trouble with this account."

Rep: "Sure I can see that."

Scott: "Well, I'm hoping that there is some kind of way we could negotiate better payoff terms or an amount because she's running out of options. Would you be the person to speak with about this?"

Rep: "Okay, about getting a better payment option?"

Scott: "I mean like this. Another friend of mine was having some trouble with their Pug Bank account and they, Pug Bank, cut the balance in half if my friend paid that amount in full. Can you do that for her, Mr. Mite?"

Rep: "Well let me take a look."

Pause...

Rep: "Let me transfer you over to that department okay?"

Scott: "Okay."

Rep: "Hold on one moment..."

On hold...

Rep: "Komondor Bankcard services, this is Ms. Scorpion speaking. Can I have your account number please?"

Scott: "Hi Ms. Scorpion, actually I'm helping a friend of mine with her account. Let me get her on the phone, okay?"

Rep: "Yes, may I have your account number please?"

Cindy: (Gives her the number).

Rep: "And your name and address for verification."

Cindy: (Gives her the address).

Rep: "Okay, I am showing that there is a minimum payment of $311 due on this account. Can you pay that today?"

Cindy: "Actually, I would like a friend of mine who handles my bills to speak to you about my account."

Scott: "That would be me."

Rep: "Would you like for me to put that authorization on the account for him to discuss it in the future too?"

Cindy: "Uh, yeah. Thanks."

Rep: "Okay, what is his name."

Cindy: "Scott Bilker."

Rep: "Okay, I'll put a permanent memo on here that Scott can discuss the account when he calls in."

Cindy: "Okay. Thanks. Bye-bye."

Rep: "Bye. Okay, Mr. Bilker."

Scott: "Yes."

Rep: "What did you want to discuss?"

Scott: "Okay, well, I've been helping Cindy out with her bills here, and she's having some trouble with the account, just in general. And actually another friend of mine had a Pug Bank account and umm, what happened with them was when they were having trouble, Pug Bank cut the total balance due in half if it was paid in full in one payment."

Rep: "In other words you wanted to discuss possibly doing a settlement on the account?"

Scott: "That's correct."

Rep: "Okay, let me see what she would be eligible for...She would be eligible for a 90% settlement, which would be $4,766."

Scott: "That might not cut it, Ms. Scorpion. I'll tell you why, because her options right now are basically just, umm bankruptcy. I mean that's basically her option."

Rep: "Okay."

Scott: "In which case it'll be negotiated basically to zero. However, she has..."

Rep: "What about, is it that she would want to settle for?"

Scott: "She can settle up to 50%, and I'll tell you what her situation is. She has a friend of hers that is going to lend her half that money for that account. But she is only going to borrow it if she can pay it off in full, otherwise it's not worth it."
Note: This approach is really a deal breaker. It explains why Cindy doesn't have the money now but how she can get it under certain conditions.

Rep: "Okay. Now there is a couple of things I need to advise you of regarding a settlement. The way that works is that it negatively impacts your credit report for 7 years that this account is settled. And she may have to pay taxes and have to get a 1099 on the remaining bill. These are two things that she needs to be aware of."

Scott: "Okay."

Rep: "Okay, now what I can do is submit this to a supervisor and see if they will accept it for 50%. So, if that is what you would like me to do, I'd put that through and you know, see what they do with it."

Scott: "Uh, when would I be able to hear back on that."

Rep: "Umm, I would try to call you back within the next 2 days."

Scott: "Okay. Alright Ms. Scorpion, are you going to call me directly?"

Rep: "Sure, hang on one second. What I have to do is complete a form, so I am going to need to ask you some questions. Hopefully you are going to be able to answer them."

Scott: "Okay."

Rep: "Bear with me one minute. Okay, 50% would be $2,648.23."

Scott: "Okay."

Rep: "And if they do accept this she would have 14 days from the date of the acceptance to make the payment. She would be making that in one installment then?"

Scott: "Yes."

Rep: "Okay. Now, do you know if she owns or rents her own residence?"

Scott: "Owns."

Rep: "Okay, and in order to complete this form I need roughly her monthly income and monthly expenses."

Scott: "Okay. Roughly..."

Rep: "Just an estimate."

Scott: "Uh, I think like $200 a week. What's that; $800 a month?"
Note: I'm just winging it here. I didn't have all her information. That's why you should be completely prepared with the numbers prior to calling.

Rep: "$800 a month. And roughly her monthly expenses?"

Scott: "Uh, umm, well much more than that. Ha. I think about...does that include food and everything?"

Rep: "Yeah, whatever her expenses come to."

Scott: "Okay, that's going to be about, probably $3,000."

Rep: "Oh boy. Okay, her primary place of employment?"

Scott: "Umm, place of employment uh, she works in a doctor's office."

Rep: "Okay, umm and the reason she wants to do the settlement is it's either this or bankruptcy?"

Scott: "That's basically her choices. Of course she is taking on a risk by borrowing it from a friend, but she'll take that risk if she can save money. Otherwise, there is no need to even do that. She wants to fulfill her obligations, but she just can't do it."

Note: It's important that they know that bankruptcy is a main option.

Rep: "Okay, now what number can I reach you at?"

Scott: "You can reach me at (609) 660-0682. And do you have a direct phone Ms. Scorpion?"

Rep: "No, unfortunately. When you call in you just get any operator. You can't get back to me."

Scott: "Ever?"

Rep: "So, yeah pretty much. So umm, it is going to be better for me to contact you."

Scott: "Okay."

Rep: "Okay, I mean the number that you just called in is a number that any operator will answer. So what I'll do is try to contact you as soon as, within the next 3 days. By Thursday or Friday morning you should hear from me. Umm, I have to wait for a supervisor to review this, okay?"

Scott: "Okay."

Rep: "And I'll call you back with the results of that. Umm, is there a way I can call back, Cindy? I can't submit this without her place of employment and date of hire."

Scott: (I give her the information.)

Rep: "Okay, alright thank you very much and I'll be getting back to you about that okay?"

Scott: "Okay, thanks Ms. Scorpion."

Rep: "Thank you, bye-bye."

Scott: "Bye-bye."

CALL #7.02: IT MAY TAKE TIME

Reason For Call:	Negotiate settlement
Result:	Completed application to settle account with 50% lump-sum offer.
Difficulty Level:	Medium
Call Time:	19 minutes
Total Saved:	$0.00
$/hour to make call:	$0.00

Be calm and persistent. Handle the settlement with care because it will probably require more than a single call to get the best settlement terms. In this call for Cindy to another credit card account, I end up talking about a few options plus I put in an application for a settlement.

SUMMARY

I spoke with Mrs. Millipede who transferred me to Ms. Treehopper in the settlement department. Ms. Treehopper suggested their in-house debt management program. They handle everything. Accounts are brought current. The bank receives one payment and pays other creditors.

I spoke to Darner (customer advocate). He took down Cindy's info, i.e., utilities, income, etc. Darner said he's going to call me back, at 0682, later in the week about settlement options.

TRANSCRIPT

Scott: "This is for Cindy Rogers..."
Note: Putting notes on the tape recording.

Voice Menu: "The next available representative will be with you shortly."

Rep: "Thank you for calling, and may I have your name please?"

Cindy: "Cindy Rogers."

Rep: "Ms. Rogers, may I have your account number please?"

Cindy: (Gives her the number.)

Rep: "Thank you so much Ms. Rogers. And your home phone number please starting with the area code first."

Cindy: (Gives her the number.)

Rep: "And how may I help you today with your Platinum Card."

Cindy: "Actually, I would like to know if my friend who handles my bills for me could speak with you about my account?"

Rep: "Absolutely, go ahead."

Cindy: "Okay, thanks."

Scott: "Hi."

Rep: "Hi. Your name please."

Scott: "My name is Scott."

Rep: "Okay, Scott."

Scott: "And what's your name?"

Rep: "Mrs. Millipede."

Scott: "Mrs. Millipede. Okay umm, well, I'm trying to help Cindy out here with her financial situation and umm, she is just basically at a point where she needs to settle the account."

Rep: "Alright, then let me go ahead and have you speak directly with an account manager. He will be able to give the proper information."

Scott: "Okay."

Rep: "Okay, let me go ahead and put an account manager on the line. He will be able to further assist you."

Scott: "Okay, thanks."

Rep: "Account manager, that's the settlement area for customer assistance. I'll have to transfer you, hold on."

Scott: "Alright, thank you."

Rep: "Thank you, you have a good day."

Scott: "You too."

On hold...

Manager: "May I have your name?"

Scott: "My name is Scott."

Manager: "And your account number sir?"

Scott: "Well, the account number I'm talking about is..." (I give her the number.)

Manager: "Thank you sir, just one moment."

Scott: "What's your name again?"
Note: Always get the names of all the people you speak with for your notes.

Manager: "My name is Ms. Treehopper."

Scott: "Okay, thanks."

Manager: "And your relationship to Cindy Rogers?"

Scott: "I'm a friend of Cindy's."

Manager: "Okay, and how can I help you?"

Scott: "Well, I'm helping Cindy out with her finances, and umm, she is just at a point where she needs some settlement options on this account."

Manager: "Okay. I see that we do have permission to speak with you."

Scott: "That's correct."

Manager: "Okay. Scott, what is your last name?"

Scott: "Bilker, B-I-L-K-E-R."

Manager: "Okay. What's financially going on for the cardholder?"

Scott: "Umm, reduction in income, and umm, basically she is looking at either being able to settle it or claim bankruptcy. It's one of those options."

Manager: "Are you an attorney?"

Scott: "No. I am not an attorney."

Manager: "Okay. So, is she definitely considering bankruptcy?"

Scott: "Oh yeah."

Manager: "Okay. Has she retained an attorney?"

Scott: "No, not yet. She is going to try to work it out, so she asked me if I could give her a hand. And uh, she has someone who would lend her some money to help, but she is only going to borrow money from a friend if she can settle an account for a reasonable amount, like 50% on the account or something like that. Otherwise, you know, but she will take that risk with a friend, for you know…"

Manager: "The loss of income, was it due to a job. I mean, I understand loss of income, but I mean is she working…So she's overextended?"

Scott: "Overextended, yes. Severely overextended."

Manager: "Has she considered debt management?"

Scott: "Umm, yes actually that's basically what we are doing right now."

Manager: "Okay, well, I mean a settlement and debt management are two different things."

Scott: "Right. Well what kind of terms, Ms. Treehopper, would you have for debt management?"
Note: Never hurts to ask about your options.

Manager: "Okay, how debt management works, the requirements; we do have one in-house, okay?"

Scott: "Okay."

Manager: "The requirements are that you have two other credit cards, outside of the Pomeranian Bank accounts."

Scott: "Okay."

Manager: "Obviously I think she does because she has a total of $19,000 revolving outside."

Scott: "Okay."

Manager: "And she has an income coming in."

Scott: "Okay."

Manager: "Okay. And what they do is they work with all your creditors to maintain and get lower payments and lower rates. Now instead of making three...How many cards does she have outside?"

Scott: "Uh, like three I believe."

Manager: "Instead of making three payments."

Scott: "Uh huh."

Manager: "You would make one. Okay?"

Scott: "Umm hmm."

Manager: "And what they do is at that point in time you make one payment and they disburse it to your creditors. Once you get established with the debt-management program they stop your fees going forward for you. Okay. Drop your interest down..."

Scott: "Drop it down to what?"

Manager: "Well, I mean I am not a specialist in that area. I mean I can tell you the basics."

Scott: "Okay."

Manager: "Okay. They drop your interest, drop your fees, the account would be brought to a current status. Umm, after three of the special payments of the proposed amount."

Scott: "Okay."

Manager: "Umm, and umm, like I said you make one payment. It takes between 4 to 7 years to pay everything down."

Scott: "Okay, 4 to 7 years, one affordable payment. And I know that you can't tell me rates from other banks, what about rates from..."

Manager: "I mean, I can't, I can actually put you over to a financial management specialist. What they would actually need to do is take a debt-to-income application."

Scott: "Well, you know what Ms. Treehopper..."

Manager: "Do you have that information?"

Scott: "Yes I do."

Manager: "Okay. So what I will do is I will put you through to them."

Scott: "Okay."

Manager: "To see if she can get qualified."

Scott: "Okay, well let's look at some settlement options while we are here."

Manager: "As far as settlement options, I mean, what I am looking at here is, I need to know, her minimum payments are under $145 a month. Can she maintain those?"

Scott: "No."

Manager: "Okay. Because she is overextended?"

Scott: "Right, overextended."

Manager: "What can she afford to do?"

Scott: "That's a good question. Basically she can afford to maybe borrow the money from a friend to settle the accounts, or go bankrupt. At this point, you know, that's what it's looking like."

Manager: "Well, I mean she might need to look at other options before bankruptcy or settlement. That's why I discussed the debt management. At this point in time right now, what I'm looking at here is settlement may not be an option."

Scott: "Really?"

Note: As is usually the case, the person you're speaking with may not be able to help you so even when they say, "settlements may not be an option" you have to keep pressing them further.

Manager: "Correct, I mean, if she can maintain her minimum, on the account. I mean, I know she is overextended, I understand that, but there are other programs as far as getting her to where she can afford her minimum payments."

Scott: "She is not going to want to do these things. I mean I'll bring them up with her, but basically..."

Manager: "She doesn't want to do debt management, or anything like that?"

Scott: "I'll research it for her, and talk to her about it. Of course that would be a nice plan, but I can tell you that in, you know, she is going to first talk to a bankruptcy attorney."

Manager: "Okay. She is really considering bankruptcy, I wasn't getting that from you."

Scott: "Oh yeah."

Manager: "If she is really considering bankruptcy, then I need to actually put you through to our bankruptcy unit, Customer Advocates."
Note: The "bankruptcy unit" kind of sounds like the ER doesn't it. ☺ You can see how important it is to make it clear to these reps that the next step is bankruptcy. That is what's going to make them consider a settlement.

Scott: "Okay."

Manager: "They have other things that they can talk to you about, but you might want to talk to her about debt management. To see if that is something that she wants to look into, before she files bankruptcy."

Scott: "Umm, I guess we can go back to the debt management place. First I might want to talk to the bankruptcy people first."

Manager: "Okay. Just one second Scott, okay?"

Scott: "Sure Ms. Treehopper."

On hold...

Manager: "Scott?"

Scott: "Yes, I'm here."

Manager: "Thank you for holding Scott. I do have Darner on the line, he is a Customer Advocate who will further assist you, okay?"

Scott: "Okay."

Customer Advocate: "How are you doing today sir?"

Scott: "Okay Darner. How are you?"

Customer Advocate: "I'm doing well, thank you. I understand that umm, that Cindy is overextended and that she is looking to do a settlement on her account."

Scott: "Well, she is really looking to do a bankruptcy, but I suggested that we talk about some settlement options first before she does that."

Customer Advocate: "Okay."

Scott: "You know, that's what I suggested to her. I know there's the debt management option Darner, but we'll start with some settlement options before, you know, she goes to the bankruptcy attorney."

Customer Advocate: "Okay. And she has only had the account...she just opened it? Oh, okay, I'm sorry, I was looking at something else. She has had the account for a couple of years now."

Scott: "Uh huh."

Customer Advocate: "Okay. And how much is she prepared to offer as a settlement?"

Scott: "50%."
Note: In hindsight I should have started with a lower number—maybe 25%.

Customer Advocate: "50%. Okay. And to be perfectly honest I couldn't agree to a settlement with you, I would need to actually speak with her, because it is going to affect her credit."

Scott: "Of course."

Customer Advocate: "Umm, and I would also need to take a debt-to-income application from her with regards to that as well."

Scott: "I have the info for her application."

Customer Advocate: "Yeah, I can take that from you then?"

Scott: "Okay."

Customer Advocate: "Yeah, let's go ahead and do that and just get that out of the way so we have that on file."

Scott: "Sure."

Customer Advocate: "What is her income sir?"

Scott: "$200 a week."

Customer Advocate: "And where does she work at?"

Scott: (I give him the name and address.)

Customer Advocate: "I don't need all that."

Scott: "Oh. Okay."

Customer Advocate: "Yeah, I just...how about her utilities? How much does she spend a month on utilities?"

Scott: "Utilities? Umm, let me think here. About $500."

Customer Advocate: "Okay, and how about medical expenses? Does she have any prescription drugs that she pays for each month, or is she paying on any medical bills?"

Scott: "I don't believe so."

Customer Advocate: "Okay."

Scott: "Do you have a direct number there, by the way Darner?"

Customer Advocate: "Yeah, absolutely, let me give you my number and my extension."

Scott: "Okay."

Customer Advocate: (He gives me the number.)

Scott: "Okay, let me read that back to you...(I read him the number). This way when, you know, when we are further along we can all talk together."

Customer Advocate: "That's fine, I can appreciate that. Umm, how about a car payment? Does she have a car payment each month."

Scott: "That's a good question. I don't know that exactly. I don't think so."

Customer Advocate: "Okay, what about groceries? How much do you think she spends on groceries each month?"

Scott: "Oh, groceries, probably a couple hundred a week, so whatever that is..."

Customer Advocate: "A couple hundred a week, so $800 a month in groceries?"

Scott: "Yeah, I would say that's fairly reasonable, yeah. Even if we went to $175. Yeah, I'd say, yeah, let's get a better number here. Yeah, $750 let's say, that's very reasonable I'd say."

Customer Advocate: "$750 a month in groceries?"

Scott: "Yeah."

Customer Advocate: "How many kids does she have?"

Scott: "Two."

Customer Advocate: "Why don't we do this, why don't we have her call in because I can't imagine her spending $750 a month in groceries."

Scott: "Really, I spend more than $750 a month in groceries."

Customer Advocate: "But you don't make $800 a month."

Scott: "Good point."
Note: I should have been more prepared. It doesn't matter because I can get in touch with Cindy for the details. Again, when you call you should certainly be ready with numbers that make sense.

Customer Advocate: "And you also don't know if she has a car payment or not. Why don't we have her call in with this information?"

Scott: "You know what, let me...she just stepped out. Let me see if I can reach her on her cell phone. If I can then maybe we can do a three-way. Can you hold on a second Darner?"

Customer Advocate: "Yeah, absolutely."

I call and get Cindy on another line...

Cindy: "He's really, really, really faint, I can barely hear him."

Scott: "That's okay. I'll relay it if you can't hear it Cindy."

Customer Advocate: "I can speak louder, is that better?"

Cindy: "Yeah, that's better."

Customer Advocate: "Okay. Umm, I wanted to know how much you spend a month for groceries."

Cindy: "A month. Oh god, that varies. About $450."

Customer Advocate: "Okay, and is there a car payment?"

Cindy: "No."

Customer Advocate: "How much for life insurance, health insurance, and car insurance?"

Cindy: "Umm, car insurance a month is $143. Really right now, I was with my ex-husbands insurance policy that got dropped. So right now I am only paying, I really don't have insurance. I have a big bill coming up, but I don't have insurance."

Scott: "And a medical bill? What kind of medical bill coming up?"

Cindy: "Well, I just got back from the doctor's so all…I have an AARP, but what happened was all that does is…it didn't take care of anything, you know I thought it would. But I was on Blue Cross Blue Shield, but not anymore."

Scott: "Right."

Cindy: "Umm, so that's the car payment…"

Scott: "I figure utilities like $500 a month. Would you say that's accurate, or that's just my guess? What do you think of utilities, just to get a good number?"

Cindy: "Umm, about $450."

Scott: "Medical per month."

Cindy: "Right now, I haven't been sick."

Scott: "So we'll say it's nothing right now. And then we have say your income, I said $200. You said between $200 and $250."

Cindy: "$250 per week."

Customer Advocate: "Does she rent or own?"

Scott: "Own. What's your mortgage?"

Cindy: "Umm, $204, but I also pay taxes. My taxes are every three months for $900. That's not included in the $200."

Scott: "Okay, that's $300, so it's $504 for the mortgage with taxes."

Customer Advocate: "How much is the house valued at?"

Cindy: "Uh, what do you mean by that, if I sold it?"

Scott: "Yeah, I mean, yeah, what's the value of your house?"

Cindy: "About $155,000."

Scott: "$155,000 and uh yeah, $155,000."

Customer Advocate: "How much does she owe on that?"

Scott: "We would really have to look that up. Do you know that off-hand, or do we need to look that up?"

Cindy: "I don't know that off-hand."

Customer Advocate: "Okay, I would need to know that."

Cindy: "Okay, let's just guess right now and say $130,000."

Customer Advocate: "How long have you had the mortgage?"

Cindy: "Not long. Five years."

Customer Advocate: "Okay. And do you want to offer a 50% settlement?"

Scott: "Yes."

Customer Advocate: "Would it be one lump sum, or would it be...umm, you can let her go if she wants...oh actually let me just mention this to her."

Cindy: "Okay."

Customer Advocate: "Okay, what I wanted to let you know is that a settlement, although it is a more positive mark than a bankruptcy, I just want to make sure that you understand that it is a negative mark on your credit history. I have to make you aware of that before we can consider a settlement."

Cindy: "Right. Run that by me Scott, to make it more clear."

Scott: "Oh, in other words a settlement isn't as negative on your credit history as a bankruptcy, but it is negative. He has to make you aware of that."

Cindy: "Okay."

Scott: "Okay, do we need to keep Cindy?"

Customer Advocate: "No you can let her go. Thank you very much ma'am."

Cindy: "And thank you Scott for helping. It was good that you helped out."

Scott: "Okay, I'll talk to you later."

Cindy: "Alright, thank you, bye."

Scott: "Bye-bye. Okay Darner."

Customer Advocate: "Okay."

Scott: "All right, so uh, yeah, yes one lump sum."

Customer Advocate: "Okay. What has happened to create her being overextended? Has she taken a loss of income, or..."

Scott: "Oh, maybe we should have kept her. Yeah, she has taken a loss of income. I believe she lost child support for one of her kids, because one of her kids got beyond that age."

Customer Advocate: "Okay."

Scott: "And sometimes she got money from her ex-husband, but that's not going well. Or I think she was also dating someone and they were kind of, you know, together and now they are not. It was one of those things."

Customer Advocate: "Okay. Let me go ahead and review this account, and I'll give you a call back in regards to this. Umm, where can I reach you at?"

Scott: "You can reach me at (609) 660-0682. When do you think you will be able to give me a call back?"

Customer Advocate: "Within the week."

Scott: "Okay great Darner."

Customer Advocate: "And thank you sir."

Scott: "Thank you. Bye-bye."

CALL #7.03: 55¢ ON THE DOLLAR!

Reason For Call:	Negotiate settlement
Result:	55% settlement in a lump-sum payment or 65% settlement with 12 equal monthly payments.
Difficulty Level:	Easy
Call Time:	9 minutes
Total Saved:	$2,900.00
$/hour to make call:	$19,333.33

This is the follow-up call from call #7.02. Darner called back and offered a great deal! There were many follow-up calls after this to make sure that I received all the proper paperwork. You need to make sure that their offer is in writing before you send the check!

SUMMARY

Darner called at 11:35 AM ET and left a message asking me to call him back. I called back at 3:02 PM ET and spoke to Darner.

He explained that one option is to pay off the account at the settled amount of $4,155.00 at 0% APR. That's a 65% settlement to pay off in one year, or $346.25 per month for 12 months. Cindy also has the option to settle at 55% with a lump sum payment of $3,512.00 (that's 55%—she owes about $6,400.00). Darner said he's going to send Cindy a letter and fax me a letter with the instructions. This saves Cindy approximately $2,900.00!

TRANSCRIPT

Voice Menu: Thank you for calling Pomeranian Bank..."

Rep: "Pomeranian Bank. Ms. Pincer speaking."

Scott: "Hi Ms. Pincer, I need to get extension..." (I give her Darner's extension.)

Rep: "Just a moment. Okay, and who are you trying to reach?"

Scott: "Darner."

Rep: "And your name is?"

Scott: "Scott Bilker."

Rep: "Okay, Mr. Bilker, and do you have an account to reference?"

Scott: "Yeah, I do. Umm, I need to get that real quick."

Rep: "Sure that would be great. Or if you don't have that readily available your social security number would be fine."

Scott: (I give her Cindy's number.)

Rep: "Okay, just one moment sir."

Scott: "Okay thanks."

On hold...

Scott: "Hello."

Rep: "Mr. Bilker. Hi, this is Darner, how are you doing sir?"

Scott: "Very good."

Rep: "Good, I'm glad to hear that."

Scott: "I got your message earlier."

Rep: "Okay. What I was calling for, you know, that umm, we wanted to speak with umm, with Ms. Rogers before we could consider the settlement, because it is a negative mark. And I just wanted to know if she had gotten that message."

Scott: "Umm, did you leave a message for her today, or..."

Rep: "You know what, I don't know. I've called too many people today...let me just review this for a second. I should have called her, I might have thought that I was calling her. Did I leave a message for you or for her?"

Scott: "Well, you might have left a message for her, but I definitely got a message from you too, Darner."

Rep: "Okay. You know what, I believe that I called you and I should have been calling her. So let me do that, let me give her a call and let her know that."

Scott: "Okay, well, she wants me to talk with you anyway."

Rep: "Okay, well you know what, okay, thank you. I know this account now, I'm sorry. Yeah, I did speak with her because you called her over the phone. Thank you. Be patient with me for one second."

Note: Okay, just for one second, then I will lose my patience! ☺

Scott: "I'm sure you've got a million customers, so I'm with you Darner. There are a lot of people at that bank there so I will give you a moment to get your notes together."

Rep: "Yeah, I've got it in here, I've just got to find it. Yeah, first I wasn't remembering the specifics, but I remember...I don't remember the exact stuff, but I do remember specifically speaking with you now. I remember you calling her on her cellular phone and having to conference her in."

Scott: "That's it, we did a three-way conversation."

Rep: "Yeah, okay. Yeah, here is my information here. She was going to be doing a lump sum, or was she going to be paying on it for a year?"

Scott: "Well, what are all her options?"

Rep: "Okay. What we can do is we can settle on the account for $4,155. And she can either do it as one lump sum payment, or, if she would prefer to have a year to pay on it. Essentially it's an interest-free loan on that amount and she can take a year to pay on it. That would be $346.25 a month."
Note: That's pretty good. It's 65% of her current balance and she has one year to pay it!

Scott: "Okay. I'm just going to write that down for her. Alright, let me just look back on this account. Alright, so that's about $4,155, divided by, whatever it was originally."

Rep: "$6,386.89."

Scott: "Okay. Umm, can she get more of a discount if she does a lump sum?"

Rep: "You know that's a good question. I don't know, certainly I could consider that. I mean there are advantages to a lump sum, so I could certainly consider that."

Scott: "Okay. Can you consider it right now, or do have to go back to..."
Note: Push to find out if there are any better options. If you have the cash saved, or can get cash, then make sure you see what the deal is for a lump-sum settlement.

Rep: "Well, I could consider it now. Go ahead and, how much do you think she could do as a lump sum?"

Scott: "She can do 50% as a lump sum."
Note: Again, in hindsight, I should have started lower—probably at 25%.

Rep: Okay. Yeah, we are not going to go with the 50%. That is what you offered initially."

Scott: "Right."

Rep: "And what is this, this is like 61% right?"

Scott: "Yeah, something like that, 65%."

Rep: "65%? I'll tell you what, I could go as low as...If she could do a lump sum, I could go as low as 55%."
Note: Look at that. There's always a card up their sleeve.

Scott: "Okay. So that's going to be...let me just break out the calculator..."

Rep: "I can tell you, it's $3,512. We'll even round down, there's 30 cents."

Scott: "Okay, there's $3,000, what is it?"

Rep: "$3,512."

Scott: "$3,512. Okay Darner. That sounds very feasible. How would we go about initiating this?"

Rep: "What happens is I am going to go ahead and submit the paperwork today. I probably won't have approval until next Friday."

Scott: "Okay."

Rep: "If you want to give me a call back Friday, I'll let you know at that time if it got approved or not."

Scott: "Umm, you don't know if it is going to get approved?"

Rep: "I don't know at this time. It goes through several different stages."

Scott: "You sound confident or you wouldn't make the offer."

Rep: "Yeah, I am very confident. I mean I deal with this every day and if I...I have yet to have one turned down."

Scott: "Okay. So if that's the case and it gets approved, then what would be the next step. How would it work?"

Rep: "What would happen is once she sends in the payment...she'll want a letter stating the agreements beforehand. We can go ahead and mail that out to her. And once she receives it then we will mail out a letter saying, or once we receive the payment, we will send out a letter saying that the settlement was approved and the obligations have been met. Some people prefer to have the letter showing that the settlement was approved before they actually send in the payment. So if she would prefer that then I can mail that out to her."

Scott: "Yeah, I certainly...that would be good. That way there is no confusion."
Note: Always get the deal in writing before sending the check.

Rep: "Okay."

Scott: "You know, just in case for some reason we can't get a hold of you."

Rep: "Okay."

Scott: "Is it possible for you to send her that letter and also fax a copy to me?"

Rep: "Yeah, absolutely."

Scott: "Okay, great. Let me give you my fax number."

Rep: "Okay."

Scott: "It's..." (I give him the number.)

Rep: "Okay."

Scott: "And you can just mail her one. But as soon as one's available, if you could, just fax it to me directly. That way at least, before it even gets here, I could start to get her things together because she is going to borrow money from a friend to do this, you know. But it will settle her obligation, so she will take the risk."

Rep: "Umm hmm."

Scott: "So that's very reasonable. If it goes through it sounds like it is going to work out well."

Rep: "Alright. Well thank you sir. You have a great day."

Scott: "You too, bye-bye."
Note: It was approved. I knew it would be because Darner really sounded confident. So confident that he probably already had approval before he even offered the 55% settlement option. I did receive the fax with all the details discussed in the call.

CHAPTER 8

DISPUTES, CHARGEBACKS, AND ERRORS

KEEP PAPERWORK AND AVOID ERRORS

As mentioned previously, when you apply for a new credit card, or take advantage of a credit offer, you should always keep a copy of the original information sent to you in the offer. Also, make a copy of your completed application.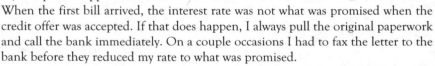

Keep this paperwork in your files. You want to make sure that you received all the terms you were promised when you applied for the card. It has happened to me, and I have heard the same stories from other people, that the promised terms were not delivered. In all the cases I'm aware of, the person applied for the new card based on the offer. When the first bill arrived, the interest rate was not what was promised when the credit offer was accepted. If that does happen, I always pull the original paperwork and call the bank immediately. On a couple occasions I had to fax the letter to the bank before they reduced my rate to what was promised.

By the way, when you call the bank, be sure to take careful notes. Get the full name of the person you spoke with and document the time of day. You never know when you'll need this information.

WHAT IS A CHARGEBACK?

One of the most important reasons for using your credit card for purchases is the protection you have from merchants. This same protection covers you if your card is lost, stolen, or someone tries to charge your card the incorrect amount and much more!

When you use your credit card, you're protected! Well, not totally, but far more than if you paid with cash, check, or debit card. That's because the Fair Credit Billing Act is a law that gives us, the consumer, the right to dispute charges for a number of reasons.

For example, let's say you buy a $200.00 television at your local discount store and pay with your credit card. You get home and find out that it doesn't work. When you bring it back, the store manager says that they don't accept returns and only give store-credits. You find this unacceptable, leave the TV at the front desk, demand your credit card be credited, and the store refuses. By the way, there are no signs in the store about this policy nor is it written on your sales receipt. What do you do?

First, pat yourself on the back for using your credit card, because you can now contact your bank about the situation. Give the bank a call and explain that you returned the merchandise to the store, and they did not credit your account. Tell the bank that you want to "dispute" the charge. As long as you're within the limits of the law, the bank will investigate the matter and you will not be held responsible for that charge until the investigation is complete. In many cases the merchant is going to have to chargeback that amount.

Many banks will tell you that there is a 60-day time limit for this procedure. However, you can still dispute the matter after the 60-day limit. In this chapter I'll do just that—with success!

Final important tip: Although you may be able to dispute charges over 60 days, it is more difficult. One way to avoid that is to not wait until you see a refund on your credit statement. If a merchant says that they'll be "giving you a credit that you'll see on your next statement," ask them when that credit is actually going to happen (usually within a few days). Then call your bank to see if that refund posted to your account promptly. If it did not, dispute the charge right then and there!

FAIR CREDIT BILLING ACT (FCBA)

(http://www.ftc.gov/bcp/conline/pubs/credit/fcb.htm)
Note: The following section is reproduced from the Federal Trade Commission. It is a very good summary of the FCBA for explaining the dispute procedures. Follow this advice if you ever need to dispute a credit card charge. This information is current as of the date of publishing only and may not be current when you read this passage. Check the FTC.gov web site for updates.

Have you ever been billed for merchandise you returned or never received? Has your credit card company ever charged you twice for the same item or failed to credit a payment to your account? While frustrating, these errors can be corrected. It takes a little patience and knowledge of the dispute settlement procedures provided by the Fair Credit Billing Act (FCBA).

The law applies to "open end" credit accounts, such as credit cards, and revolving charge accounts—such as department store accounts. It does not cover installment contracts—loans or extensions of credit you repay on a fixed schedule. Consumers often buy cars, furniture and major appliances on an installment basis, and repay personal loans in installments as well.

What types of disputes are covered?
The FCBA settlement procedures apply only to disputes about "billing errors." For example:
- Unauthorized charges. Federal law limits your responsibility for unauthorized charges to $50.
- Charges that list the wrong date or amount.
- Charges for goods and services you didn't accept or weren't delivered as agreed.

- Math errors.
- Failure to post payments and other credits, such as returns.
- Failure to send bills to your current address—provided the creditor receives your change of address, in writing, at least 20 days before the billing period ends.
- Charges for which you ask for an explanation or written proof of purchase along with a claimed error or request for clarification.

To take advantage of the law's consumer protections, you must:

- Write to the creditor at the address given for "billing inquiries," not the address for sending your payments, and include your name, address, account number and a description of the billing error.
- Send your letter so that it reaches the creditor within 60 days after the first bill containing the error was mailed to you.
- Send your letter by certified mail, return receipt requested, so you have proof of what the creditor received. Include copies (not originals) of sales slips or other documents that support your position. Keep a copy of your dispute letter.
- The creditor must acknowledge your complaint in writing within 30 days after receiving it, unless the problem has been resolved. The creditor must resolve the dispute within two billing cycles (but not more than 90 days) after receiving your letter.

What happens while my bill is in dispute?

You may withhold payment on the disputed amount (and related charges), during the investigation. You must pay any part of the bill not in question, including finance charges on the undisputed amount.

The creditor may not take any legal or other action to collect the disputed amount and related charges (including finance charges) during the investigation. While your account cannot be closed or restricted, the disputed amount may be applied against your credit limit.

Will my credit rating be affected?

The creditor may not threaten your credit rating or report you as delinquent while your bill is in dispute. However, the creditor may report that you are challenging your bill. In addition, the Equal Credit Opportunity Act prohibits creditors from discriminating against credit applicants who exercise their rights, in good faith, under the FCBA. Simply put, you cannot be denied credit simply because you've disputed a bill.

What if the bill is incorrect?

If your bill contains an error, the creditor must explain to you—in writing—the corrections that will be made to your account. In addition to crediting your account, the creditor must remove all finance charges, late fees or other charges related to the error.

If the creditor determines that you owe a portion of the disputed amount, you must get a written explanation. You may request copies of documents proving you owe the money.

What if the bill is correct?

If the creditor's investigation determines the bill is correct, you must be told promptly and in writing how much you owe and why. You may ask for copies of relevant documents. At this point, you'll owe the disputed amount, plus any finance charges that accumulated while the amount was in dispute. You also may have to pay the minimum amount you missed paying because of the dispute.

If you disagree with the results of the investigation, you may write to the creditor, but you must act within 10 days after receiving the explanation, and you may indicate that you refuse to pay the disputed amount. At this point, the creditor may begin collection procedures. However, if the creditor reports you to a credit bureau as delinquent, the report also must state that you don't think you owe the money. The creditor must tell you who gets these reports.

What if the creditor fails to follow the procedure?

Any creditor who fails to follow the settlement procedure may not collect the amount in dispute, or any related finance charges, up to $50, even if the bill turns out to be correct. For example, if a creditor acknowledges your complaint in 45 days—15 days too late—or takes more than two billing cycles to resolve a dispute, the penalty applies. The penalty also applies if a creditor threatens to report—or improperly reports—your failure to pay to anyone during the dispute period.

An important caveat: Disputes about the quality of goods and services are not "billing errors," so the dispute procedure does not apply. However, if you buy unsatisfactory goods or services with a credit or charge card, you can take the same legal actions against the card issuer as you can take under state law against the seller.

To take advantage of this protection regarding the quality of goods or services, you must:

- Have made the purchase (it must be for more than $50) in your home state or within 100 miles of your current billing address.
- Make a **good faith effort** to resolve the dispute with the seller first.
- The dollar and distance limitations don't apply if the seller also is the card issuer—or if a special business relationship exists between the seller and the card issuer.

Other billing rights. Businesses that offer "open end" credit also must:

- Give you a written notice when you open a new account—and at certain other times—that describes your right to dispute billing errors.
- Provide a statement for each billing period in which you owe—or they owe you—more than one dollar.

- Send your bill at least 14 days before the payment is due—if you have a period within which to pay the bill without incurring additional charges.
- Credit all payments to your account on the date they're received, unless no extra charges would result if they failed to do so. Creditors are permitted to set some reasonable rules for making payments, say setting a reasonable deadline for payment to be received to be credited on the same date.
- Promptly credit or refund overpayments and other amounts owed to your account. This applies to instances where your account is owed more than one dollar. Your account must be credited promptly with the amount owed. If you prefer a refund, it must be sent within seven business days after the creditor receives your written request. The creditor must also make a good faith effort to refund a credit balance that has remained on your account for more than six months.

You can sue a creditor who violates the FCBA. If you win, you may be awarded damages, plus twice the amount of any finance charge—as long as it's between $100 and $1,000. The court also may order the creditor to pay your attorney's fees and costs.

If possible, hire a lawyer who is willing to accept the amount awarded to you by the court as the entire fee for representing you. Some lawyers may not take your case unless you agree to pay their fee—win or lose—or add to the court-awarded amount if they think it's too low.

MORE ON GOOD FAITH

The below section of law is what will be referenced in call #8.03. More legal information can be found online at the Office of the Law Revision Counsel at http://uscode.house.gov/uscode.htm

Note: The following is "Title 15, Chapter 41, Subchapter I, Part D, Sec. 1666i. - Assertion by cardholder against card issuer of claims and defenses arising out of credit card transaction; prerequisites; limitation on amount of claims or defenses"

(a) Claims and defenses assertible

Subject to the limitation contained in subsection (b) of this section, a card issuer who has issued a credit card to a cardholder pursuant to an open end consumer credit plan shall be subject to all claims (other than tort claims) and defenses arising out of any transaction in which the credit card is used as a method of payment or extension of credit if

(1) the obligor has made a good faith attempt to obtain satisfactory resolution of a disagreement or problem relative to the transaction from the person honoring the credit card;

(2) the amount of the initial transaction exceeds $50; and

(3) the place where the initial transaction occurred was in the same State as the mailing address previously provided by the cardholder or was within 100 miles from such address, except that the limitations set forth in clauses (2) and (3) with respect to an obligor's right to assert claims and defenses against a card issuer shall not be applicable to any transaction in which the person honoring the credit card

(A) is the same person as the card issuer,

(B) is controlled by the card issuer,

(C) is under direct or indirect common control with the card issuer,

(D) is a franchised dealer in the card issuer's products or services, or

(E) has obtained the order for such transaction through a mail solicitation made by or participated in by the card issuer in which the cardholder is solicited to enter into such transaction by using the credit card issued by the card issuer.

(b) Amount of claims and defenses assertible

The amount of claims or defenses asserted by the cardholder may not exceed the amount of credit outstanding with respect to such transaction at the time the cardholder first notifies the card issuer or the person honoring the credit card of such claim or defense. For the purpose of determining the amount of credit outstanding in the preceding sentence, payments and credits to the cardholder's account are deemed to have been applied, in the order indicated, to the payment of:

(1) late charges in the order of their entry to the account;

(2) finance charges in order of their entry to the account; and

(3) debits to the account other than those set forth above, in the order in which each debit entry to the account was made.

SOURCE
(Pub. L. 90-321, title I, Sec. 170, as added Pub. L. 93-495, title III, Sec. 306, Oct. 28, 1974, 88 Stat. 1515.)

Call #8.01: Make Them Keep Their Promises

Reason For Call:	Correct error in interest rate
Result:	Adjusted current rate from 17.22% to 3.99%.
Difficulty Level:	Hard
Call Time:	11 minutes
Total Saved:	$60.10
$/hour to make call:	$327.82

This call is an example of why you always need to keep the original paperwork from the bank. When you take advantage of low rate offers you must check to make sure that the bank is charging you the correct rate shown in the offer. You know, in all my years of having credit, and with all my accounts, I have never had the bank make an error in my favor—go figure.

SUMMARY

I used a balance transfer offer that gave me a 3.99% rate through my January billing statement if used by November 1st. I used check number #7211. The November statement showed the 3.99% rate, but the December statement showed a 17.22% rate. The balance of $2,590.79 at the correct 3.99% for 32 days (the billing period) has a finance charge of $9.06. The charge for 17.22% is $39.11. They owe us $30.05.

I called and spoke to Mr. Dung Beetle who told me that my rate ended in December. I explained that it ends in January and he continued to disagree even after I quoted the letter. I asked to speak to a supervisor and was transferred into a voice mailbox.

I called back and spoke to Ms. Stinkbug. We went through the same dance. She said it ends in December. I read the letter that said it ends in January. Ms. Stinkbug explained that I have to send the letter to "corporate" and they'll straighten it out. I told her that I want to straighten it out now. Then I asked to speak to a supervisor.

Ms. Stinkbug spoke to a supervisor, Mr. Dragonfly, who said that he'd take care of the account. Ms. Stinkbug indicated that I would get the proper credits and rate by the next billing statement.

The total savings here is $30.05 for two months (if they didn't change the rate back), which comes out to $60.10.

TRANSCRIPT

Rep: "Thank you for calling Pointer Bankcard services. My name is Mr. Dung Beetle, may I have your account number please?"

Larissa: (Gives him the number.)

Rep: "Mrs. Bilker."

Larissa: "Yes."

Rep: "For verification may I have your social security number please?"

Larissa: (Gives him the number.) "I'd like to have my husband talk to you about my account."

Rep: "Alright."

Scott: "Hi Mr. Dung Beetle."

Rep: "Hi, how may I help you today sir?"

Scott: "Okay, umm, can you see that account?"

Rep: "Oh, I have the account."

Scott: "Okay good, the interest rate isn't correct. It's showing here as 17.22%. It should be 3.99%."

Pause...

Rep: "Let's see, actually the 3.9% was expired on December 1st."

Scott: "Actually, it's not."

Rep: "Okay, why not?"

Scott: "Well, according to the letter I was sent, it expires January 1st."

Rep: "I show December 1st sir."

Scott: "Well, it's showing incorrectly. You have the check number? You should have the check number."

Rep: "7211."

Scott: "That's correct. Then you should know, there should be something linking it to the offer that was sent. I'm looking at the letter right in front of me. I'm holding it. Gee, it says specifically 'Your balance transfer has been reduced to 3.99% fixed until the 1st day of your billing cycle, which includes January 1st. Use these by November 1st.'"

Rep: "Alright, let's see."

Scott: "In fact, if you go back, well, you'll see that it's on there the previous month."

Rep: "Right I do show it, in fact I show that it expires in October, but they put the extension on until December. It should have expired 10/1, but they put the end date to be 12/1."

Scott: "Well it should be 1/1."

Rep: "Okay, unfortunately it's not sir, it's 12/1."

Scott: "Okay, can you change that?"

Rep: "No, we can't actually."

Scott: "Okay great, can I speak to your supervisor then?"

Rep: "Unfortunately, no sir."
Note: This rep is really annoying to deal with.

Scott: "And why is that?"

Rep: "We would have to speak with your wife sir, on that account."

Scott: "Okay, umm, if she let's me speak for her then I may, yes?"

Rep: "Umm, sure but they'll have to talk to her again to verify that."

Scott: "Okay, let's put him on, let's get him on."

Rep: "Sure, sure. Hold on for a moment sir."

On hold...

Voice Mail: "Thank you for calling Pointer Bank, you have reached the voice mailbox of..."

Scott: (I hang up totally frustrated.)

Second call...

Voice Menu: "Thank you for calling Pointer Bank cardmember services. Please listen carefully, the options may have changed since your last call. Please enter your account number."

Rep: "Thank you for Pointer Bank credit card services, my name is Ms. Stinkbug, may I have your name please?"

Larissa: "Larissa Bilker."

Rep: "For further verification may I have your mother's maiden name."

Larissa: (Gives her the name.)

Rep: "Thank you and how may I assist you with your account?"

Larissa: "Umm, eh, may my husband speak on behalf of my account for me?"

Rep: "Most certainly."

Larissa: "Thanks."

Scott: "Hi Ms. Stinkbug."

Rep: "Hi, how may I help you Mr. Bilker?"

Scott: "Okay, well I just got disconnected from Mr. Dung Beetle, the last guy. Here's the story. If you look at the account and you look at the rate it's 17.2%, it's supposed to be 3.99%."

Rep: "Okay, and may I ask why it's supposed to be at 3.9%?"

Scott: "Okay, because I received a letter from Pointer Bank that gave me a Preferred Pointer Bank Select Cardholder rate of 3.99% until the 1st of next year."

Rep: "Okay, let me see what we've got here."

Scott: "Okay."

Rep: "Okay so up until the most current statement you were getting the 3.99% on there?"

Scott: "That's correct."

Rep: "Okay, so let's see what caused it to go away."

Pause...

Rep: "Okay it says it's to end on 12/1."

Scott: "Right, but that's incorrect. Unless the letters they send are wrong."

Rep: "Okay, do you have a copy of that letter?"

Scott: "It's in my hand."

Rep: "Okay, what you need to do is send it over to, fax it over to our corporate office so that they can correct it."

Scott: "That's a lot of hassle. Is there a code on here that I could give you? I'm sure there are all kinds of little numbers on here that designate everything."

Rep: "That's what I'm telling you, our codes say that it's to expire on December 1st."

Scott: "Right, but there is some kind of little number at the bottom of this letter that I'm sure might correspond with this whole thing."

Rep: "But it won't, I have no way of putting that in. There is no way for me to change that. That's why it needs to go to the corporate office."

Scott: "Umm, do you have a supervisor there that I could speak with?"

Rep: "I do have a supervisor here, but they can't adjust the rate either."
Note: The usual line. I've come this far and I'm not stopping now!

Scott: "Okay, can I speak to them anyway?"

Rep: "I will see if I can locate one. Okay?"

Scott: "Alright. Thank you."

Rep: "I'm going to place you on hold."

Scott: "Sure."

On hold...

Scott: "Okay."

Rep: "Okay, and the time frame that this is to expire..."

Scott: "Uh huh."

Rep: "What date is that?"

Scott: "January 1ˢᵗ."

Rep: "Okay, what I, what the manager is going to do is I'm going to give him the account number, he will send the information over to corporate for them to correct it."
Note: Being persistent pays off. All of the sudden it can be adjusted.

Scott: "Beautiful."

Rep: "Okay, so you are going to bear with me for just a moment while I get all the information of your account."

Scott: "Sure."

Rep: "Okay I'm going to place you back on hold."

Scott: "Okay."

Rep: "Thank you."

On hold...

Rep: "Thanks for holding. I've gone ahead and forwarded that information over to him for him to make that correction, okay."

Scott: "Okay."

Rep: "I do show that you made a large payment."

Scott: "Yes."

Rep: "Just to let you know that the bulk of that payment did go towards that lower rate okay."

Scott: "Yeah, I'm sure..."

Rep: "Just so you know that."

Scott: "Right, but everything was...Yeah the bulk of the payment of course went towards the lower rate, but the entire balance was at the low rate."

Rep: "Okay."

Scott: "So whatever the balance is today should be at the low rate."

Rep: "Okay. Is there anything else I can do for you at this time?"

Scott: "Uh, well, can you tell me the manager's name?"

Rep: "Uh, the manager's name is Mr. Dragonfly."

Scott: "Will they have that corrected by the next billing statement?"

Rep: "Yes."

Scott: "Excellent, Ms. Stinkbug."

Rep: "Okay."

Scott: "Thank you very much."

Rep: "Thank you for calling."

Scott: "Bye-bye."

Rep: "Bye."

CALL #8.02: BASIC DISPUTES ARE EASY!

Reason For Call:	Dispute charge for web hosting
Result:	Mission completed
Difficulty Level:	Easy
Call Time:	7 minutes
Total Saved:	$874.47
$/hour to make call:	$7,495.46

The web host of DebtSmart.com notified me that they were being sold to another company and that there would be a transition to their new computers. The transition did not go too well because we lost some of the functionality of the web site. This was a major problem.

The solution required moving the web site to another host. I signed up with a few new hosting companies to see if their services could handle the function requirements of DebtSmart.com. Many could not. I cancelled those accounts and was promised a refund. Well, most of the refunds didn't happen. In fact, one place said that I violated one of their rules, which I did not, and they were not going to give me a refund! Good luck Mr. Host Merchant, because I used my credit card for the purchase. I'm going to dispute that charge and get a refund anyway!

In the end, I won all the disputes and received all of the refunds! There was only one problem. One of the hosts kept charging me month-after-month for service and I had to dispute it every time. But, eventually I got every penny back!

SUMMARY

The below charges appeared on my March 25th statement. I called to dispute all these charges. These charges are from web hosting companies (names have been changed), all of which I cancelled within days of signing up.

Date	Merchant	Amount
2/28	VirusInfected Hosting	$297.52
3/7	NoTechSupport Hosting	$60.00
3/12	ServerDown Hosting	$466.95
3/12	ServerDown Hosting	$79.95
3/21	ServerDown Hosting	($29.95)
	Total	$874.47

I need to say that I'm not going to pay $874.47 because it's being disputed. The total on the statement is $2,377.09 so the adjusted, pay-in-full amount is $1,502.62.

I also need to ask if any of these credits have already appeared.

I spoke with Ms. Billbug and explained the situation. She said they're going to start an investigation of the charges. She also verified that my outstanding balance is now $1,502.62 after the adjustments.

TRANSCRIPT

Voice Menu: "For quality purposes your call may be recorded."

Scott: "Okay. Yours too."

On hold...

Rep: "Hello. This is Ms. Billbug. How may I help you?"

Scott: "Hi Ms. Billbug. I have some problems, I think, with my account...I have umm, let me give you my account number." (I give her the number.)

Rep: "And your name sir?"

Scott: "Scott Bilker."

Rep: "And how may I help you?"

Scott: "Well, I guess I should first ask; are there any other credits on my account right now?"

Note: Many of these companies promised that I would receive a refund. I'm not going to wait until the next statement arrives to see if the refund happens. It makes it more difficult to dispute the charges if I go over 60 days. So if you're promised a refund within a certain period, be sure to call your bank to see if it happened. If it didn't, dispute the charge right away!

Rep: "Well, let's see here. March 25th statement had a few, but let's see...the only credit I see is $0.26 for, probably, on a gasoline purchase. Yeah, it is for gasoline purchase."

Scott: "Okay, alright. Well then, 'cause there are a few charges. I'll go through them. On February 28th, VirusInfected Hosting. Then you have on, March 7th, NoTechSupport Hosting."

Rep: "Okay. Are they all the same merchant?"

Scott: "No."

Rep: "No. Okay. Now, let's go through them one at a time. Now what is the issue with VirusInfected Hosting?"

Scott: "Alright. Well the issue with all of them is the same issue. They are just different places. They are places I signed up for with web hosting and within 24 hours cancelled my account because they just didn't have the technical aspects for me to use."

Rep: "Okay. So they are all cancelled?"

Scott: "Yeah."

Rep: "Do you have any cancellation numbers from those firms?"

Scott: "Some. In the instance of VirusInfected Hosting, I called them and they said that because it was such a short time period they weren't going to run the charge. But apparently they did so."
Note: I didn't have a cancellation notice from the one that said they would not give me the refund.

Rep: "Yeah."

Scott: "And then with the other ones, I do have...Well that's the issue with VirusInfected Hosting."

Rep: "Okay. And how about NoTechSupport Hosting?"

Scott: "Okay. Now they know that the account is cancelled. However they should have posted a credit, they haven't."
Note: This is the hosting company that I mentioned earlier. They claimed that I violated their policies and, therefore, they would not give me a refund. We'll just see about that!

Rep: "Okay."

Scott: "And ServerDown Hosting. I do have a cancellation number from them. They're the 3rd one."

Rep: "Right, and which charge is it now. The $466, or all 3 of them."

Scott: "All of them."

Rep: "Yeah, all 3 of them. Well actually there is a credit for $29.95, but is it the $466.95 as well?"

Scott: "All those should equal zero. You know, all the credits and charges should add up to zero. And I do have a cancellation number for them."

Rep: "Okay and that is?"

Scott: "Let me look it up. Okay, cancellation request...Well, I don't have an actual cancellation number. I have an email that says that they have received it."

Rep: "Alright. Then just save that email in case you need to forward it to our Dispute Handling Department. But we'll go ahead and suspend all of those amounts on your account and start an investigation. And is there anything else I can help you with today?"

Note: I never had to forward that email or produce any physical proof.

Scott: Uh, no that'll be all. I'm just going to deduct that from my balance."

Rep: "That's correct."

Scott: "Which would be...So the new pay-in-full amount would be $1,502.62?"

Rep: "It is."

Scott: "Okay great."

Rep: "Okay."

Scott: "I'll do that. So yeah, I don't even know what the $29.95 is about, or even the $79.95 is. So who knows. They were just charging and crediting and who knows?"

Rep: "Yeah."

Scott: "It should just be zero. Whatever it adds up to be, it should be zero."

Rep: "Right. Okay sir, we'll go ahead and process those for you and go ahead and deduct the $904.42, plus the $29.95, which will give you $1,502.62."

Scott: "Okay great. Thank you very much Ms. Billbug."

Rep: "You're more than welcome Mr. Bilker. Thanks for calling. You have a good day sir."

Scott: "You too. Bye-bye."

Call #8.03: Dispute over 60 days

Reason For Call:	Dispute charge
Result:	Dispute and refund for purchase older than 60 days.
Difficulty Level:	Hard
Call Time:	10 minutes
Total Saved:	$99.00
$/hour to make call:	$594.00

When you make a return to a merchant, and they say they're going to credit your account, be sure to follow up and make sure it's done. Watch for the credit to be posted on your account statement because you don't want to be past the 60-day limit for disputes. Being past that limit will make it more difficult to dispute the charge. However, you can, and should, dispute invalid charges no matter how old the charge is!

SUMMARY

I returned a smart-card reader to Weasel Computer Supplies and they haven't yet given me the $99 credit. The original purchase was charged to my account on 12/3. I called the bank and spoke to Mrs. Praying Mantis. She said that because the charge is over 60 days old, it would not be investigated.

I needed to make them do an investigation. They said that I have only 60 days to make the complaint, but I did complain, to the merchant, within that time period!

Mrs. Praying Mantis gave me the address for mailing my written dispute, and I did just that. They responded via email and the charge was reversed!

TRANSCRIPT

Voice Menu: "Thank you for calling Spaniel Bank services. Please have your card available. For quality purposes this call may be recorded."

Scott: "Yours too."

Voice Menu: "Please enter your account number now. If your number is not available, please hold for assistance."

Scott: "I'm holding!"

Rep: "This is Mrs. Praying Mantis, how can I assist you?"

Scott: "Hi, umm, let me give you my account number."

Rep: "What is it please?"

Scott: "Account number is..." (I give her the number.) "You said Mrs. Praying Mantis?

Rep: "My name is Mrs. Praying Mantis."

Scott: "Okay."

Rep: "And what is your name please?"

Scott: "Scott Bilker."

Rep: "Mr. Bilker for the security of the account, what is your date of birth please."

Scott: (I give her the date.)

Rep: "Thanks, what can I do for you?"

Scott: "Okay, back in December, on December 3rd actually, I made a purchase at a place called Weasel Computer Supplies."

Rep: "December 3rd. Okay let me go back to December. Okay this is December 3rd, this is Weasel Computer Supplies incorporated, uh huh."

Scott: "Yeah. Okay, well I got the stuff except I made a return. One of the items that I purchased, I returned. And I returned that in January. Uh, January 3rd I believe. Uh yes, January 3rd it was delivered by Airborne Express back to them. I followed all their procedures and got the Return Merchandise Number (RMN) and they were supposed to give me a credit of $99 for one of the items. And they haven't to date. I sent them an email. They replied back and said they would, back in January, but they haven't. I've sent other emails following up on that, plus I tried to call them. Their line is busy 24 hours a day. I've attempted to contact the merchant, nothing has happened. I would just like to charge it back."

Rep: "Okay, well there is no way for us to charge it back, but we can go ahead and open up a customer service inquiry saying that you returned $99 worth of the merchandise, and you are requesting credit for $99."

Scott: "Yes, that's fine. We'll do that."

Rep: "And again the purchased merchandise is returned on the 3rd of January?"

Scott: "That's correct. And I have documentation showing that it was returned there, signed for. And all that good stuff, and their emails with the RMN. I've got all the documentation that you'll need."

Rep: "And how did...did you say they picked it up?"

Pause...

Rep: "Okay, in regard to the customer service inquiry, the umm, the resolution that I got back is that to advise the cardmember we cannot investigate this claim based on the age of the question. I suggest that the cardmember contact the merchant directly."

Scott: "What do you mean the age of the question?"

Rep: "Okay, let me finish reading and we will explain to you. It says 'advise the cardmember in the event they have questions on the...' I'm sorry. 'Advise the cardmember if they have questions about an item under billing statement in the future to contact us within 60 days of the billing to ensure their rights are preserved.' So because this charge is billed to your Spaniel Bankcard over 60 days ago, that's the reason why we are not going to be able to dispute the charge of the vendor."

Scott: "Well according to like, the credit card laws there is no time limit on disputes."

Rep: "That is not correct."

Scott: "Oh really."

Rep: "No, I can send you a copy of your cardmember agreement, it clearly states in your cardmember agreement that you have 60 days to dispute charges."

Scott: "Umm hmm, well it might say that in the cardmember agreement, but the law says that you can dispute it, and there is no time limit given in the law."

Rep: "Which part of the law are you looking at because, I...you are going to need to provide us with a copy of that, 'cause this has been a part of Spaniel Bank's policy since we started issuing credit cards approximately, over 40-some years ago."

Scott: "Okay, well then I guess..."

Rep: "And this is also the policy of other credit cards in regarding the 60 days."

Scott: "Alright, well I guess we will have to actually pull a copy and tell it to you. It's the Fair Credit Reporting Act, you know, it says in..."

Rep: "Okay the Fair Credit Reporting Act is a different, it's completely different from disputes."

Scott: "I don't know the name of it right now, but I will dig it up, and I will, I can read it to you and whatever. All I can tell you is that when they promise that they are going to give the credit within a certain amount of time, I gave them a chance to do it, one of your merchants. And they didn't do it in that time period."
Note: United States Code, Title 15, Chapter 41 (Consumer Credit Protection), section 1666i does not mention any time limitation for a "good faith" stop. That's when a "good faith effort to resolve the dispute" is made with the seller first. See the FTC section in this chapter, "What if the creditor fails to follow the procedure?" and "More on Good Faith."

Rep: "Okay."

Scott: "And it takes time to see if it is actually going to come through."

Rep: "Okay."

Scott: "Well, umm, I would like this investigated."

Rep: "We cannot investigate it."

Scott: "Okay."

Rep: "Because the charge is over 60 days old. You are going to need to do it directly with the vendor."

Scott: "Okay. Well I'm going to have to call back then, and well how can I address the legal department about this?"

Rep: "The legal department wouldn't be able to handle this. The only department, umm, the only thing that you will be able to do is to send a letter to our consumer relations department."

Scott: "Right."

Rep: "And they will be, pretty much they will be able to tell you the same information because they are working off the same system. They are basically going to go ahead and run the charge through our dispute handling system, and if the system cannot investigate the charge, then there is no way for us to investigate the charge."
Note: It's the usual response intended to make me give up.

Scott: "Hmm."

Rep: "I can give the address for Spaniel Bank consumer relations department."

Scott: "Okay, let's do that."

Rep: "Sure. It's Spaniel Bank, care of consumer relations."

Scott: "Okay."

Rep: "The next line you need to put this..."

Scott: "Is there a phone number?"

Rep: "Umm, there is no phone number."

Scott: "Okay, so there is no phone number."

Rep: "No, it's an address where you go ahead and put your request, or your feedback. It's basically consumer relations for cardmembers who are not satisfied with the information they are getting from the customer service representatives or from the customer service..."

Scott: "Okay, what is the address?"

Rep: "It's umm..."

Scott: "Okay so let's start again. What is it? Spaniel Bank..."

Rep: "Spaniel Bank, care of consumer relations."

Scott: "Okay, okay, hold on a second. Okay, consumer relations, okay."

Rep: (She gives me the address.)

Scott: "Okay."

Rep: "Okay, have a great day."

Scott: "You too."

Rep: "Thank you, bye."

Scott: "Bye."

Copy of my dispute letter to the Spaniel Bank:

Spaniel Bank Customer Service:

On December 3, (YEAR) I purchased camera equipment from Weasel Computer Supplies in the amount of $1,565.00 (see enclosed statement).

On January 2, (YEAR) I returned $99.00 worth of merchandise with the approval of Weasel Computer Supplies (see enclosed email). Weasel Computer Supplies, on January 3rd, received the merchandise (see enclosed Airborne Express delivery confirmation).

To date I have not received the promised $99.00 credit for returned merchandise. I have sent follow-up emails with no response and their phone is always busy. After checking The Weasel Computer Supplies' web site I discovered that they're out of business (see enclosed print out).

Please investigate this matter and credit my account $99.00 for the return pursuant to United States Code, Title 15, Chapter 41 (Consumer Credit Protection), section 1666i.

You can contact me at (609) 660-0682 or by email at scott@debtsmart.com.

Thank you for your prompt attention to this matter.

Regards,
Scott Bilker

Spaniel Bank's Email Response:

Thank you for your correspondence received in the Executive Offices of Spaniel Bank. I welcome the opportunity to be of assistance. I have noted your comments regarding the difficulties you have experienced with Weasel Computer Supplies and regret your dissatisfaction.

As a courtesy to you as a valued Member, and a gesture of goodwill, I have issued a credit to your account in the amount of $99.00. The credit will appear on an upcoming statement.

I trust that I have resolved the situation to your satisfaction. Thank you for bringing this matter to our attention.

Sincerely,
R. Tapeworm
Executive Assistant

CHAPTER 9

TECHNIQUE SUMMARIES, IDEAS, & TIPS

LIST OF TECHNIQUES AND OTHER IDEAS

1) Banks are charging many of us too much for their loans. It's time for everyone to take a stand and stop the banks from forcing us to pay exorbitant amounts in interest charges and fees! Whether you make $100,000 a year or $10,000 a year, the techniques discussed in this book will work to some degree in lowering the cost of your debts!

2) Reread transcripts of the calls that are similar to the call you're about to make regarding your account. This will help get you mentally prepared, as well as suggest deal breaker ideas and how to handle responses from bank reps.

3) Always review each monthly billing statement. Check the interest rate, interest charges, any fees, and all purchases to make sure they're correct.

4) Be sure to use all your credit cards for at least two weeks each year. Buy a few things like gas or groceries that you would normally purchase, then pay off the cards in full each month. This is going to let the credit-card company's computers know that you're still using the card. Then, if you call to get a better deal or get a fee waived, they'll see that your account is "active."

5) Always take detailed notes about your phone conversations. Include the time of day, name of the rep(s), what happened, and any new offers your received during the call.

6) Don't get stressed out or overly emotional while trying to get the deal. Maybe you can have a friend do the talking.

7) Have your deal breaker ready before you call and be prepared to use it.

8) Use low-rate transfer offers that you receive in the mail, from your existing accounts, as deal breakers. Also, use your junk mail credit offers as a negotiating tool. Read these offers to the reps to let them know that you're prepared to take your business elsewhere if they can't satisfy you right now!

9) Be prepared by researching your own account history. Add up how much you've charged and repaid. Also, add up how much you've paid in interest over the past year. Let the reps and managers know these numbers by saying something like, "Do you see how much I've paid in interest this year? Well I've added it up and it's about $240! Now what's more important to you, the $30 annual fee or the $240 in interest payments, because if you don't waive that fee, I'll transfer my balance and let Pug Bank make the $240."

10) Start by asking nicely for fees to be waived, rates to be lowered, etc. "Can you assist me with lowering my rate...can you assist me with waiving that fee, or do I need to speak to someone else."

11) Take the pressure off the bank representative you're speaking with by not directing the problem at them personally. Tell them, "I know you don't make the rules, but I'm hoping you can help me find an answer to my problem." Or, "I know you can only do what you're allowed to based on the bank's policy. Is there someone else you can direct me to who will have more power to help me with this situation?" However, it may not be wise to give them an excuse to stop working to get you a better deal so think carefully before speaking.

12) Throw them a bone. Tell them that you'll use the card for transfers if they do what you want. Tell them that you're about to use their latest offer. However, you're waiting to see if they're going to do something for you first, like waive a fee or lower a rate on an existing balance.

13) Ask the bank representative for their help. Say, "Who do you suggest I speak with about getting this rate lowered (fee waived)? What do you suggest I say to them?" You may be surprised to find that some reps may be willing to give you good advice.

14) Sometimes you run into a bank representative that may help you get around the system. If the rep simply says, "we cannot lower your rate," ask, "What do I need to do to get my rate reduced?"

15) Always ask for a supervisor if the first bank representative cannot help you.

16) When you're transferred to a supervisor, be certain to notice if the supervisor asks you for your name again. If that happens it may indicate that they haven't been debriefed by the first rep. Tell your story, then say, "The first rep, Mr. Drone, said that you would be able to help me lower the rate, waive the fee, etc."

17) If a bank representative asks you about your other credit card rates, be sure to name other banks specifically by name along with some competitive rates. Tell them, "I'm looking at this offer from Elkhound Bank and their offering me 1.99% for 12 months."

18) Ask for a credit line increase while you're on the phone. The more available credit you have, used wisely to help reduce your rates, the more competition you create between banks for your business.

19) Tell them that you'll use the card more often if the interest rate is something more reasonable.

20) Change the card product. Ask if you can "upgrade" your account to a different account that has a lower interest rate or no annual fee.

21) No matter the reason or circumstances, always call and attempt to get fees waived. Even if you think it's your fault. Don't blame yourself and don't let the banks blame you. Make them treat you with respect! Remember you are the customer and "the customer is always right!"

22) Whenever you call, for any reason, always ask to have your interest rate reduced. It never hurts to ask. You may be surprised at how low they can go. Hey, and while you're lowering the rate, ask about balance transfer options.

23) Any time you get the bank to reduce your interest rate, thank them, and then ask for a credit for the difference in the two interest rates in the current month's statement. For example, if you owe $5,000 at 20%, then the interest charges for the month are $83.33 (5,000*0.20/12), bringing the balance to $5,083.33. If the bank representative lowers the rate to 15%, ask for a credit of (20-15)/20 or 5/20th's of the interest charges or $21.83 ($83.33 x 5/20). You're asking that they charge you for the current month at the new rate, because that's what it really should have been in the first place.

24) Always ask if there are any transfer fees on balance transfer offers.

25) Many low-rate credit offers you receive through the mail will require transfer fees. It is sometimes possible to have those fees waived if you do the transfer by calling instead of using the transfer checks that accompany the mail offer.

26) If you're shopping for a low-rate promotional offer, with an existing credit card, and one is available, you have to be careful to make sure that your balance is zero before taking advantage of that offer. That's because banks typically have the right to apply payments to your account as they choose, and no doubt they will choose to apply payments to the balance with the lower rate. This method for applying payments effectively locks your other balance at the greater rate. Here's how that trick works. Let's say you have a credit card with a $5,000 balance at 13% and a $2,000 balance at 2.9%. Every time you make a payment, your balance at 2.9% is being reduced but you'll still owe $5,000 at 13%, until you pay off the 2.9% balance. To make sure you don't get caught by this trick, transfer your balance off of any cards which are offering you a low rate and then transfer it back at the new low rate.

27) Call your credit cards before making a major credit purchase, for example, a large appliance. Tell them, "I'm buying a large-screen TV today for $1,500.00. Here's the deal, give me a low rate for purchases for the next 6 months, and I'll use your card today. Otherwise I'll be using my Schnauzer Bankcard." Use this same technique if you're going on a vacation. Tell your credit card bank that you can use them for the next two weeks while you're "buying like crazy" or use their competitor's card.

28) You've got to ask specific questions after negotiating with the bank to get your deal. Don't assume anything. Ask questions like, "Exactly how long is that interest rate good for?" Or, "When will I see that credit refund on my statement and in what amount?"

29) Although you may be able to successfully dispute charges over 60 days, it is more difficult. One way to avoid that is to not wait until you see a refund on your credit statement. If a merchant says that they'll be "giving you a credit that you'll see on your next statement," ask them when that credit is actually going to happen (usually within a few days). Then call your bank to see if that refund has been posted to your account. If it hasn't, dispute the charge right then and there!

30) Many times, fixing your credit, negotiating rates and terms, is not going to be a one-step process. That is, you won't be able to fix it all in a single day, but you have to start somewhere. You might be able to get some fees waived or you might be able to negotiate a slightly lower rate—maybe only a couple points lower on your first try. As you get better with your credit card and debt management, you'll improve your bargaining power.

31) If you have excellent credit and you're paying on time but still have cards with extremely high rates, such as the case with Kathy Boyd (call #5.02), it's going to be relatively easy to make the bank adjust what they're charging. On the other hand, as we see in Tony's case (call #5.07), the greater the number of late or missed payments, and the more mismanaged the credit, the more difficult negotiating the rate becomes.

32) It is very important to have credit options. Even if you only have high-interest credit options, at least you have something. You have to start making those banks fight for your business. You have to make them participate in a bidding war for your money. If you're stuck shopping for money in only one store, that store is going to keep its prices very high, because they know you have no other place to shop. Once you have many places to shop (credit options) then you really have some power. Keep that in mind.

33) Although you're bargaining for a particular outcome, you may have to hang up or settle for something less. This doesn't mean that you failed. It means that you have just pushed them to their best deal, at least at this time. And remember, they might have another deal to offer you in the future, so you must always call back. In the meantime, be prepared to call other banks.

34) Vary your techniques. Be careful to avoid overusing the same approach with the same banks, call after call. Techniques will also have to be adjusted to your unique situation. Banks are always changing the policies and bank representative scripts, your credit history is changing, your financial condition is changing, your income is changing, your purchases and purchase habits are changing, the amount of available credit you have is changing, and your spending is always changing. It's a fact that things change, so keep that in mind when preparing to speak with a bank.

35) Don't be so determined to get your way in any particular situation to the point where you miss a big opportunity. Even if you don't get the rate lowered or the fee waived, you may be presented with other options by the representative or the supervisor; for example, converting your card to a different type of account that's going to have a lower rate, or getting a higher credit limit, or a reduced cash advance fee. Don't be blind to your other options because you're not getting your way. Take every opportunity to save money!

36) From time to time, you're going to encounter banks that are going to be inflexible about changing their terms. That's why it's so important to have options, a good credit record, and positive relations with alternate banks. You cannot allow one bank to rule your financial destiny! There are so many credit card lenders out there, competing for your business, that you'll eventually find one that will give you a better deal. There's no reason to stay with any single bank.

37) If you've been late paying past bills, then chances are it will be difficult to get the banks to give you a better rate. In that case you may have to try again at a later date. Your first step will be to get organized and start paying your bills on time. Consider these unadjusted rates to be the fee for getting your credit back on track. If you have to pay 20% for six months and get gouged for a few hundred dollars before being able to negotiate a better rate, then so be it. Your ability to make consistent timely payments will be recognized by lenders. In time this will open the doors for negotiation.

38) Don't be hasty in closing accounts once they're paid off. If you close your accounts you close your credit options.

39) By using the negotiation techniques in the book, and starting to apply good credit card and debt management strategies, it will only be a matter of time before you are getting better credit offers. Perhaps even offers at rates as low as 0% that you can use to save thousands of dollars on your existing debts!

40) Review your credit card statements and start calling right now!

CHAPTER 10

TABLE OF SAVING RESULTS BY CALL

TOTALS FOR ALL CALLS

Total Number of Calls:	52 calls in this book
Total Phone Time:	403 minutes (6 hours, 43 minutes)
Total Saved from Calling:	$43,147.68
Saved per Hour of Calling:	$6,423.97 per hour
Saved per Minute of Calling:	$107.07 per minute

CALL RESULT SUMMARIES

Call	Result	Time	Saved	$/hour
2.01	Annual fee waived.	2	$40.00	$1,200.00
2.02	Annual fee waived.	2	$50.00	$1,500.00
2.03	Annual fee waived.	4	$28.00	$420.00
2.04	Annual fee waived.	4	$40.00	$600.00
2.05	Annual fee waived.	2	$20.00	$600.00
2.06	Annual fee and related interest charges waived.	5	$51.71	$620.52
2.07	Annual fee waived.	6	$28.00	$280.00
2.08	Changed card to type that does not have annual fee.	7	$28.00	$240.00
2.09	Cancel account to avoid annual fee.	5	$20.00	$240.00
2.10	Annual fee waived.	7	$28.00	$240.00
2.11	Annual fee waived.	6	$29.00	$290.00
3.01	Late fee waived.	4	$20.00	$300.00
3.02	Cash advance fees and overlimit fees waived.	7	$285.00	$2,442.86
3.03	Overlimit and late fees waived.	3	$50.00	$1,000.00
3.04	Transfer fee waived.	11	$10.00	$54.55
3.05	Late fee waived.	11	$35.00	$190.91

Call	Result	Time	Saved	$/hour
3.06	Late fee waived.	4	$25.00	$375.00
3.07	Transfer fee waived.	8	$41.24	$309.30
3.08	Cash advance fee waived.	5	$29.00	$348.00
4.01	Late fee waived and finance charges refunded.	4	$37.59	$563.85
4.02	Called to have late fee waived and the bank did not waive the fee.	9	$0.00	$0.00
4.03	Called to have late fee waived and the bank did not waive the fee.	5	$0.00	$0.00
4.04	They called me! Late fee waived, interest rate reduced from 17.99% to 9.99%, and 6.9% offer!	12	$25.00	$125.00
5.01	Rate lowered from 22.55% to 8.75% plus $40 refund!	11	$13,673.00	$74,580.00
5.02	Rate lowered from 21.4% to 15.9%.	8	$77.00	$577.50
5.03	Rate lowered from 16.71% to 11.9%.	12	$864.00	$4,320.00
5.04	Rate lowered from 23.99% to 19.8%.	12	$128.00	$640.00
5.05	Rate lowered from 21.08% to 15.9%.	5	$160.00	$1,920.00
5.06	Rate lowered from 19.8% to 16.9% and $199 refund.	13	$479.00	$2,210.77
5.07	Waived a late fee but did not lower the rate.	7	$25.00	$214.29
5.08	Interest charges waived for no reason at all!	2	$6.43	$192.90
5.09	Rate reduced from 16.99% to 9.99% and promotional rate reduced from 8.9% to 6.9%!	7	$7,098.00	$60,840.00
5.10	Rate dropped from 22.99% to 13.99%.	8	$0.00	$0.00
5.11	Rate reduced from 13.99% to 9.99% and $26.59 interest charge refund!	8	$1,632.00	$12,240.00
5.12	Wouldn't lower the rate on the existing balance but did lower purchase rate to 9.9% and gave offer for 2.9% transfer.	8	$354.92	$2,661.90
5.13	Rate reduced from 11.97% to 9.9%.	16	$730.00	$2,737.50

Call	Result	Time	Saved	$/hour
5.14	They don't reduce the minimum payment. However, I got the rate reduced from 16.74% to 12.65% and got an offer of 3.9% with no transfer fees.	5	$1,141.00	$13,692.00
5.15	Rate reduced from 13.72% to 8.76%.	10	$4,320.00	$25,920.00
5.16	Rate reduced from 13.72% to 8.75%.	10	$2,811.34	$16,868.04
6.01	Received offer of 6.9% on existing account and transferred balance.	16	$129.01	$483.79
6.02	Fight to get offer of 9.9% but that is still too high for my purposes.	6	$0.00	$0.00
6.03	Didn't reduce the rate but did offer a 5.99% transfer deal. I punish them in the next call (#6.04).	7	$0.00	$0.00
6.04	9.99% fixed transfer offer.	13	$3,727.44	$17,203.57
6.05	Transferred money at 6.9% and got transfer fee waived.	7	$138.00	$1,182.86
6.06	Increased limit on the spot by $500 and put in application to raise to $5,000.	3	$0.00	$0.00
6.07	Took advantage of low rate offer to transfer balance from 13% to 6.9%.	7	$323.43	$2,772.26
7.01	Offer of 90% settlement.	10	$476.00	$2,856.00
7.02	Completed application to settle account with 50% lump-sum offer.	19	$0.00	$0.00
7.03	55% settlement in a lump-sum payment or 65% settlement with 12 equal monthly payments.	9	$2,900.00	$19,333.33
8.01	Adjusted current rate from 17.22% to 3.99%.	11	$60.10	$327.82
8.02	Dispute and refund for web hosting charges.	7	$874.47	$7,495.46
8.03	Dispute and refund for purchase older than 60 days.	10	$99.00	$594.00

CHAPTER 11

CALCULATING YOUR SAVINGS

KEEP TRACK OF YOUR SAVINGS!

After all that work calling the banks, dealing with voice menus, talking to the bank representatives, and making your case, you will want to keep score!

You must be able to compare the results of your calls and analyze all credit offers. That's why the math is so important! The bad news is that the actual math formulas may be daunting. However, the good news is that I've included four tables that reduce the work to simple addition, subtraction, multiplication, and division. You only need a pen, paper, and standard calculator to get an accurate measure of your savings success!

The four tables are the Time Remaining Table, 3-Month Balance Factor Table, 6-Month Balance Factor Table, and 12-Month Balance Factor Table. They are located at the end of this chapter (starting on page 302).

TWO MAIN CASES

There are two main methods to calculate savings from reduced interest rates. The first is when the current interest rate is reduced to a lower fixed rate. "Fixed" meaning that the new rate will not change while making payments to that card. The second case is when the current interest rate is reduced for a limited time period (short-term rate reductions). The most popular time periods for credit offers are 3, 6, and 12 months.

FINDING THE RATIO

In my first book, *Credit Card and Debt Management*, I used the RATIO to represent a unique relationship between the amount you owe (principal) and how much you're paying (monthly payment). The ratio is simply the principal divided by the payment.

Example 11.01
What's the RATIO for a loan with a principal amount owed of $5,000 with monthly payments of $100?

Solution 11.01
RATIO = Principal ÷ Monthly Payment
RATIO=$5,000÷$100=50

It's that easy! By the way, the inverse of the RATIO is the percentage of your balance that's being paid. In this case it's $1/50^{th}$ or 2%. Many credit cards have a minimum payment policy of 2%. Here's another problem just to give one more example.

Example 11.02
What's the RATIO for a loan with a principal amount owed of $8,500 with monthly payments of $425?

Solution 11.02
RATIO=$8,500÷$425=20

SAVINGS FROM REDUCTION TO A LOWER FIXED RATE

Let's say you owe $5,000 on your credit card at 20% and you're paying $100 per month. You read this book, call your bank, and get them to reduce the rate to a fixed 10%—awesome! The question is "How much did you save?" The steps to solving that problem are:
1) Find the RATIO
2) Use the Time Remaining Table to find the number of months to pay off a loan with that RATIO at the high rate.
3) Use the Time Remaining Table to find the number of months to pay off a loan with that RATIO at the lower fixed rate.
4) Subtract the months found in step 3 from the months found in step 2. The result is the number of monthly payments you save by getting the rate reduction.
5) Multiply the number of months saved by the monthly payment to find the total savings.
6) Subtract balance transfer fees (if any).

I know that may be hard to digest quickly. So, instead of continuing to go into more detail, let's just go through a specific example for clarity.

Example 11.03
You owe $5,000 at 20% APR and are paying the minimum payment of $100 per month. You call the bank and get them to reduce the rate to a fixed 10% APR until it's paid off. How much did you save by making the call?

Solution 11.03
Step 1:
Find the RATIO
RATIO=$5,000÷$100=50

Step 2:
Find the number of months required to pay off the loan at 20% using the Time Remaining Table (page 302). The top row of the table contains the RATIO numbers, the left column contains the APR. Look down the column for a RATIO of 50 and across the row for 20%. The corresponding number in the table is the number of months required to pay off the loan. In this case it's 108.40 months. See figure 11.01.

APR/r	60	55	50	45	40
17%	134.86	107.37	87.59	72.13	59.45
18%	154.65	117.07	93.11	75.49	61.54
19%	190.70	130.28	97.85	79.35	63.87
20%	n/a	153.63	108.40	83.87	66.46
21%	n/a	189.26	119.86	89.28	69.40
22%	n/a	n/a	136.78	95.94	72.75
23%	n/a	n/a	167.40	104.51	76.65

Figure 11.01: Time Remaining Table Example

Step 3:
Find the number of months required to pay off the loan at 10% using the Time Remaining Table (page 302). Look down the column for a RATIO of 50 and across the row for 10%. The corresponding number in the table is the number of months required to pay off the loan. In this case it's 64.95 months.

Step 4:
Find the number of monthly payments saved by subtracting the payoff time at 10% from the payoff time at 20%. At 20% it takes 108.40 monthly payments of $100 to pay back the debt but at 10%, it only takes 64.95 months. That means you save 43.45 monthly payments.

Months Saved=108.4-64.95=43.45 months

Step 5:
Find the total amount saved by multiplying the months saved by the monthly payment. In this case you're saved from making 43.45 monthly payments of $100 or a total of $4,345.00 saved!

Total Saved=$100 x 43.45 months=$4,345.00

Step 6:
Since there weren't any balance transfer fees, nothing needs to be subtracted. Therefore the total saved remains at $4,345.00.

I must caution that your solution will not be exact unless the numbers in the table exactly match your situation. However, you can get a really close estimate by rounding to the nearest number shown in the tables. In example 11.03 we calculated the savings going from 20% to 10%. If in that example the rates were changing from 19.8% to 9.99%, we would use the same numbers from the table. Of course, this means we would compute the identical savings amounts, but they would be an approximation.

Let's look at one more practical example right out of the book! This one is an estimate for the savings in call #5.16.

Example 11.04
What are the savings of going from 13.72% to 8.75% with a balance of $11,592.93 and monthly payments of $232?

Solution 11.04
Step 1:
RATIO=$11,592.93÷$232.00=49.97
It's so close to 50 that we will use 50 as the RATIO.

Step 2:
Months to pay off balance with RATIO 50 at 14% (close to 13.72%) are 75.48.

Step 3:
Months to pay off balance with RATIO 50 at 9% (close to 8.75%) are 62.9.

Step 4:
Months Saved=75.48-62.9=12.58 months

Step 5:
Total Saved=$232 x 12.58 months=$2,918.56 (estimated)

Step 6:
Since there weren't any balance transfer fees, nothing needs to be subtracted.

The exact answer is $2,811.34, so you can see how very close the estimate is to the actual amount. The estimate is within 3.8% of the exact solution.

SAVINGS FROM SHORT-TERM RATE REDUCTIONS

In many cases you'll be able to lower your interest rate for a limited time period. Perhaps you'll take advantage of a transfer offer that reduces your APR for several months. You also may end up doing a balance transfer to punish a bank that's not giving you the low rate you deserve.

The most frequent time periods for balance transfers are 3 months, 6 months, and 12 months. The question you need to answer is how much you'll save by taking advantage of these low rate offers.

To do this calculation, you'll use one of the appropriate tables in the last three pages of this chapter. They are the 3-Month, 6-Month, or 12-Month Balance Factor Tables.

What exactly is a Balance Factor? Simply stated, it's the balance remaining from your principal amount after making payments for a certain period of time at a certain interest rate, divided by the original principal amount. For example, if you owe $10,000 and after 3 months your Balance Factor is 0.950, you will owe $9,500 because $9,500=$10,000 x 0.950.

The steps for estimating your savings, after transferring your balance for a limited time period, are as follows:

1) Find the RATIO
2) Use the appropriate Balance Factor Table to find the Balance Factor with that RATIO at the high rate.
3) Use the appropriate Balance Factor Table to find the Balance Factor with that RATIO at the lower, short-term rate.
4) Subtract the Balance Factor found in step 3 from the Balance Factor found in step 2. The result, the Balance Transfer Fraction, represents the difference in the unpaid balances of loans at both rates, at the end of the transfer period as a fraction of the original principal.
5) Multiply the Balance Transfer Fraction by the loan principal to find the total savings from taking advantage of the lower short-term interest rate.
6) Subtract balance transfer fees (if any).

Follow the below example (11.05) to see how each step applies when using this method to compute savings.

Example 11.05
You owe $5,000 at 20% APR and are paying the minimum payment of $100 per month. You call the bank and cannot get them to reduce the rate, so you call another bank and do a balance transfer at 7% for 3-months with a flat, $30 transfer fee. Of course, your rate will increase after 3 months. How much will you have saved during the 3-months of having the lower 7% rate?

Solution 11.05
Step 1:
Find the RATIO

RATIO=$5,000÷$100=50

Step 2:
Use the appropriate Balance Factor Table (3-Month on page 303) to find the Balance Factor for a loan with that RATIO at the high rate. The top row of the table contains the

RATIO numbers and the left column contains the APR. Look down the column for a RATIO of 50 and across the row for 20%. The corresponding number in the table is the Balance Factor of the loan or the percentage that's unpaid after 6 months. In this case it's 0.990 months. See figure 11.02.

APR/r	60	55	50	45	40
17%	0.992	0.988	0.982	0.975	0.967
18%	0.995	0.990	0.985	0.978	0.970
19%	0.997	0.993	0.987	0.981	0.972
20%	1.000	0.995	0.990	0.983	0.975
21%	1.003	0.998	0.992	0.986	0.977
22%	1.005	1.000	0.995	0.988	0.980
23%	1.008	1.003	0.997	0.991	0.982

Figure 11.02: 3-Month Balance Factor Table

Step 3:
Use the appropriate Balance Factor Table (page 303) to find the balance factor loan with that RATIO at the lower, transfer rate. Look down the column for a RATIO of 50 and across the row for 7%. The corresponding number in the table is the Balance Factor for the loan. In this case it's 0.957.

Step 4:
Subtract the Balance Factor found in step 3 from the Balance Factor found in step 2. The result is the Balance Transfer Fraction of the differences in the unpaid balances at the end of the transfer period.

Balance Fraction=0.990—0.957 = 0.033

Step 5:
Multiply the Balance Transfer Fraction by the loan principal to find the total savings from using the transfer balance for the offer period.

Total Saved=$5,000 x 0.033=$165

Step 6:
Subtract balance transfer fees.
Total Saved=$165—$30=$135

As mentioned previously, your calculations using the tables are estimates unless the numbers for the RATIO and interest rate (APR) match exactly. If your numbers are not exactly the same, simply use the table numbers that are the closest to your RATIO and rates.

Let's look at one more practical example right out of the book! This one is an estimate for the savings in call #6.07.

Example 11.06
In call #6.07 I transferred $10,700 from a 13% credit card to a 6.9% offer for 6 months. Mike was paying $214 per month toward that debt. How much money did Mike save in that 6-month period?

Solution 11.06
Step 1:
RATIO=$10,700÷$214=50

Step 2:
Use the 6-Month Balance Factor Table (page 304) to find the Balance Factor for a loan with a RATIO of 50 at 13% to be 0.943.

Step 3:
Use the 6-Month Balance Factor Table (page 304) to find the Balance Factor for a loan with a RATIO of 50 at 7% (close to 6.9%) to be 0.914.

Step 4:
Balance Fraction=0.943−0.914 = 0.029

Step 5:
Total Savings=$10,700 x 0.029=$310.30

Step 6:
Since there weren't any balance transfer fees, nothing needs to be subtracted.

The exact answer is $323.43. You can see how very close the estimate is to the actual amount. The estimate is within 4.1% of the exact solution.

TIME REMAINING TABLE

APR/r	60	55	50	45	40	35	30	25	20	15
0%	60.00	55.00	50.00	45.00	40.00	35.00	30.00	25.00	20.00	15.00
1%	61.58	56.32	51.09	45.88	40.70	35.54	30.39	25.27	20.18	15.10
2%	63.27	57.73	52.25	46.82	41.43	36.09	30.80	25.56	20.36	15.20
3%	65.09	59.24	53.48	47.80	42.20	36.67	31.22	25.85	20.54	15.31
4%	67.05	60.86	54.79	48.84	43.00	37.28	31.66	26.15	20.73	15.41
5%	69.19	62.60	56.18	49.94	43.85	37.91	32.11	26.46	20.93	15.52
6%	71.51	64.48	57.68	51.11	44.74	38.57	32.58	26.77	21.12	15.63
7%	74.06	66.52	59.29	52.35	45.68	39.26	33.07	27.10	21.33	15.74
8%	76.88	68.74	61.02	53.68	46.68	39.99	33.58	27.44	21.54	15.86
9%	80.01	71.18	62.90	55.10	47.73	40.75	34.11	27.79	21.75	15.97
10%	83.52	73.88	64.95	56.64	48.86	41.55	34.67	28.15	21.97	16.09
11%	87.51	76.88	67.19	58.29	50.06	42.40	35.24	28.52	22.19	16.21
12%	92.09	80.25	69.66	60.08	51.34	43.29	35.85	28.91	22.43	16.33
13%	97.43	84.08	72.40	62.04	52.71	44.24	36.48	29.31	22.66	16.46
14%	103.80	88.48	75.48	64.18	54.19	45.25	37.14	29.73	22.91	16.59
15%	111.60	93.63	78.96	66.55	55.80	46.32	37.83	30.16	23.16	16.71
16%	121.51	99.79	82.94	69.18	57.54	47.46	38.57	30.61	23.42	16.85
17%	134.86	107.37	87.59	72.13	59.45	48.68	39.34	31.08	23.68	16.98
18%	154.65	117.07	93.11	75.49	61.54	50.00	40.15	31.57	23.96	17.12
19%	190.70	130.28	99.85	79.35	63.87	51.42	41.02	32.08	24.24	17.26
20%	n/a	150.33	108.40	83.87	66.46	52.96	41.93	32.61	24.53	17.40
21%	n/a	189.26	119.86	89.28	69.40	54.65	42.91	33.16	24.83	17.55
22%	n/a	n/a	136.78	95.94	72.75	56.49	43.95	33.75	25.14	17.70
23%	n/a	n/a	167.40	104.51	76.65	58.53	45.07	34.36	25.46	17.85
24%	n/a	n/a	n/a	116.28	81.27	60.80	46.27	35.00	25.80	18.01
25%	n/a	n/a	n/a	134.47	86.90	63.35	47.57	35.68	26.14	18.17
26%	n/a	n/a	n/a	172.09	94.00	66.26	48.98	36.40	26.50	18.34
27%	n/a	n/a	n/a	n/a	103.48	69.61	50.51	37.15	26.87	18.50
28%	n/a	n/a	n/a	n/a	117.41	73.55	52.20	37.96	27.25	18.68
29%	n/a	n/a	n/a	n/a	142.43	78.30	54.06	38.81	27.65	18.85
30%	n/a	n/a	n/a	n/a	n/a	84.21	56.14	39.72	28.07	19.03

3-MONTH BALANCE FACTOR TABLE

APR/r	60	55	50	45	40	35	30	25	20	15
0%	0.950	0.945	0.940	0.933	0.925	0.914	0.900	0.880	0.850	0.800
1%	0.952	0.948	0.942	0.936	0.927	0.917	0.902	0.882	0.852	0.802
2%	0.955	0.950	0.945	0.938	0.930	0.919	0.905	0.885	0.855	0.805
3%	0.957	0.953	0.947	0.941	0.932	0.922	0.907	0.887	0.857	0.807
4%	0.960	0.955	0.950	0.943	0.935	0.924	0.910	0.890	0.860	0.809
5%	0.962	0.958	0.952	0.946	0.937	0.926	0.912	0.892	0.862	0.812
6%	0.965	0.960	0.955	0.948	0.940	0.929	0.915	0.894	0.864	0.814
7%	0.967	0.963	0.957	0.951	0.942	0.931	0.917	0.897	0.867	0.816
8%	0.970	0.965	0.960	0.953	0.945	0.934	0.919	0.899	0.869	0.819
9%	0.972	0.968	0.962	0.956	0.947	0.936	0.922	0.902	0.872	0.821
10%	0.975	0.970	0.965	0.958	0.950	0.939	0.924	0.904	0.874	0.824
11%	0.977	0.973	0.967	0.960	0.952	0.941	0.927	0.907	0.876	0.826
12%	0.980	0.975	0.970	0.963	0.955	0.944	0.929	0.909	0.879	0.828
13%	0.982	0.978	0.972	0.965	0.957	0.946	0.932	0.912	0.881	0.831
14%	0.985	0.980	0.975	0.968	0.960	0.949	0.934	0.914	0.884	0.833
15%	0.987	0.983	0.977	0.970	0.962	0.951	0.937	0.916	0.886	0.835
16%	0.990	0.985	0.980	0.973	0.965	0.954	0.939	0.919	0.889	0.838
17%	0.992	0.988	0.982	0.975	0.967	0.956	0.942	0.921	0.891	0.840
18%	0.995	0.990	0.985	0.978	0.970	0.959	0.944	0.924	0.893	0.843
19%	0.997	0.993	0.987	0.981	0.972	0.961	0.947	0.926	0.896	0.845
20%	1.000	0.995	0.990	0.983	0.975	0.964	0.949	0.929	0.898	0.847
21%	1.003	0.998	0.992	0.986	0.977	0.966	0.952	0.931	0.901	0.850
22%	1.005	1.000	0.995	0.988	0.980	0.969	0.954	0.934	0.903	0.852
23%	1.008	1.003	0.997	0.991	0.982	0.971	0.957	0.936	0.906	0.855
24%	1.010	1.006	1.000	0.993	0.985	0.974	0.959	0.939	0.908	0.857
25%	1.013	1.008	1.003	0.996	0.987	0.976	0.962	0.941	0.911	0.860
26%	1.015	1.011	1.005	0.998	0.990	0.979	0.964	0.944	0.913	0.862
27%	1.018	1.013	1.008	1.001	0.992	0.981	0.967	0.946	0.916	0.864
28%	1.020	1.016	1.010	1.003	0.995	0.984	0.969	0.949	0.918	0.867
29%	1.023	1.018	1.013	1.006	0.997	0.986	0.972	0.951	0.921	0.869
30%	1.026	1.021	1.015	1.009	1.000	0.989	0.974	0.954	0.923	0.872

6-MONTH BALANCE FACTOR TABLE

APR/r	60	55	50	45	40	35	30	25	20	15
0%	0.900	0.891	0.880	0.867	0.850	0.829	0.800	0.760	0.700	0.600
1%	0.905	0.896	0.885	0.871	0.855	0.833	0.805	0.765	0.704	0.604
2%	0.910	0.900	0.890	0.876	0.859	0.838	0.809	0.769	0.709	0.608
3%	0.914	0.905	0.894	0.881	0.864	0.843	0.814	0.774	0.713	0.613
4%	0.919	0.910	0.899	0.886	0.869	0.847	0.818	0.778	0.718	0.617
5%	0.924	0.915	0.904	0.891	0.874	0.852	0.823	0.783	0.722	0.621
6%	0.929	0.920	0.909	0.895	0.878	0.857	0.828	0.787	0.727	0.625
7%	0.934	0.925	0.914	0.900	0.883	0.862	0.833	0.792	0.731	0.630
8%	0.939	0.930	0.919	0.905	0.888	0.866	0.837	0.797	0.736	0.634
9%	0.944	0.935	0.924	0.910	0.893	0.871	0.842	0.801	0.740	0.638
10%	0.949	0.940	0.929	0.915	0.898	0.876	0.847	0.806	0.745	0.643
11%	0.954	0.945	0.933	0.920	0.903	0.881	0.852	0.811	0.749	0.647
12%	0.959	0.950	0.938	0.925	0.908	0.886	0.856	0.815	0.754	0.651
13%	0.964	0.955	0.943	0.930	0.913	0.891	0.861	0.820	0.759	0.656
14%	0.969	0.960	0.949	0.935	0.918	0.896	0.866	0.825	0.763	0.660
15%	0.974	0.965	0.954	0.940	0.923	0.901	0.871	0.830	0.768	0.665
16%	0.979	0.970	0.959	0.945	0.928	0.905	0.876	0.835	0.773	0.669
17%	0.984	0.975	0.964	0.950	0.933	0.910	0.881	0.839	0.777	0.674
18%	0.990	0.980	0.969	0.955	0.938	0.915	0.886	0.844	0.782	0.678
19%	0.995	0.985	0.974	0.960	0.943	0.920	0.891	0.849	0.787	0.683
20%	1.000	0.991	0.979	0.965	0.948	0.926	0.896	0.854	0.791	0.687
21%	1.005	0.996	0.984	0.970	0.953	0.931	0.901	0.859	0.796	0.692
22%	1.010	1.001	0.990	0.976	0.958	0.936	0.906	0.864	0.801	0.696
23%	1.016	1.006	0.995	0.981	0.963	0.941	0.911	0.869	0.806	0.701
24%	1.021	1.011	1.000	0.986	0.968	0.946	0.916	0.874	0.811	0.706
25%	1.026	1.017	1.005	0.991	0.974	0.951	0.921	0.879	0.816	0.710
26%	1.032	1.022	1.011	0.996	0.979	0.956	0.926	0.884	0.821	0.715
27%	1.037	1.027	1.016	1.002	0.984	0.961	0.931	0.889	0.825	0.720
28%	1.042	1.033	1.021	1.007	0.989	0.967	0.936	0.894	0.830	0.724
29%	1.048	1.038	1.027	1.012	0.995	0.972	0.942	0.899	0.835	0.729
30%	1.053	1.044	1.032	1.018	1.000	0.977	0.947	0.904	0.840	0.734

12-MONTH BALANCE FACTOR TABLE

APR/r	60	55	50	45	40	35	30	25	20	15
0%	0.800	0.782	0.760	0.733	0.700	0.657	0.600	0.520	0.400	0.200
1%	0.809	0.791	0.769	0.742	0.709	0.666	0.608	0.528	0.407	0.206
2%	0.818	0.800	0.778	0.751	0.717	0.674	0.616	0.536	0.415	0.213
3%	0.828	0.809	0.787	0.760	0.726	0.683	0.625	0.544	0.422	0.219
4%	0.837	0.819	0.796	0.769	0.735	0.692	0.633	0.552	0.430	0.226
5%	0.847	0.828	0.806	0.778	0.744	0.700	0.642	0.560	0.437	0.233
6%	0.856	0.837	0.815	0.788	0.753	0.709	0.650	0.568	0.445	0.239
7%	0.866	0.847	0.824	0.797	0.762	0.718	0.659	0.577	0.453	0.246
8%	0.876	0.857	0.834	0.806	0.772	0.727	0.668	0.585	0.461	0.253
9%	0.885	0.866	0.844	0.816	0.781	0.736	0.677	0.594	0.468	0.260
10%	0.895	0.876	0.853	0.825	0.791	0.746	0.686	0.602	0.476	0.267
11%	0.905	0.886	0.863	0.835	0.800	0.755	0.695	0.611	0.485	0.274
12%	0.915	0.896	0.873	0.845	0.810	0.764	0.704	0.620	0.493	0.281
13%	0.926	0.906	0.883	0.855	0.819	0.774	0.713	0.628	0.501	0.289
14%	0.936	0.917	0.893	0.865	0.829	0.784	0.723	0.637	0.509	0.296
15%	0.946	0.927	0.904	0.875	0.839	0.793	0.732	0.646	0.518	0.303
16%	0.957	0.937	0.914	0.885	0.849	0.803	0.742	0.655	0.526	0.311
17%	0.968	0.948	0.924	0.895	0.859	0.813	0.751	0.665	0.535	0.319
18%	0.978	0.959	0.935	0.906	0.870	0.823	0.761	0.674	0.544	0.326
19%	0.989	0.969	0.945	0.916	0.880	0.833	0.771	0.683	0.552	0.334
20%	1.000	0.980	0.956	0.927	0.890	0.843	0.781	0.693	0.561	0.342
21%	1.011	0.991	0.967	0.938	0.901	0.854	0.791	0.702	0.570	0.350
22%	1.022	1.002	0.978	0.948	0.911	0.864	0.801	0.712	0.579	0.358
23%	1.033	1.013	0.989	0.959	0.922	0.874	0.811	0.722	0.588	0.366
24%	1.045	1.024	1.000	0.970	0.933	0.885	0.821	0.732	0.598	0.374
25%	1.056	1.036	1.011	0.981	0.944	0.896	0.832	0.742	0.607	0.382
26%	1.068	1.047	1.023	0.992	0.955	0.907	0.842	0.752	0.616	0.391
27%	1.079	1.059	1.034	1.004	0.966	0.917	0.853	0.762	0.626	0.399
28%	1.091	1.070	1.046	1.015	0.977	0.928	0.863	0.772	0.636	0.408
29%	1.103	1.082	1.057	1.027	0.989	0.940	0.874	0.783	0.645	0.416
30%	1.115	1.094	1.069	1.038	1.000	0.951	0.885	0.793	0.655	0.425

CHAPTER 12

KEEPING YOUR OWN NOTES

YOU MADE IT

How often do you need your notes? It's like Murphy's Law. The one time that you don't take careful notes is when you can be sure that you needed to have them! At least that's how it happens to me. Maybe you'll be luckier. But, just in case that doesn't happen, I do suggest you take precautions.

If you've read everything up to this point, you're certainly well-prepared to call your banks and get results! The only thing I can do for you now is create a place for you to keep notes about your calls. I cannot stress the importance of keeping good notes. You'll be surprised how many times you may need to refer to them to make sure that the bank is delivering on their promises.

Even when you take good notes, there may still be times that the bank will argue about what was said in previous calls. This happened to me in call #6.04. I had notes and even tape recordings of the bank rep offering me 6.9%. However, they lost their notes. I didn't really pursue the original offer in this call because I still had many other credit options.

Of course, like in call #8.01, it's easier to make your point with copies of their letters. You should always keep the bank's original offer letters as well as photocopies of your applications for new credit. It's also good to note letters, check numbers, dates, and offers so you have a handy reference at your fingertips.

By the way, if you get great results from your calls, or should I say, when you do, please let me know! Send your results to phonecalls@debtsmart.com. I won't tell anyone about them without asking your permission first. I would just love to hear all about your success!

CALL #12.01: TITLE: _____

Bank/Account:	
Date/Time:	
Phone Number:	
Reason For Call:	
Preparation:	How much have you charged on this account in the past? How much interest have you already paid this year on this account?
Rep Names:	
Call Summary:	
Memorable Quotes:	
Result:	
Difficulty Level:	
Call Time:	
Total Saved:	
$ saved/hour to make call:	

CALL #12.02: TITLE: _____

Bank/Account:	
Date/Time:	
Phone Number:	
Reason For Call:	
Preparation:	How much have you charged on this account in the past? How much interest have you already paid this year on this account?
Rep Names:	
Call Summary:	
Memorable Quotes:	
Result:	
Difficulty Level:	
Call Time:	
Total Saved:	
$ saved/hour to make call:	

CALL #12.03: *TITLE:* _____

Bank/Account:	
Date/Time:	
Phone Number:	
Reason For Call:	
Preparation:	How much have you charged on this account in the past? How much interest have you already paid this year on this account?
Rep Names:	
Call Summary:	
Memorable Quotes:	
Result:	
Difficulty Level:	
Call Time:	
Total Saved:	
$saved/hour to make call:	

CALL #12.04: TITLE: _____

Bank/Account:	
Date/Time:	
Phone Number:	
Reason For Call:	
Preparation:	How much have you charged on this account in the past? How much interest have you already paid this year on this account?
Rep Names:	
Call Summary:	
Memorable Quotes:	
Result:	
Difficulty Level:	
Call Time:	
Total Saved:	
$saved/hour to make call:	

CALL #12.05: TITLE: _____

Bank/Account:	
Date/Time:	
Phone Number:	
Reason For Call:	
Preparation:	How much have you charged on this account in the past? How much interest have you already paid this year on this account?
Rep Names:	
Call Summary:	
Memorable Quotes:	
Result:	
Difficulty Level:	
Call Time:	
Total Saved:	
$saved/hour to make call:	

INDEX

BOOKS, SOFTWARE, AND NEWSLETTER

Order online at http://www.debtsmart.com/offers or by calling (609) 660-0682 or toll-free 1-888-775-4410

Credit Card and Debt Management
by Scott Bilker
ISBN: 0-9648401-9-7
Over 107,000 copies in print!

"...this book could be a big help to those experiencing a rather common burden."—*Booklist* (American Library Association)

"*Credit Card and Debt Management* shows how to master the financial techniques and disciplines that will emancipate you from the stress of indebtedness for the rest of your life."—*Reviewer's Bookwatch*

"I recommend this book, only if you want to become a master of your credit cards, not a slave to them...It is easy to read and very detailed and concise...It's amazing the amount of time I will be able to save just filing away the bills faster using Bilker's system."—Sue Seppo, Staff Writer, theWhiz.com

"...you can be sure that if I recommend it, this book contains easy-to-understand and has fairly painless instructions for everything having to do with credit-card debt..."—Mary Hunt, author of *Debt-Proof Living*

"How refreshing it was for me to pick up a book and be able to grasp the concepts without taking 25 courses in higher finance. The book offered quite clearly many topics I have longed to know, but didn't know how or where to learn them."
—Carol F. Peck, Germantown, OH

"This book is so helpful to me. I borrowed it from the library twice and then said, 'I have to buy this!' It's AWESOME! It's my money management bible."
—Ann Marie Yorke, Bayville, NJ

How to be more Credit Card and Debt Smart
(Volume 1)
by Scott Bilker
ISBN: 0-9648401-3-8

The most demanded information from DebtSmart®! How to stop the banks from taking advantage of you, get the best lending deals, get financially organized, pick the right mortgage, make more money, finance your next car, personal stories, Q&A, and much more!

"I have enjoyed reading it! What I like about *How to be more Credit Card and Debt Smart* is the way it is written. It's like having a conversation with a friend. Picture it like this, instead of two people, just one person and the book sitting at a table with a nice warm mug of Starbucks (that I brewed of course) and learning about credit issues in a relaxing and easy-to-remember format."—Susie Marion

DebtSmart® Email Newsletter
by Scott Bilker
Subscribe FREE at http://www.debtsmart.com

This biweekly ezine keeps you posted with the latest ways to save on your debt! Includes Household Math™, reader surveys, and much more!

5-Year Loan Amortization and Analysis Worksheet
by Scott Bilker
Runs with MS Excel

Free for subscribing to the *DebtSmart® Email Newsletter*. Immediately after you subscribe, you'll be sent an email with the download link. This spreadsheet calculates results for loans ranging from 0 to 5 years.

Order online at http://www.debtsmart.com/offers or by calling (609) 660-0682 or toll-free 1-888-775-4410